WHAT TO DO
IN AN
EMERGENCY

WHAT TO DO
IN AN
EMERGENCY

PRACTICAL ADVICE FOR EVERY SITUATION

JG PRESS

contents

⚞ ACCIDENTS AND INJURIES
79–120

HOUSEHOLD EMERGENCIES
121–162

CRIMINAL ACTS
163–186

PUBLIC EMERGENCIES 187–218

DRIVING EMERGENCIES 219–248

OUTDOOR INCIDENTS 249–276

✈ TRAVEL EMERGENCIES 277–302

ANIMAL ENCOUNTERS
303–322

TECHNOLOGY CRISES
323–332

READY REFERENCE
333–352

⚠ WARNING

● **MEDICATION:** Always follow the packet instructions when taking medication and be aware of any contraindications. If you're unsure, consult a pharmacist or your doctor for advice.

● **EMERGENCY CALLS:** It is unsafe, and in most places illegal, to use a hand-held mobile phone while driving. You must try to pull over to a safe spot before making a phone call, even in an emergency.

how to use this book

WHAT TO DO IN AN EMERGENCY assumes that you may have to deal with a difficult and dangerous situation without the opportunity to seek professional help. The instructions should enable you to minimise injury and damage and get effective help as swiftly as possible.

This book has been designed to help you to cope with a range of possible situations, some that all of us may face one day; others much rarer. The first three chapters focus on medical emergencies, including key life-saving techniques and critical signs. The next four chapters deal with problems arising in your home; as a result of crime; public emergencies such as fire, weather and bomb attacks; and crises while driving. The book aims to help prepare you even for emergencies that arise when you are abroad or in unfamiliar terrain, or faced with a dangerous animal. Finally, there are useful fixes to deadline-busting technology problems.

1 PRECAUTIONS
Practical tips help you avoid potential hazards and prepare you for an emergency situation

2 ASSESSMENT
Gives a clear order for evaluating the extent of the emergency and assessing resources

3 WARNINGS
Highlight dangers in the particular emergency that you should be aware of

4 ACTION
Step-by-step sequences with clear explanatory diagrams and photographs suggest action you can take to help relieve the situation

5 TAKE CARE
Points out important safety information to help ensure that you do not put yourself or others at further risk

6 LEARN MORE
A series of boxes give detailed additional information on particular points of interest

LIFE-SAVING
FIRST AID

attending to a casualty

When dealing with someone who is injured, stay calm and follow a clear plan of action. Consider your own safety above all. Once you are sure that it is safe to do so, assess and treat the casualty and get appropriate help.

assessment

Check your own – and the casualty's – safety and then identify and treat conditions that are an immediate threat to life. The most important of these is unconsciousness – from whatever cause (see pages 14–19). Next are conditions that affect breathing or blood circulation.

1 CHECK THAT IT IS SAFE TO APPROACH THE CASUALTY If it isn't, call the emergency services and keep your distance while keeping an eye on the casualty. Do not approach even if his condition worsens.

2 CHECK THE CASUALTY'S SAFETY Only move someone if his life is in immediate danger (and if there is no risk of you injuring yourself).

3 ASSESS AND TREAT Deal with potentially life-threatening injuries or conditions, such as unconsciousness (see opposite) before attending to other conditions or injuries.

4 GET APPROPRIATE HELP You may need to call the emergency services or enlist the help of someone nearby.

Getting help

Call for emergency help if a casualty is seriously injured and/or needs to be transported by stretcher. If a casualty needs hospital treatment, but he can walk or sit and his condition is unlikely to deteriorate, you can go by car or taxi. For other injuries, call the local emergency number for advice and/or assistance. For a list of phone numbers in different countries see page 338.

You'll need to tell the emergency services:
● Your telephone number, your exact location, including any landmarks, and the type of incident.
● The number of casualties, their approximate ages and a description of their injuries. **Stay on the line** to answer any questions and receive first-aid advice. The emergency call-taker will also contact the police or fire service.

action

IS THE CASUALTY CONSCIOUS? Talk to the person. If he is conscious, he will respond by making a gesture or eye contact with you. If there is no response, gently squeeze his shoulders. If there is still no response, he is unconscious. Shout for help, and move on to the next step.

He is unconscious

He is conscious

OPEN AIRWAY Tilt the casualty's head back and lift his chin to open the airway. See **unconscious adult** (page 14).

CHECK AIRWAY Make sure that the airway is open and clear. Treat **choking** (see page 24) or remove anything covering the mouth or preventing normal chest movement.

CHECK BREATHING Look for chest movement, and listen and feel for breaths for up to 10 seconds. See **unconscious adult** (page 14).

CHECK BREATHING Monitor the casualty's breathing and check it is normal. Treat any condition that could be affecting his breathing, such as **asthma** (see pages 42–43).

He is breathing normally

He is not breathing

CIRCULATION Check and treat conditions that affect circulation, such as **severe bleeding** (see page 22) or **burns** (see page 23).

GIVE CPR Call the emergency services, then start **CPR** (see pages 16–17).

CIRCULATION Check and treat any conditions that affect circulation, such as **severe bleeding** (see page 22) or **burns** (see page 23).

CHECK WHAT ELSE IT COULD BE If there is no life-threatening injury or illness, assess what else it could be (see pages 28–29). Call for emergency help if necessary.

PLACE IN THE RECOVERY POSITION If safe to do so, place the casualty in the **recovery position** (see page 15) and call for emergency help. Monitor the casualty and then check for possible causes.

⚠ WARNING
If the casualty is a child or an infant less than one year old, go straight to pages 18–19. There are important differences in the way that unconsciousness is managed in children.

▶▶See also: **MAKING FURTHER CHECKS** pp28–29

unconscious adult

An unconscious person has no muscle control in his throat so the tongue can fall back and block the airway, preventing breathing. He cannot cough or swallow so risks choking on fluid or vomit. Fast action can be life-saving.

✔ CHECK
Make sure the area is safe for you to approach.

⚠ WARNING
● If a person is not breathing, the heart can stop, so begin CPR immediately (see step 4).
● If the casualty is a child or baby, go to pages 18–19 as there are important differences in the way unconsciousness is managed in children.

👁 GET HELP
● Find out whether or not an unconscious casualty is breathing before you call the emergency services, as this is likely to be the first question you will be asked.
● If you are not alone, send someone to call for help as soon as you have checked breathing. Ask the person to come back and confirm that the call has been made.
● If you have help, when you place the casualty in the recovery position, one person can support his head while you roll him onto his side.

1 TILT HEAD Kneel next to the casualty – level with his shoulders – put one hand on his forehead in front of the hairline, then tilt the head back. His mouth will fall open slightly.

2 LIFT CHIN Place two fingers of your other hand on the point of the casualty's chin, then lift it. This action will lift the tongue away from the back of the throat, opening the air passage to the lungs.

3 CHECK BREATHING Put your ear as near as possible to the casualty's mouth and nose, and look towards his chest. Listen for breathing sounds, feel for breaths against your face and look to see if the chest is moving. Do this for up to 10 seconds.

4 IF NOT BREATHING Call for emergency help. Start cardio-pulmonary resuscitation (CPR) (see pages 16–17). If you are in a public place, ask someone to fetch an AED machine (see page 17), which may correct the heart rhythm.

5 IF BREATHING NORMALLY Check for and treat conditions that affect circulation, such as severe bleeding (see page 22) or burns (see page 23). Call for emergency help. If possible, place the casualty in the recovery position (see opposite). Note any change in the casualty's condition while you are waiting for help.

▶▶See also: ATTENDING TO A CASUALTY pp12–13 • UNCONSCIOUS CHILD/BABY pp18–19

recovery position

If the casualty is breathing normally, place him in the recovery position (unless you suspect serious back injury, see pages 84–85). In this position his airway is open, fluid and/or vomit can drain and he cannot roll forward. Try not to leave a casualty, unless you need to go and call for help.

1 POSITION ARMS AND LEGS Remove anything bulky from the casualty's pockets. Ensure his legs are straight, then kneel beside him, level with his chest. Place the arm nearest to you at a right angle to his body with the palm facing upwards. Pull his far leg up at the knee until his foot is resting flat on the ground. Lift his other arm, bring it across his body towards you and hold the back of his hand against his cheek.

2 TURN THE CASUALTY Grasp his raised knee with one hand and support the hand against his cheek with your other hand. Pull on the knee and gently roll the casualty towards you. Keep the casualty's head, back and neck aligned during turning. If you have help, one person can support the casualty's head while you roll him onto his side.

3 ADJUST THE HEAD POSITION Tilt his head back slightly to keep the airway open. The casualty's uppermost hand should be under his cheek to help maintain the correct position.

4 ADJUST THE LEG AND ARM Make sure the casualty's upper leg is at a right angle at his hip and knee, his lower leg and back align, and his lower arm is at a right angle at the shoulder and elbow.

5 MONITOR THE CASUALTY While you are waiting for help, monitor the casualty's level of consciousness, breathing and pulse and note any changes (see page 30). If normal breathing stops, begin CPR (see pages 16–17).

▶▶See also: **BACK AND NECK INJURY** pp84–85

cardiopulmonary resuscitation (CPR)

If a person is not breathing, his heartbeat will stop. Do CPR (chest compressions and rescue breaths) to help the circulation and get oxygen into the body. Early use of a machine called an AED (automated external defibrillator – see opposite) can restart a heart with an abnormal rhythm.

✓ CHECK
Open the airway and check breathing (see page 14). Do not begin CPR if a casualty is breathing normally.

👁 GET HELP
If you are not alone, send someone to call for help as soon as you have checked breathing. Ask the person to come back and confirm that the call has been made.

⚠ WARNING
● **DO NOT press on the ribs, the lower tip of the breastbone or the upper abdomen when giving chest compressions to a casualty.**
● **If the chest does not rise and fall with a rescue breath, adjust the head position and try again. DO NOT try more than twice before going on to repeat chest compressions.**

❓ WHAT NEXT
Continue giving CPR until emergency help arrives; the casualty starts to breathe normally; or you are too tired to keep going. If normal breathing begins at any point, place him in the recovery position (see page 15) and await help.

1 **POSITION YOUR HAND** Make sure the casualty is lying on his back on a firm surface. Kneel beside him and place the heel of your hand on the centre of his chest.

2 **INTERLOCK FINGERS** Keeping your arms straight, cover the first hand with the heel of your other hand and interlock the fingers of both hands together. Keep your fingers raised so they do not touch the casualty's chest or ribcage.

3 **GIVE CHEST COMPRESSIONS** Lean forward so that your shoulders are directly over the casualty's chest and press straight down on the chest about 4–5cm. Release the pressure, but not your hands, and let the chest come back up. Repeat to give 30 compressions at a rate of 100 compressions per minute.

chest compressions x **30**

4 **OPEN THE AIRWAY** Move to the casualty's head. Tilt his head and lift his chin to open the airway again. Let his mouth fall open slightly.

5 **GIVE RESCUE BREATHS** Pinch the nostrils closed with the hand that was on the forehead and support the casualty's chin with your other hand. Take a normal breath, put your mouth over the casualty's and blow until you can see his chest rise.

rescue breaths x **2**

6 **WATCH CHEST FALL** Remove your mouth from the casualty's and look along the chest, watching the chest fall. Repeat steps 5 and 6 once.

7 **REPEAT CHEST COMPRESSIONS AND RESCUE BREATHS** Place your hands on the chest again and repeat the cycle of 30 chest compressions, followed by two rescue breaths. Continue the cycle until emergency help arrives.

chest compressions x **30**
rescue breaths x **2**

Using an automated external defibrillator (AED)

Give CPR while you wait for the AED. If there is no one trained in its use available, follow the machine's instructions.

1 **ATTACH PADS** Switch on AED. Position pads against the skin as shown on the pack.

2 **LISTEN TO MACHINE PROMPTS** Stand away from the casualty and make sure that no one is touching him while the AED is analysing. It will tell you whether or not a shock is advised.

● **IF SHOCK ADVISED** Make sure no one is touching the casualty and stand clear. Press the shock button; the casualty may 'jump'. Continue CPR for 2 more minutes, then the AED will re-analyse the casualty. Follow the instructions. Leave pads attached if casualty recovers.

● **IF NO SHOCK ADVISED** Continue CPR for 2 more minutes, then the AED will re-analyse the casualty. Leave pads attached and keep following the AED's instructions.

▶▶See also: **UNCONSCIOUS ADULT/CHILD/BABY** pp14–19

unconscious child

Use this sequence to treat a child aged between one year and puberty. If a child stops breathing, the cause is more likely to be a breathing difficulty than a heart problem, so begin by giving rescue breaths to raise blood oxygen levels.

✅ CHECK

If the chest does not rise and fall with a rescue breath, adjust the head position and try again.

👁 GET HELP

- If you have help, ask the person to call the emergency services as soon as you know the child is not breathing.
- If you are on your own and the child is not breathing, carry out CPR for one minute before stopping to make the call for emergency help.

⚠ WARNING

DO NOT press on the ribs, the lower tip of the breastbone or the upper abdomen when giving chest compressions.

❓ WHAT NEXT

- Continue giving CPR until emergency help arrives and takes over; the child starts to breathe normally; or you are too tired to carry on. If normal breathing begins, place the child in the recovery position and wait for emergency help.
- If there is an AED machine available (see page 17), it can be used on a child.

1 OPEN THE AIRWAY AND CHECK BREATHING
Tilt the child's head back and lift the chin. Put your ear next to her mouth: look, listen and feel for breaths for up to 10 seconds. If she is not breathing, go to step 2. **If breathing normally**, place the child in the **recovery position**, as for an adult (see page 15).

2 GIVE RESCUE BREATHS
Tilt her head and lift her chin; let the child's mouth fall open slightly. Pick out any visible obstruction from the mouth – do not do a finger sweep. Pinch the nostrils closed, take a breath, put your mouth over the child's and blow gently until you see her chest rise. Remove your mouth and watch the chest fall. Give the casualty two rescue breaths.

rescue breaths x **2**

3 GIVE CHEST COMPRESSIONS
Place the heel of ONE hand on the centre of the chest. With your shoulder directly over your hand, press straight down about one-third of the depth of the chest. Release the pressure, but not your hand; let the chest relax. Give 30 compressions at a rate of 100 compressions per minute.

chest compressions x **30**

4 REPEAT RESCUE BREATHS AND CHEST COMPRESSIONS
Tilt the child's head, lift her chin and repeat the two rescue breaths. Continue a cycle of 30 chest compressions followed by two rescue breaths.

rescue breaths x **2**
chest compressions x **30**

unconscious baby

Use this sequence to treat an infant less than one year old. Talk to the baby and tap the foot to assess consciousness; never shake a baby. If a baby's breathing stops, begin by giving rescue breaths. Place the baby on a firm surface before you start.

✓ CHECK

If the chest does not rise and fall with a rescue breath, adjust the head position and try again.

👁 GET HELP

● If you have help, ask the person to call the emergency services as soon you know the baby is not breathing.

● If you are on your own and the baby is not breathing, carry out rescue breaths and chest compressions (CPR) for one minute before stopping to make the call for emergency help.

⚠ WARNING

● **DO NOT press on the ribs, the lower tip of the breastbone or the upper abdomen when giving chest compressions.**
● **An AED cannot be used on an infant aged less than one year old.**

❓ WHAT NEXT

Continue giving CPR until emergency help arrives; the baby starts to breathe normally; or you are too tired to carry on. If normal breathing begins, hold the baby in the recovery position (see right) and await emergency help.

1 OPEN THE AIRWAY AND CHECK BREATHING Tilt the baby's head back and lift the chin. Put your ear next to the baby's mouth: look, listen and feel for breaths for up to 10 seconds. If she is not breathing, go to step 2. **If breathing normally**, go to step 5.

2 GIVE RESCUE BREATHS Tilt the baby's head slightly and lift the chin. Pick out any visible obstruction from the mouth and nose – do not do a finger sweep. Put your mouth over the baby's mouth and nose, and puff steadily until you see the chest rise. Remove your mouth and watch the chest fall. Give two rescue breaths.

rescue breaths x **2**

3 GIVE CHEST COMPRESSIONS Place two fingers on the centre of the chest. With your shoulder over your hand, press straight down about one-third of the depth of the chest. Release the pressure, but not your fingers; let the chest relax. Give 30 compressions at a rate of 100 per minute.

chest compressions x **30**

4 REPEAT RESCUE BREATHS AND CHEST COMPRESSIONS Tilt the baby's head, lift the chin and repeat the two rescue breaths. Continue a cycle of 30 chest compressions followed by two rescue breaths.

chest compressions x **30**
rescue breaths x **2**

5 IF BREATHING NORMALLY Hold the baby in the recovery position, with the head lower than the body. Call for emergency help and monitor the level of consciousness, breathing and pulse (see page 30) while waiting.

▶▶See also: **ATTENDING TO A CASUALTY** pp12–13 • **UNCONSCIOUS ADULT** pp14–17

severe allergic reaction

A severe allergic reaction affects the whole body and can develop within seconds or minutes of contact with an allergen. Act quickly and call for help as the person urgently needs adrenaline (epinephrine). Help administer the autoinjector if the casualty has one.

✔ ASSESSMENT

Signs of severe allergic reaction include:
- Red, watery and puffy eyes
- General flushed appearance
- Red itchy rash, especially around the mouth and throat
- Swelling of mouth and throat, causing difficulty swallowing
- Difficulty breathing – chest may be tight and casualty may gasp for air
- Abdominal cramps and possible nausea and vomiting
- The casualty may be very agitated, frightened or experience a sense of impending doom

☎ GET HELP

If the casualty does not have an autoinjector, tell the emergency services when you make the call.

⚠ WARNING
- If the casualty becomes very pale and the pulse is weak, lay her down with her legs raised above the level of her heart.
- If the casualty becomes unconscious, open the airway and check breathing (see page 14). Be prepared to begin CPR (see page 16).

1 CALL FOR HELP Call for emergency help immediately and explain that the casualty is having a severe allergic reaction. If there is a bee stinger still in the casualty, remove it immediately (see page 322) before calling for help.

2 GIVE MEDICATION Find the casualty's autoinjector and give it to her. If she cannot use it, you can help her. Hold it with your fist, remove the safety cap and press the end firmly against the thigh through any clothing for at least 10 seconds. Massage the area for 10 seconds.

3 SIT THE CASUALTY DOWN Help her to sit down in whatever position she finds most comfortable for breathing. The best position is leaning forward slightly with her back straight.

4 MONITOR THE CASUALTY Check her level of consciousness, breathing and pulse (see page 30) while waiting for emergency help. Make a note of any change in her condition. If the symptoms return, you can repeat the dose of adrenaline (epinephrine) every 5 minutes.

asthma attack

When a person has an asthma attack, the air passages narrow and the muscles tighten, making breathing difficult. In addition the membrane that lines the air passages becomes sticky with mucus. The casualty will need prompt help to use his inhaler.

✓ ASSESSMENT

Signs of asthma include:
- Difficulty breathing, especially breathing out
- Wheezing and coughing
- Difficulty talking
- Blueness around lips and earlobes as condition worsens

☎ GET HELP

If this is a first asthma attack, or the casualty does not have an inhaler, call for emergency help straightaway.

⚠ WARNING

- Make sure the casualty is using the reliever inhaler (blue or grey) and not the preventer inhaler (brown, red or white) as this will not help during the attack.
- If the attack worsens and the casualty becomes unconscious, open the airway and check breathing (see page 14). Be prepared to begin CPR (see page 16).

1 GIVE INHALER Help the casualty find his reliever inhaler (normally blue or grey). If he has a spacer, follow the 4 x 4 routine as follows:
1. Shake the puffer and fire one puff into the spacer
2. Take 4 breaths from the spacer
3. Repeat steps 1 and 2 until 4 puffs of medication have been taken.
If he does not have a spacer, let him take 4 puffs directly from the inhaler – taking a breath with each puff. Tell him to breathe slowly and deeply while he does this.

2 SIT THE CASUALTY DOWN Help him to sit down in whatever position he finds most comfortable for breathing. The best position is leaning forward slightly with his back straight. Do not let him lie down. If the attack does not improve after 4 minutes, repeat step 1, giving another 4 puffs.

3 CALL FOR HELP If his breathing does not improve, the casualty's condition becomes worse, or he finds it difficult to talk because of his breathlessness and/or he is becoming exhausted, call for emergency help.

4 MONITOR THE CASUALTY Help the casualty to use his inhaler and spacer as necessary every 4 minutes and monitor his level of consciousness, breathing and pulse (see page 30) while you are waiting for emergency help. Make a note of any change in his condition.

▶▶See also: **UNCONSCIOUS ADULT/CHILD/BABY** pp14–19 • **ASTHMA ATTACK** pp42–43

severe **bleeding**

Profuse bleeding can be life-threatening as vital body fluids are lost from the circulatory system. It is critical to control the casualty's blood loss or he will lose consciousness and there is a risk that his breathing and heartbeat may stop.

⚠ TAKE CARE

Put on disposable gloves if you have them. Use non-latex gloves to avoid any irritation.

⚠ WARNING

- **DO NOT use a tourniquet to control bleeding.**
- **If there is an object such as a piece of glass in the wound, press either side of it to control bleeding.**
- **DO NOT give the casualty anything to eat or drink as he may need to have an anaesthetic later.**
- **If the casualty becomes unconscious, open the airway and check breathing (see page 14). Be prepared to begin CPR (see page 16).**

👁 GET HELP

Ideally get someone else to call the emergency services while you attend to the casualty.

❓ WHAT NEXT

- Monitor the casualty's level of consciousness, breathing and pulse (see page 30) while you wait for emergency help.
- Make sure that the bandage is not too tight. Press on a fingernail until it turns white. Release the pressure; colour should return straightaway. If it does not, loosen and reapply the bandage and check it every 10 minutes.

1 **APPLY PRESSURE** Place a dressing pad directly over the wound and press firmly. Remove or cut away clothing to expose the wound if necessary. The casualty may be willing and able to apply pressure to his own wound while you find some dressings and a bandage.

2 **RAISE AND SUPPORT** Raise the injured limb so that it is higher than the casualty's heart; this will slow down the blood flow to the area.

3 **LAY THE CASUALTY DOWN** Help the casualty to lie down, while keeping the injured area raised and supported. Raise his legs above the level of his heart and support them on a chair. This reduces the risk of shock (see pages 38–39), a life-threatening condition that can develop after serious loss of fluids.

4 **SECURE DRESSING WITH BANDAGE** Tie a bandage around the dressing and limb to hold the pad in place; maintain pressure. Call for emergency help. If blood seeps through the dressing, cover it with another one, secured with a second bandage. If blood comes through the second bandage, take off both dressings and apply a new one.

press against wound

raise and support limb

severe **burns** and **scalds**

This type of injury carries major risks: body fluids are lost from the circulatory system, and infection is likely because the body's protective layer is damaged. Your aim is to stop the burning process by cooling the burn as soon as possible.

✓ ASSESSMENT

Establish the severity of the burn. There may be:
- Severe pain at the site of injury, although deep burns may be pain-free
- Blisters around the site of the injury
- Redness and swelling at the site of injury, or charred skin if the burn is severe

⚠ TAKE CARE

Put on disposable gloves if you have them. Use non-latex gloves to avoid any irritation.

⚠ WARNING

- **DO NOT cover the burn with adhesive dressings.**
- **Never put ointments or creams on a burn.**
- **DO NOT give the casualty food or drink as he may need an anaesthetic later.**
- **If the casualty becomes unconscious, open the airway and check breathing (see page 14). Be prepared to begin CPR (see page 16).**

☺ GET HELP

Seek medical advice for any burn larger than 2.5cm. All deep burns or burns on children need hospital treatment.

❓ WHAT NEXT

Monitor the casualty's level of consciousness, breathing and pulse (see page 30) while you wait for emergency help.

1 **COOL THE BURN** Run cool or tepid water over the burn for at least 10 minutes, or until the pain eases. Sit the casualty down and raise the injured area. Make her as comfortable as possible. Call for emergency help.

cool with water

2 **REMOVE CONSTRICTIONS** Remove or cut away any clothing or jewellery from the affected area while you are cooling it. Do not try to remove anything that is stuck to the burn.

3 **PROTECT THE BURN** Cover the burn, ideally with plastic wrap or a clean plastic bag. If you do not have either of these available, use a sterile dressing large enough to cover the burn or a clean, non-fluffy material such as a cotton pillowcase.

cover to protect from infection

4 **LAY THE CASUALTY DOWN** Help the casualty to lie down, while keeping the injured area raised and supported. Raise her legs above the level of her heart and support them on a chair. This reduces the risk of shock (see pages 38–39), a life-threatening condition that can develop after serious loss of fluids.

▶▶See also: **UNCONSCIOUS ADULT/CHILD/BABY** pp14–19 • **SHOCK** pp38–39 • **BURNS AND SCALDS** pp112–113

choking adult/child

An object lodged in a casualty's airway can prevent him from breathing, speaking or even coughing. If the casualty cannot clear the blockage by coughing, take fast action to intervene and call the emergency services.

✓ ASSESSMENT

- The casualty suddenly starts coughing and gasping for breath
- If the obstruction is partial, the casualty can speak, cough and breathe
- If the obstruction is complete, the casualty is unable to speak, cough or breathe
- **DO NOT** intervene until the obstruction is severe as the person may be able to clear the blockage by coughing

⚠ WARNING

Pick out anything obvious but don't sweep a finger around in the mouth. You're more likely to push the object back down the throat or damage the tissues in the throat.

❓ WHAT NEXT

- Continue the cycle of five back blows followed by five chest thrusts until the obstruction is clear or emergency help arrives and takes over.
- If the casualty loses consciousness, go to page 14: the throat may relax, freeing the blockage.
- Anyone who has been given chest thrusts must be checked by a doctor.

1 ENCOURAGE COUGHING Tell the casualty to cough and clear a mild obstruction himself if he can. Remove any obvious object from a child's mouth.

2 GIVE BACK BLOWS If the obstruction is severe, stand beside the casualty. Support her upper body and give up to five sharp back blows with the heel of your hand between the shoulder blades. Check the mouth. A child may need you to remove any obvious object. If the mouth is still not clear, go to step 3.

back blows x **5**

3 GIVE CHEST THRUSTS Put a hand on her back for support and put the heel of your other hand in the CPR position on her chest (see page 16) and give up to five thrusts, checking her between thrusts.

4 CALL FOR HELP Check the mouth. If necessary repeat steps 2 and 3 up to three times. If you have not been able to clear the obstruction, call the emergency services. Continue with the cycle of back blows and chest thrusts until help arrives.

chest thrusts x **5**

choking baby

When an infant less than one year old has a small object or piece of food lodged in the airway, you will have to act very quickly to clear the obstruction. If the baby has stopped breathing, giving back blows and chest thrusts may dislodge the object.

✓ ASSESSMENT

- The casualty suddenly starts coughing and gasping for breath
- If the obstruction is partial, the baby can cough, but finds it difficult to make a noise or to cry
- If the obstruction is complete, the baby will not be able to breathe or make any noise

⚠ WARNING

Pick out anything obvious but don't sweep a finger around in the mouth. You're more likely to push the object back down the throat or damage the tissues in the throat.

❓ WHAT NEXT

- Continue the cycle of five back blows followed by five chest thrusts until the obstruction is clear or emergency help arrives.
- If the baby loses consciousness go to page 19: the throat may relax, freeing the blockage.
- A baby who has been given chest thrusts must be seen by a doctor.

1 GIVE BACK BLOWS If a baby can't breathe, lay her face down along the length of your forearm, supporting her head. Sit down and support a larger baby across your thigh. Using the heel of one hand give up to five firm blows between the baby's shoulder blades.

back blows x **5**

2 CHECK MOUTH Turn the baby over so that her back is along your forearm. Cradle her head with your hand. Keeping her head as low as possible, look in the mouth and remove any obvious object. If the mouth is not clear, go to step 3.

3 GIVE CHEST THRUSTS With the baby along your forearm, support her head and rest your arm against, along or across your thigh. Place two fingers a finger's breadth below the nipple line. Press sharply inward up to five times. Check the mouth again.

4 CALL FOR HELP Repeat steps 1 to 3 up to three times. If the mouth is still not clear, take the baby with you and call the emergency services. Continue with the cycle of back blows and mouth checks until help arrives.

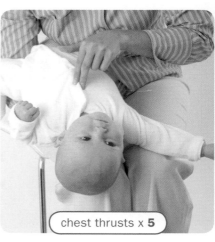
chest thrusts x **5**

▶▶See also: **DIFFICULTY BREATHING** pp40–41

heart attack

A person who is having a heart attack needs urgent medical help because there is a risk that the heart will stop. Your aim is to comfort, support and monitor the casualty while you are waiting for the emergency services to arrive.

✅ ASSESSMENT

Signs of a heart attack include the following:

- Vice-like chest pain that does not ease when the casualty rests. Pain often extends down one or both arms and up towards the jaw
- Breathlessness, possibly gasping for air
- Rapid, weak and irregular pulse
- Pale, grey, clammy or sweaty skin
- Discomfort high in the abdomen. Nausea and vomiting
- Feels faint and dizzy and may collapse

⚠ WARNING

If the casualty becomes unconscious, open the airway and check breathing (see page 14). Be prepared to begin CPR (see page 16).

1 MAKE THE CASUALTY COMFORTABLE
Reassure the casualty, sit him in a half-sitting position and make him as comfortable as possible. Loosen clothing at his neck, chest and waist. Raise his knees slightly and place cushions underneath them; this eases any strain in the heart.

2 CALL FOR EMERGENCY HELP
Call the emergency services and explain that you have a casualty with a suspected heart attack.

3 GIVE MEDICATION If the casualty suffers from angina (see page 32), he may have medication for this – help him take it. If he is fully conscious, give him one full-dose (300mg) aspirin tablet. Tell him to chew it slowly so that it dissolves and can get into the bloodstream as quickly as possible.

4 MONITOR THE CASUALTY Monitor his breathing and pulse as well as his level of consciousness (see page 30) while you are waiting for emergency help. Make a note of any change in his condition.

stroke

If you suspect that someone is having a stroke, use the FAST test – check Face, Arms, Speech and know when it is Time to call for emergency help. If the person fails any one of the face, arm or speech tests, call the emergency services.

✓ ASSESSMENT

Signs of a stroke include sudden onset of:
- Weakness on one or both sides of the body that affects face, arms and/or legs
- Speech problems, difficulty understanding and/or confusion
- Loss of sight or blurred vision
- Sudden severe headache
- Collapse

👁 GET HELP

Tell the emergency services that you have assessed the casualty using the FAST test and you suspect a stroke.

⚠ WARNING

- **DO NOT give the casualty anything to eat or drink as she may not be able to swallow and could choke.**
- **If the casualty becomes unconscious, open the airway and check breathing (see page 14). Be prepared to begin CPR (see page 16).**

1 CHECK FACE Look at the casualty. Do you notice any facial weakness? Ask her to smile. If she has had a stroke she may only be able to smile on one side. The other side of her face may droop.

2 CHECK ARMS Ask the casualty if she can lift her arms. If she has had a stroke she may only be able to lift one arm – on the same side of the body that she can smile.

3 CHECK SPEECH Talk to the casualty. Can she understand what you are saying and can she speak clearly? If the casualty has had a stroke, her speech may be impaired and she may not understand you.

4 CALL FOR EMERGENCY HELP If the answer is yes to any **one** of these assessments, suspect a stroke. Call for emergency help immediately. Reassure the casualty and monitor her breathing and pulse as well as her level of consciousness (see page 30) while you are waiting for help.

▶▶See also: UNCONSCIOUS ADULT pp14–17 • STROKE pp34–35

making **further checks**

If you have established that a casualty does not have a life-threatening injury or condition but you are not sure what is wrong, carry out a methodical assessment. Also assess him if his condition has stabilised and you want to check for other problems.

DETAILED ASSESSMENT Establish what happened (the history) and listen to what the casualty tells you about how he feels (his symptoms). Look, listen and feel for other possible injuries that you can see (the signs). Do not move the casualty.

What is the history?

What are the symptoms?

What are the signs?

ASK WHAT HAPPENED How far did he fall and how did he land? Was anyone else involved? The point of impact can indicate likely injury.

LISTEN CAREFULLY Try not to interrupt the casualty when he talks. He may be able to say what happened. Ask for as much detail as possible.

CHECK THE SKIN Check the colour and temperature of the casualty's skin – is it pale or flushed, grey or bluish, hot or cold, clammy or dry?

TALK TO WITNESSES They may be able to give additional clues about the casualty's injury – this is especially important if a casualty is not fully conscious.

IS HE IN PAIN? If so, ask him to describe it. Where does it hurt? Is it a dull ache, a stabbing pain, or vice-like pain? Does anything improve it or make it worse?

ASSESS VITAL SIGNS Is he fully conscious? Listen to his breathing – is it normal or laboured, noisy or quiet? Check his pulse – is it fast or slow, weak or strong?

FIND OUT HIS MEDICAL HISTORY Is the casualty taking any medication? Is he allergic to anything? He may be wearing or carrying medical identification. When did he last eat or drink?

OTHER SYMPTOMS Ask the casualty to describe any other symptoms he's experiencing such as tingling, loss of feeling, dizziness, nausea and thirst. Again, find out if anything makes it worse.

MAKE A COMPARISON Make a physical check. See how the affected side of the body compares with the unaffected side – note any deformity or swelling. Is the casualty able to move normally?

assessment

Carry out a head-to-toe examination of the casualty to identify less obvious injuries. Start by checking general symptoms and signs – level of consciousness, breathing and pulse (see page 30). Complete the examination before you start treating her.

HOW TO CHECK THE CASUALTY FROM HEAD TO TOE

PART OF BODY	WHAT TO LOOK FOR
Head and neck, nose, eyes, ears, mouth and face	• Feel the scalp to check for bleeding and check for any swelling or depression that may indicate skull fracture. Do not move the head if you suspect neck injury. • Speak into each ear – can the casualty hear you? Is there any bleeding? Watery blood coming from the ears could be a sign of head injury. • Check the eyes – is there anything on the coloured part of the eye? Do the pupils (black centre) react to light? Different-sized pupils can indicate head injury. • Watery blood from the nose could result from head injury. • Bleeding from the mouth could result from a wound; soot around the mouth can indicate burns to the airway. Check lip colour. Leave well-fitting dentures in place. • Look at her face and check the skin colour and temperature – cold, clammy skin can indicate shock; hot, dry skin could indicate fever or heatstroke.
Chest, abdomen and back	• Listen to breathing sounds and ask the casualty if breathing causes her any pain. Feel both sides of the ribcage. Does the chest expand evenly on both sides? • Tenderness or a rigid abdomen may indicate an internal wound. • Feel as far along the spine as you can. Do not move the casualty. Suspect a back injury if she is in pain or unable to move her arms or legs.
Shoulders and arms	• Feel across collarbones, shoulders and down arms as far as the fingers. Can she move her hands or fingers? Look for bracelets warning of a medical condition. Check for needlemarks and the skin colour of the fingertips.
Hips and pelvis	• Carefully feel both sides to check for fracture. Check clothing for signs of incontinence or bleeding as this may indicate internal injury.
Legs and feet	• Compare both legs for any signs of swelling, bruising or deformity. Ask the casualty if she can move her legs. If there is no obvious injury, ask her to raise her legs one at a time. • Compare her feet. Look at the skin colour of her feet and toes.

monitoring the casualty

A casualty's level of consciousness, breathing and pulse together give an indication of how the body is responding to an illness or injury. Assess all three when you carry out your detailed examination of a person, and repeat the checks regularly (about every 10 minutes) while you wait for help. Note down any changes as this helps the medical team decide on the best treatment.

assessment

LEVEL OF CONSCIOUSNESS
Between being conscious and unconscious there are several stages – any change can indicate deterioration or improvement.
● **ALERT AND AWAKE** The casualty's eyes are open and he answers questions normally
● **RESPONDS TO VOICE** The casualty is not fully conscious, but can respond to commands
● **RESPONDS TO PAIN** He is not very responsive, but aware of pain. Do not try to cause pain
● **UNCONSCIOUS** The casualty does not respond at all to any stimulus (see page 13)

BREATHING
An adult normally breathes at a rate of about 12–18 times per minute, but children breathe about 20–30 times per minute.
● Watch and time the number of breaths a person takes in one minute. For a child it may be easier to put one hand on the chest and count breaths
● Listen to the quality of the casualty's breaths – are they quiet or unusually noisy; difficult or easy; or deep or shallow?
● A casualty with breathing difficulties may find it difficult to talk, so do not insist on this

How to check a pulse

Each heartbeat sends a wave of pressure along the arteries (the vessels that take blood to the tissues of the body). This is called the pulse – it can be felt where an artery is close to the surface of the body.
● The heart pumps blood around the body. It normally beats 60–80 times per minute in an adult, and faster – up to 120 times per minute – in babies and children.
● The easiest points to check the pulse are at the wrist (radial pulse) in adults and children, or the upper arm in babies (brachial pulse).
● Place the pads (not the tips) of your fingers on the pulse point and, using a watch, count the number of beats in a minute.
● You can also check the pulse at the neck (the carotid pulse) by placing two fingers between the windpipe and the large neck muscle, although it is more difficult to find the carotid pulse.
● While you count the beats, try to be aware of the quality of the pulse – is it regular or irregular, and is it weak or strong?

● **FOR AN ADULT OR CHILD**
Place three fingers in the wrist crease on the thumb side (radial pulse).

● **FOR A BABY**
Press two fingers on the inner side of the upper arm (brachial pulse).

MEDICAL EMERGENCIES

potential **heart attack**

A heart attack is caused by an obstruction of the blood supply to the heart muscle (usually by a blood clot in the coronary blood vessels). The outcome depends on how much of the muscle is affected and how quickly help can be given. If you think someone is having a heart attack, always call for emergency medical help rather than waiting to see if the symptoms subside.

assessment

These are the common signs and symptoms of a heart attack. A casualty will experience some, but not necessarily all. If the pain subsides with rest, it could be angina (see below).

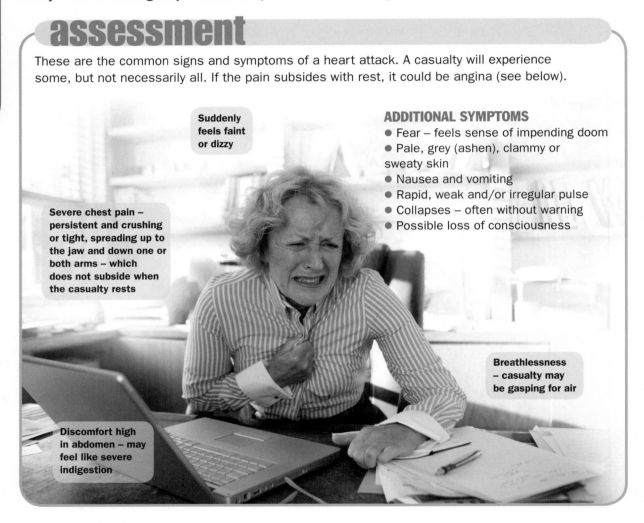

Suddenly feels faint or dizzy

ADDITIONAL SYMPTOMS
- Fear – feels sense of impending doom
- Pale, grey (ashen), clammy or sweaty skin
- Nausea and vomiting
- Rapid, weak and/or irregular pulse
- Collapses – often without warning
- Possible loss of consciousness

Severe chest pain – persistent and crushing or tight, spreading up to the jaw and down one or both arms – which does not subside when the casualty rests

Breathlessness – casualty may be gasping for air

Discomfort high in abdomen – may feel like severe indigestion

Angina

If the pain subsides after the person rests for a few minutes, it is likely that it is an angina attack. This is a long-term condition in which the coronary (heart) arteries are narrowed, so that the heart muscle cannot get enough blood to meet its demands. Someone diagnosed with angina will have been given medication for use in an attack.

- **REASSURE** Keep the casualty calm; sit her down.
- **ASSIST WITH MEDICATION** Help the casualty to find her medication – usually a tablet or spray. If necessary, help her to take it.
- **KEEP WATCH** The attack should ease within a few minutes. If the pain does not ease or the person has no medication, treat as a heart attack.

GET HELP If you suspect a heart attack, call for emergency help and state that it is for a heart attack. Or get someone else to make the call while you stay with the casualty.

TIME TO ACT The casualty is three times more likely to survive if he receives advanced medical help within an hour of having a heart attack.

WATCHPOINT If the casualty is suffering from an angina attack (see box, opposite) but has no medication to hand, call for emergency help immediately.

action

A CONSCIOUS CASUALTY

1 EASE STRAIN ON HEART Make the casualty as comfortable as possible, in a half-sitting position, with his head and shoulders well supported and knees bent to ease strain on the heart. Loosen clothing at the neck, chest and waist.

2 CALL FOR EMERGENCY HELP Keep bystanders away from the casualty.

3 GIVE ANGINA MEDICATION If the casualty has medication for angina (see opposite), help him to take it. Keep him calm and encourage him to rest.

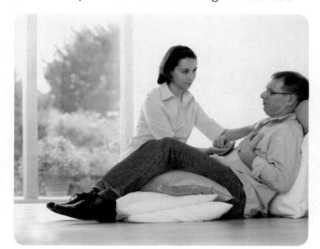

4 GIVE ASPIRIN If the casualty is fully conscious, give him a full-dose (300mg) aspirin tablet. Tell him to chew it slowly so that it dissolves and is absorbed into the bloodstream more quickly when it reaches the stomach. Aspirin helps to break down blood clots, minimising muscle damage.

5 MONITOR THE CASUALTY Regularly check and make a note of the casualty's consciousness, breathing and pulse.

AN UNCONSCIOUS CASUALTY

1 OPEN THE AIRWAY Check for breathing (see page 14) and be prepared to begin CPR (see pages 16–17) as the heart may stop.

2 SEND FOR AED Ask someone to bring an AED (automated external defibrillator – see page 17), if possible, while you treat the casualty. AEDs can deliver a shock to correct an abnormal heart rhythm called ventricular fibrillation – the cause of some cardiac arrests. The machines may be found in public places such as shopping centres and train stations, for example. If there isn't one, you will have to wait for the emergency services to arrive.

3 OPERATE AED Attach the pads, as indicated on the machine, then the machine will guide you through the process. An AED will only deliver a shock if the casualty's condition indicates that it is necessary. If you have attached an AED to a casualty, leave the machine switched on and the pads attached, even if the casualty recovers.

what next?

● Wait for the emergency services. The earlier a person receives advanced medical help, the greater the chances of survival. There is a risk that the heart may stop, so the emergency team will bring resuscitation equipment.
● Diagnosis will be confirmed at the hospital with an electrocardiogram (ECG) and blood tests. Advanced care may include a short stay in a coronary care unit and treatment with balloon angioplasty (using a balloon to open the clotted artery) and medication.
● Hospital treatment for a heart attack will be followed by a period of rehabilitation.

suspected Stroke

Also known as a brain attack, a stroke occurs when the blood supply to part of the brain is cut off or reduced because of a ruptured blood vessel or a clot in one of the blood vessels that supplies the brain. The effects will depend on the part of the brain that is affected. The sooner a casualty receives hospital treatment, the better the chances of recovery.

assessment

Damage to the brain caused by a stroke affects bodily functions. This can be most obvious in facial expressions, arm movement and speech. If you notice any one of these symptoms, call for emergency help immediately:

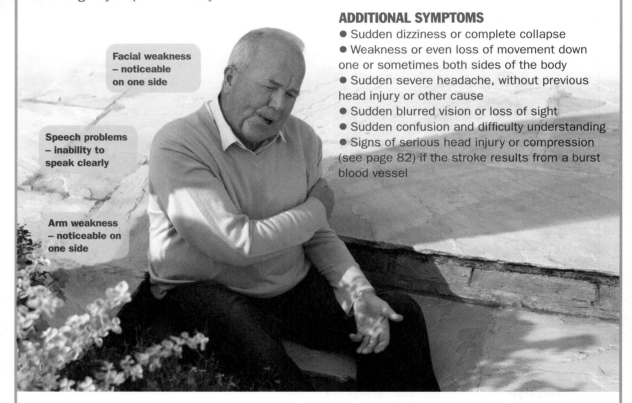

Facial weakness – noticeable on one side

Speech problems – inability to speak clearly

Arm weakness – noticeable on one side

ADDITIONAL SYMPTOMS
- Sudden dizziness or complete collapse
- Weakness or even loss of movement down one or sometimes both sides of the body
- Sudden severe headache, without previous head injury or other cause
- Sudden blurred vision or loss of sight
- Sudden confusion and difficulty understanding
- Signs of serious head injury or compression (see page 82) if the stroke results from a burst blood vessel

THE 'FAST' TEST
A quick test to help check for the most obvious signs of a stroke, FAST requires an assessment of three specific symptoms. If the casualty fails any one of these tests, call for emergency help.
- Facial weakness: Can the person smile? Does his mouth or eye droop?
- Arm weakness: Can the person raise both of his arms together?
- Speech problems: Can the person speak clearly and understand what you say?

MINI-STROKE
A transient ischaemic attack (TIA), often called a mini-stroke, happens when the brain's blood supply is temporarily interrupted. Symptoms are similar to a stroke (such as weakness on one side of the body, visual disturbance and slurred speech), but they usually disappear within 24 hours, and often within minutes. If a TIA occurs, call for emergency help as there is a risk of a more serious stroke in the future.

GET HELP If you suspect a stroke, make a 'FAST' assessment (see below) and call for emergency help. Prompt action can help to prevent further damage to the brain.

WATCHPOINT If you suspect a TIA or mini-stroke (see box, opposite) get emergency help. Although the symptoms may only last for a few minutes, a full stroke could follow.

action

F – CHECK HER FACE

Look at the casualty. Do you notice any facial weakness? Ask her to smile. If she has had a stroke, she may only be able to smile on one side; the other side of her face may droop.

A – CHECK HER ARMS

Ask the casualty if she can lift both of her arms. If she has had a stroke, she may only be able to lift one arm – on the same side of the body that she is able to smile.

S – CHECK HER SPEECH

Talk to the casualty. Can she understand what you say and can she speak clearly? If she has had a stroke, **her speech may be impaired and she may not understand you.**

T – TIME TO CALL FOR EMERGENCY HELP

If the casualty fails any **one** of these tests, suspect a stroke and call for emergency help immediately. Reassure the casualty. Check and make a note of her level of consciousness, breathing and pulse (see page 30). Recheck these regularly until help arrives.

⚠ WARNING

● If the casualty becomes unconscious, open the airway and check breathing (see page 14). Be prepared to begin CPR (see pages 16–17).
● Do not give the casualty anything to eat or drink as she could choke and/or the object or fluid can enter the lungs, which leads to further complications. About 50 per cent of stroke casualties have difficulty swallowing (known as dysphagia).

what next?

● Diagnosis will be confirmed in hospital with brain scans and blood tests. A stroke caused by a blood clot might be treated with medication that breaks up the clot and limits the extent of the brain damage.
● All stroke patients are given a swallow test in hospital, and will only be allowed to drink and eat normally when they can swallow properly.
● After a stroke, the dead brain cells will not recover, but the cells around the injured area may start functioning as soon as any swelling goes down. Most recovery happens in the first few months but, depending on the area affected, people can continue to recover for several years.
● The patient is likely to be given medication to minimise the risk of further strokes.

▶▶See also: **UNCONSCIOUS ADULT** pp14–17 ● **CHOKING** pp24–25

feeling faint

Fainting is caused by a temporary reduction in the supply of blood to the brain. It can be a reaction to pain, exhaustion, stress, a sudden drop in blood pressure (the pressure at which blood is pumped around the body) or lack of food (low blood sugar). A person may feel dizzy and light-headed or pass out, but will recover as soon as the brain's blood supply is restored.

assessment

These are the common signs and symptoms of a faint. A casualty will experience some of them, but not necessarily all:

- Feeling weak and dizzy and may also feel nauseous or vomit
- Skin is very pale and feels cold and clammy
- Slow pulse that quickly returns to normal as soon as the casualty lies down
- Sudden collapse, possibly followed by a brief loss of consciousness – once this happens, the casualty's head and heart are on the same level so that the blood supply is restored more easily

 WARNING

Repeated fainting attacks should be investigated. Isolated episodes of fainting are not normally anything to worry about.

POSSIBLE CAUSES

REASON	WHAT YOU SHOULD DO
Has been sitting or standing still for a long time, especially in a hot, stuffy atmosphere	Tell the casualty to move her legs and feet to encourage circulation. Take her to a cooler place and/or open a window.
Has not eaten for a few hours and/or has diabetes	Low blood sugar causes fainting, so give the casualty something sweet to eat. If she has diabetes, tell her to see her doctor as her medication may need to be reviewed.
Is reacting to pain	Fainting is a common reaction to pain. A person in pain may be able to take normal pain relief if there is no obvious injury or serious illness that requires medical treatment. If treatment is needed, do not give the casualty anything to eat or drink in case an anaesthetic is needed later.
Is reacting to emotional stress	Fainting is a common reaction to stress or emotional shock. As the casualty recovers, talk to her and offer reassurance.
Is pregnant	Fainting in pregnancy is common as hormone changes can cause blood vessels to relax, which can lower blood pressure. Advise her to see her midwife or doctor for a check-up.
Is reacting to medication	Some prescription medications can cause low blood pressure and this can lead to fainting; tell the casualty to seek medical advice as the dose may need to be adjusted.
Is particularly tired, short of breath and very pale	Tell her to call her doctor. She could be anaemic (a condition in which the body has too few red oxygen-carrying blood cells).
Has a history of heart disease	Seek medical advice, especially if the pulse was very slow or fast before she fainted. If in doubt, call the emergency services.

 ▶▶See also: UNCONSCIOUS ADULT/CHILD pp14–18 • HEART ATTACK pp32–33 • STROKE pp34–35

GET HELP If the casualty does not recover straightaway, or the condition worsens, call for emergency help.

TIME TO ACT If a person passes out completely, try to guide her as she falls so that she does not hurt herself, provided there is no risk of you injuring yourself.

action

1 LIE THE CASUALTY DOWN If a person starts to feel faint, help her to lie down on the floor – if possible on something to protect her from the ground. If you are out of doors, make sure she is in the shade.

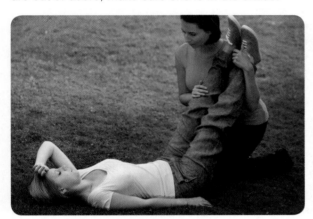

2 RAISE HER LEGS Kneel beside her hips, raise her legs and rest them on your shoulder (or place them on a chair) to help improve the blood flow to the brain. Look at the casualty's face – the skin colour should return to normal quite quickly.

3 ENSURE SUPPLY OF FRESH AIR Fan her face to cool her down. If you are inside, ask someone to open the window to improve air flow.

4 SIT THE CASUALTY UP GRADUALLY Once the casualty starts to feel better, help her to sit up slowly. If she feels faint again, help her to lie down for a bit longer.

5 IDENTIFY CAUSE Try to find out why she collapsed (see opposite). If she has not eaten and is fully conscious, give her something to eat. If she is a known diabetic, treat as described on page 58.

⚠ WARNING

● If the casualty does not make a rapid, complete recovery, call for emergency medical help. Open the airway and check breathing (see page 14).
● If a person feels faint, do not sit her on a chair with her head between her legs – if she faints, she will fall off the chair and could injure herself.
● If a woman is pregnant, she should not lie flat on her back, as the weight of the baby in the uterus can compress the blood vessels, restricting blood flow back to the heart. Help her to lie down and place a cushion under one hip. Raise her legs as high as you can.
● Do not give the casualty anything to eat or drink unless she is fully conscious.

what next?

If a person is prone to fainting, advise her to see her doctor for further investigation. The doctor will want to know how often the person faints, whether she experiences any other symptoms at the same time and whether there is a family history of fainting episodes. The doctor will assess her and may carry out tests – for example, blood analysis or an ECG (electrocardiogram) to try to identify the cause. Treating an underlying condition, such as anaemia (low red blood cells), heart disease or diabetes, can often prevent further problems.

shock

Medical, as opposed to emotional, shock is a life-threatening condition that develops if the circulatory system fails to provide sufficient oxygen-rich blood to the organs. Severe bleeding (external or internal) is the most common cause, but it can also follow fluid loss from burns, vomiting or diarrhoea, or be the result of a severe allergic reaction, back injury or heart failure.

assessment

Signs of shock worsen as the circulatory system fails. Suspect shock after, for example, severe bleeding (see page 22), but also if any of the following occur with no obvious wound:

- Rapid pulse at first, which becomes weaker. By the time half the blood is lost from the circulatory system (about 3 litres in an adult), you may not be able to feel the pulse at the wrist
- Profuse sweating with cold, clammy skin
- Fast but shallow breathing
- Skin becomes grey/blue, as the circulatory system fails or fluid loss worsens. This is seen at the ears, lips, inside the mouth and at the

fingertips. If you press a fingernail then let go, the healthy pink colour will not return quickly
- Casualty becomes weak and feels dizzy. He may feel nauseous and may even vomit
- Casualty starts to feel very thirsty
- Casualty feels restless and may become aggressive as the oxygen to the brain reduces. He will be yawning and gasping for air. **Eventually he will become unconscious and his heart may stop**

SIGNS OF INTERNAL BLEEDING

Severe internal bleeding can develop after a blow to the body or it can also be spontaneous – for example, as the result of a ruptured abdominal aortic aneurysm. Look for the following:

- Signs of shock (see above) but no obvious injury
- Bruising on the skin that matches the pattern of clothes and worsens as the area swells
- Severe abdominal or back pain
- Bleeding from body openings (see below)

- Sudden collapse and loss of consciousness some time after an injury
- Information from the casualty or a bystander that indicates possible internal injury

BLEEDING FROM BODY OPENINGS

BODY OPENING	APPEARANCE AND POSSIBLE CAUSE
Ears/Nose	Bright red blood in the ear is likely to be caused by injury to the outer part of the ear or eardrum. Bright red blood from the nose results from a ruptured blood vessel in the nose. The watery blood that appears after a head injury is fluid from around the brain mixed with blood from the ear and nose.
Mouth	Coughed-up bright red, frothy blood indicates bleeding in the lungs. Dark-reddish blood that looks like coffee grounds comes from the digestive system.
Anus	Fresh bright red blood comes from the lower part of the intestine or bowel. Darker, tar-like stools indicate injury further up the digestive system.
Urethra	Reddish urine, with possible clots, indicates possible bleeding from the kidneys, ureters, bladder or urethra.
Vagina	Fresh or dark-red blood could be a sign of menstruation, but it could also be caused by infection, a miscarriage, childbirth or sexual assault.

▶▶See also: **UNCONSCIOUS ADULT/CHILD/BABY** pp14–19

GET HELP If you suspect shock, call the emergency services or ask someone else to make the call while you look after the casualty, following the steps below.

TIME TO ACT Shock is life-threatening – suspect it if you notice any of the symptoms or signs detailed opposite, even if there is no obvious injury.

WATCHPOINT If the casualty has a suspected broken leg, do not raise the affected leg, but raise the other leg, if possible.

action

1 TREAT OBVIOUS CAUSE Treat severe bleeding by applying direct pressure to the wound (see pages 96–97). Cool any burns (see pages 112–113). Raise and support the injury.

2 LIE THE CASUALTY DOWN Reassure the casualty and tell him not to move unnecessarily. Help him to lie down on a rug or blanket. Do not put anything under his head; leave it low. Raise and support his legs as high as you can above his heart – for example, rest his feet on a chair.

3 LOOSEN CLOTHING Loosen any tight clothing, especially around his neck, chest and waist, that could restrict blood circulation around the body.

4 KEEP THE CASUALTY WARM Cover him with a blanket or coats. Do not warm him with a hot water bottle or electric blanket (see Warning, right).

5 CALL FOR HELP Call the emergency services. Tell them that you suspect shock, and give as much information as you can about the possible cause.

6 MONITOR THE CASUALTY Check and note the level of consciousness, breathing and pulse (see page 30). Recheck regularly until medical help arrives. If the casualty is thirsty, moisten his lips with a clean damp cloth.

 WARNING
● Do not warm the casualty with direct heat. The aim of treatment is to keep vital organs supplied with blood. If you put a hot water bottle on the casualty's skin, blood will be drawn to the surface of the body and away from the core where it is needed.
● Do not give the casualty anything to eat or drink as he may need an anaesthetic at the hospital.
● If the casualty loses consciousness, open the airway and check breathing (see page 14). Be prepared to begin CPR (see pages 16–17).

Understanding medical shock

If a person reacts to an emotional situation, he is described as being in 'shock'. Medical shock is different. It develops when the circulatory system fails for two main reasons: there may not be enough fluid in the body to be circulated (after bleeding) or the heart is not functioning normally and so cannot pump enough blood around the body.

difficulty **breathing**

Breathing problems are serious and must be treated as emergencies. Every part of the body needs oxygen to survive – brain cells start to die after only three minutes without it. If the body is not receiving enough oxygen, through injury or illness, and the cause is not treated, breathing (and the heartbeat) may stop.

assessment

Depending on how long the casualty has been in difficulty, you may notice any of these symptoms:

Rapid breathing, coughing, gasping for breath; difficulty in talking

Skin becomes grey-blue, especially at the ears, lips inside the mouth and at the fingertips

ADDITIONAL SYMPTOMS
● **If the airway is blocked, the casualty will not be able to cough or make a sound**
● If there is a constriction around the casualty's neck, blood vessels in the face and neck may be prominent
● An obvious cause, such as a plastic bag near the face or a chest injury that prevents normal breathing
● Casualty complains of feeling sick and may even vomit
● Possible loss of consciousness

Inability to think clearly

POSSIBLE CAUSES

REASON	WHAT HAPPENS
Blocked airway	Anything that covers the mouth, constricts the casualty's windpipe or blocks the airway (see pages 80–81) can prevent oxygen from entering the body. Swelling of the air passages after smoke inhalation (see pages 44–45) or due to an allergic reaction (see pages 54–55) will restrict breathing.
Unable to move chest	Crushing (see pages 102–103) – for example, being buried in sand – will prevent normal movement of the chest so the casualty cannot breathe in or out. Injury to the ribcage can also prevent normal movement (see pages 94–95).
Insufficient oxygen in the air (fumes)	Poisonous fumes (see pages 44–45) can prevent the body from taking up any oxygen in the air.
Illness	Long-term conditions such as asthma or allergy can affect breathing, as can an infection such as pneumonia, croup or bronchiolitis.
Head injury	Any injury or drug that affects the part of the brain or nerves that control respiration can restrict breathing.

GET HELP Your aim is to help the casualty to restore normal breathing as soon as possible. Help him into fresh air or to take medication, and call the emergency services.

TIME TO ACT If an infant less than a year old has a bad cough and high fever, it may indicate a viral lung infection called bronchiolitis. Seek medical advice.

WATCHPOINT If you are treating a casualty known to have asthma, let her use her inhaler (see pages 42–43). If she has no medication, call the emergency services.

action

1 REMOVE OBVIOUS OBSTRUCTION Remove anything that is covering the person's mouth and/or nose or that prevents normal chest movement. Treat choking if necessary (see pages 80–81).

2 CALL FOR HELP Call the emergency services even if the casualty appears to have recovered completely.

3 OBSERVE THE CASUALTY Check and make a note of the casualty's level of consciousness, breathing and pulse (see page 30). Recheck regularly until the emergency services arrive.

Hanging and strangulation

An incident that leads to compression of the windpipe prevents air getting to the lungs. It might also result in serious neck injury.

1 REMOVE CONSTRICTION Remove the cause of strangulation as quickly as you can. If the casualty has a tight constriction around the neck, cut as near to the knot as possible using shears or scissors. Slide the shears under the rope or tie and cut towards you – away from the casualty's neck.

2 SUPPORT THE CASUALTY'S WEIGHT Support the body as the ligature is removed. You may need help as the casualty could be very heavy, especially if he is unconscious.

3 CALL FOR EMERGENCY HELP Call the emergency services, or ask a helper to make the call. Check and make a note of the level of consciousness, breathing and pulse (see page 30). Recheck until medical help arrives.

⚠ WARNING

If the casualty becomes unconscious, open the airway and check breathing (see page 14). Be prepared to begin CPR (see pages 16–17).

what next?

All casualties who have experienced breathing difficulties must be assessed at a hospital even if they appear to have recovered. It is important to confirm the cause and make sure that there is no permanent damage. If a person was rescued from water there may be water in the lungs, which can cause irritation and swelling several hours later.

⚠ SAFETY FIRST WITH CHILDREN

● Make sure you keep all plastic bags locked away out of reach of children.
● Secure all curtain pulls, tie-backs and blind cords out of a child's reach.
● If a young child wants to wear a tie, use the ready tied type with a quick-release fastening.
● Remove strings from jacket or sweatshirt hoods.
● Do not give toys with very small parts to young children. All soft toys should be suitable for young children with securely affixed details.
● Stay with your child when she is eating. Never let her run around while she is eating or drinking.
● Remove ribbons that are not securely fastened from clothes or soft toys.

Always check the safety labels on toys.

▶▶See also: **INHALING FUMES** pp44–45 • **ALLERGIC REACTION** pp54–55

asthma attack

Exposure to certain triggers causes breathing difficulty in people who suffer from asthma, a chronic (long-term) disease. During an asthma attack, the muscles around the airways in the lungs contract, causing the airways to narrow. The amount of mucus that lines the air passages increases. Asthma cannot be cured, but it can be controlled with medication.

assessment

Symptoms are often worse at night and people have different patterns to their attacks. **It is vital to give the casualty his medication as soon as possible.** Common symptoms include:

Difficulty speaking

Difficulty breathing – especially breathing out

Shortness of breath – often accompanied by wheezing (noisy out-breaths)

Feeling of tightness in the chest

ADDITIONAL SYMPTOMS
● As the attack worsens, skin may become bluish, especially around the mouth and earlobes
● A moist or dry cough, especially at night

Croup

This is an infection, often viral, that causes breathing difficulty and wheezing in young children. It can be alarming and occasionally life-threatening, but there is rarely any long-term effect. It is sometimes confused with asthma but there are a number of critical differences. The child often has a fever, there will be a barking cough and the child has more difficulty breathing in. It is likely to occur at night. Seek medical advice if there is stridor – a harsh rasping sound heard only when the child breathes in.

1 SUPPORT THE CHILD If the child is happy for you to do so, sit her on your lap, supporting her chest. Stay calm, reassure her and encourage her to relax and breathe steadily.

2 SEEK MEDICAL HELP If there is stridor or the child is too unwell to eat or drink, take her to hospital. Treatment can prevent life-threatening complications.

GET HELP Asthma attacks can be life-threatening. If this is a casualty's first asthma attack, or he does not have an inhaler with him, call for emergency help straightaway.

TIME TO ACT Make sure the casualty is using his reliever inhaler (containing salbuterol or albuterol) and not his preventer inhaler as the latter will not help in an attack.

WATCHPOINT Common triggers are exercise, colds, cold air and allergens such as pollen or dust and some medications. Milk, eggs or nuts can also be triggers.

action

1 GIVE INHALER Help the casualty find his reliever inhaler (normally blue or grey). If he has a spacer, follow the 4 x 4 routine as follows:
1. Shake the puffer and fire one puff into the spacer
2. Take 4 breaths from the spacer
3. Repeat steps 1 and 2 until the casualty has taken 4 puffs.
If he does not have a spacer, let him take 4 puffs directly from the inhaler – taking a breath with each puff. Tell him to breathe slowly and deeply.

2 SIT THE CASUALTY DOWN Help him to sit down in a comfortable position. The best position is generally leaning forward slightly with his back straight. Do not let him lie down. The attack should ease after a few minutes – if it does not improve, repeat step 1, giving him another 4 puffs.

3 CALL FOR HELP If breathing does not improve, the casualty's condition is worse or he finds it difficult to talk because of breathlessness, and/or he is becoming exhausted, call for emergency help.

4 MONITOR CASUALTY Help the casualty to use his inhaler and spacer every 4 minutes as necessary and monitor his level of consciousness, breathing and pulse (see page 30) while you wait for help. Note changes in his condition.

⚠ WARNING
If the casualty becomes unconscious, open the airway and check breathing (see page 14). Be prepared to begin CPR (see pages 16–17).

Treating children

Asthma often develops in childhood and many children grow out of it. The condition is managed in the same way but young children will need help taking their medication.

1 ADMINISTER MEDICATION INTO A SPACER Young children find it difficult to use an inhaler. A spacer with a mouthpiece or mask can be used to deliver the medication. Place the inhaler into one end of the device and 'squirt' the medication into it.

2 GIVE SPACER TO THE CHILD Let the child put the mouthpiece in his mouth, or mask, if it has one, over his face. Tell him to breathe normally.

what next?

● If this is the first attack, hospital assessment is necessary. Two main types of medications are prescribed: reliever and preventer inhalers. Relievers (bronchodilators) give immediate relief for the symptoms of an attack. Preventer inhalers, normally taken every day, treat the underlying inflammation, helping to reduce symptoms.
● The person may be referred to an allergist to help identify what triggers the attacks.
● A personal plan of asthma management will be prepared. Regular medical check-ups are needed to ensure that the medication is effective.

▶▶See also: **UNCONSCIOUS ADULT/CHILD** pp14–18 • **DIFFICULTY BREATHING** pp40–41

inhaling **fumes**

The inhalation of fumes can be life-threatening as they reduce the amount of oxygen available to the body. A casualty needs urgent medical help, but rescue should only be carried out by someone wearing protective breathing apparatus.

GET HELP Never enter a fume-filled room or building, even if there are casualties. Call for emergency help. Ask for the fire service and explain that there are fumes.

assessment

Any casualty will have very low levels of oxygen in his body. Symptoms vary, depending on the gas or vapour inhaled and how long a person is exposed to it. General symptoms include:

- Rapid breathing – the casualty may cough, gasp for breath and find it difficult to talk
- Skin becomes grey-blue (called cyanosis) – this is especially noticeable at the ears, lips, inside the mouth and at the fingertips

- Inability to think clearly – as oxygen levels fall, the casualty will become increasingly restless and anxious, and possibly aggressive
- The casualty may complain of feeling nauseous and may even vomit

DANGEROUS FUMES

FUMES	SOURCE	SYMPTOMS
Smoke	Fires – as fire uses oxygen to burn, smoke contains very low oxygen levels. Smoke may also contain toxic gases given off by other materials as they burn.	Noisy breathing, coughing, hoarseness, black or grey saliva (spit) and fluids in the lungs. Skin colour may range from grey-blue to cherry-red. As the condition worsens, the casualty may lose consciousness or stop breathing. The heat may burn nose hairs and there may be burns in the throat and inside the nose.
Carbon monoxide (CO)	Colourless, odourless gas that is a by-product of incomplete burning of any fossil fuel. For example, exhausts, gas fires, faulty gas boilers or water heaters and paraffin heaters.	Mild symptoms are headache, nausea, vomiting, drowsiness and poor co-ordination. In more moderate or severe cases there may be confusion, unconsciousness, chest pain or seizures.
Solvents	Lighter fuels, glues, paints, cleaning fluids, camping gas canisters and aerosol sprays.	General symptoms of fumes, plus headaches and possible loss of consciousness. Solvent use can cause the heart to stop (cardiac arrest). The casualty may also have an obstructed airway as a result of breathing solvents from a plastic bag.
Carbon dioxide (CO_2)	Environmental gas, produced naturally and through human activities. It can accumulate in deep enclosed spaces, such as wells. High concentrations can occur in places that are crowded and have poor ventilation. The gas is normally odourless but can be detected at very high concentrations.	General symptoms of fumes, plus headache, breathlessness, a dramatic increase in breathing and pulse rate, tinnitus (ringing in the ears) and impaired vision. Eventual unconsciousness.

▶▶See also: **UNCONSCIOUS ADULT/CHILD/BABY** pp14–19

action

1 CALL THE EMERGENCY SERVICES Do not enter a room or building if you suspect fumes. Call the emergency services and ask for the fire service. State that there are people in the building.

2 HELP THE CASUALTY AWAY FROM THE FUMES If the casualty is able to get away from the source of the fumes or the building, stay outside and help him to safety. Never enter the building yourself.

3 TREAT ANY INJURY Help the casualty to sit down. Assess his injuries and treat any burns (see pages 112–113). He may have inhaled smoke and there could be burns to the mouth, throat and windpipe. Loosen any clothing around the neck and chest to help his breathing.

4 MONITOR THE CASUALTY Check and note his level of consciousness, breathing and pulse (see page 30). Recheck regularly until medical help arrives.

⚠ TAKE CARE

Make sure that everyone in your house knows how to escape if there is a fire. Install smoke detectors on every floor of your home. If they are battery operated, check them every week to ensure that they still work.

⚠ WARNING

If the casualty becomes unconscious, open the airway and check breathing (see page 14). Be prepared to begin CPR (see pages 16–17).

what next?

● The casualty may be given oxygen by the medical emergency team and taken to hospital. People with moderate symptoms who receive early treatment tend to recover completely from the experience.
● Blood tests will be carried out to assess the casualty's blood oxygen levels and to find out whether any toxic gases are present in the blood.
● Burns in the airways need hospital treatment. Fluid can collect in the lungs after smoke inhalation, causing noisy breathing, so an X-ray and other tests will be needed.

Preventing carbon monoxide poisoning

You can see and smell smoke, but carbon monoxide (CO) is colourless and odourless, as well as highly toxic. Depending on the concentration, **CO gas can render a person unconscious within hours**. There are several ways to reduce the risk of exposure.

● **SERVICE ALL APPLIANCES REGULARLY** Appliances should be checked at least annually. Carbon monoxide can accumulate if solid fuel appliances, such as gas fires, boilers or water heaters, are badly maintained or faulty.
● **INSTALL DETECTOR ALARMS** Put them in every room where there is a fossil fuel appliance. Choose alarms that give visual and audible warnings when there is a build-up of the gas.
● **CHECK DETECTORS** If the detector alarms are battery operated, check them once a week to ensure that they are still working.

▶▶See also: **DIFFICULTY BREATHING** pp40–41 ● **BURNS AND SCALDS** pp112–113

hypothermia

When the core body temperature falls below 35°C (95°F), the body shuts down the blood supply to the surface blood vessels to keep vital organs such as the heart supplied with blood. This leads to a condition known as hypothermia.

TIME TO ACT It is important to prevent body temperature dropping too low. If a casualty receives prompt medical help, mild to moderate hypothermia can usually be reversed.

assessment

Hypothermia can strike at any age, and the symptoms and signs are the same whatever the cause. You may also see signs of frostbite on the casualty's fingers and toes (see opposite).

Skin feels cold and dry, and looks pale

Lacks energy

AS HYPOTHERMIA DEEPENS
- Casualty becomes disoriented and starts to behave irrationally; she will become more lethargic and may no longer be fully conscious and alert
- **Eventually the casualty will lose consciousness**
- Breaths become very slow and shallow
- Pulse slows down and gets gradually weaker and irregular; if the casualty is not warmed up, the heart stops

Shivering in the early stages is the body's way of generating heat

action

1 WARM UP GRADUALLY If you are inside, start to warm the room, or move to a warmer room. Remove any wet clothes. Wrap her up in several layers of blankets to trap heat. Put a hat on her head.

2 GIVE WARM DRINK AND FOOD Provided the casualty is fully conscious, give her a warm (not hot) drink and a high-energy food such as chocolate for fast energy. You may need to help her.

3 CALL FOR HELP Call the emergency services as soon as possible. Regularly check and make a note of her level of consciousness, breathing and pulse (see page 30) until help arrives.

Treating a baby

Young babies have very under-developed temperature control mechanisms, so they can become hypothermic relatively quickly in a cold room. A baby will become very floppy, but may have bright pink skin. Her skin will feel very cold. She will not want to eat or drink.

1 WARM UP GRADUALLY Either warm the room or take the baby into a warmer room. Wrap the baby in warm blankets. Keep her head covered with a hat or the blanket, but leave her face exposed. Cuddle her so that you are using your own body heat for warmth.

2 GET HELP Either call the emergency services or take the baby to hospital if you can keep her warm. Check the level of consciousness, breathing and pulse (see page 30).

 TAKE CARE

● Only start to warm someone up if there is no risk of her becoming cold again.
● Warm a person gradually to prevent blood from being diverted away from the core of the body towards the skin, as this forces cold blood back to the major organs, and can cause a heart attack.
● A healthy adult or older child can be warmed up in a bath if he can climb in and out unaided and there is no risk of him becoming cold again.

 WARNING

● Do not warm up an elderly person in a bath as this may send cold blood to the heart or brain too suddenly, and may cause a stroke or heart attack.
● Do not warm the casualty with direct heat, such as a hot water bottle, or put him beside an electric fire.
● Do not give him alcohol, as this dilates the blood vessels, decreasing the body's ability to retain heat.
● Do not rub or massage the casualty as, in severe hypothermia, there is a risk of heart attack.
● If the casualty becomes unconscious, open the airway and check breathing (see page 14). Be prepared to begin CPR (see pages 16–17).
● In an elderly person signs of a stroke (see pages 34–35) or heart attack (see pages 32–33) can be masked by signs of hypothermia.

frostbite

If exposed to severe cold, the extremities, usually the fingers and toes, can literally freeze. Prompt action is needed so that tissues are not permanently damaged.

assessment

● The casualty may have pins and needles in affected areas; later he may have no feeling
● The skin may be waxy, pale, cold and hard
● The skin may turn from mottled blue/grey

action

1 STOP AND FIND SHELTER Get the casualty into a shelter. Do not warm the affected area unless there is no risk of refreezing. Do not remove her gloves or shoes if she needs to walk any further.

2 WARM UP GRADUALLY Tell the casualty to put her hands in her armpits to warm them up gently using her own body warmth. She can put her feet in your armpits to warm them up.

3 PLACE AFFECTED PARTS IN WARM WATER Once you are inside, remove the casualty's gloves or shoes and place her hands or feet in warm water. Try to remove rings or jewellery (do not force this, though). Dry the affected area and wrap it in a loose, dry, non-fluffy bandage.

4 GET MEDICAL HELP The casualty should be taken to hospital. If she is in pain, she can take the recommended dose of her normal pain relief tablet, such as paracetamol or ibuprofen.

 TAKE CARE

As the skin is warmed up, it may become bright red, feel hot and be very painful. If the tissues are damaged, the affected area may turn black.

heat-related illness

Heat exhaustion occurs in hot, humid surroundings when a person sweats profusely and loses a lot of fluids and body salts. Heatstroke is a medical emergency that occurs when the body's temperature regulation system fails and cannot cool the body. Both conditions need medical help, but heatstroke is life-threatening if untreated.

assessment

For **heat exhaustion**, the symptoms and signs are:

- Casualty complains of feeling hot but may look pale and will be sweating
- Will have a headache and may feel faint
- Skin feels cool and clammy
- May feel nauseous and vomit
- Signs of dehydration, such as cramps especially in the leg muscles (see pages 50–51)
- Breathing and pulse may be rapid and gradually become weaker

Symptoms for **heatstroke** are as follows:

- Severe headache
- Casualty complains of feeling very hot, but will not be sweating
- Skin looks flushed and feels hot, but will be dry
- Body temperature above 40°C (104°F)
- Breathing may be rapid and shallow but pulse will appear strong and bounding
- **Casualty will become confused and will rapidly lose consciousness**

 WARNING

A person who is already unwell, particularly if he has vomiting or diarrhoea, is more likely to suffer from heat exhaustion.

 TAKE CARE

Heatstroke develops if the body temperature rises to about 40°C (104°F). Take precautions in a heatwave. Stay out of the sun in the middle of the day – between 11am and 3pm. Wear light cotton clothing and a hat. Have plenty to drink (see page 50) and avoid alcohol and caffeine.

IS IT HEAT EXHAUSTION OR HEATSTROKE?

ACTION	HEAT EXHAUSTION	HEATSTROKE
Look at skin colour	Pale	Flushed
Feel the casualty's skin	Cool and clammy	Hot and dry
Check the pulse	Rapid and weakening	Strong and bounding
Check level of consciousness	Fully awake and conscious	Rapidly deteriorating level of consciousness

GET HELP Heat exhaustion can lead to the more dangerous condition heatstroke if you do not cool the casualty down. If you suspect heatstroke, call the emergency services.

 WATCHPOINT The use of some drugs such as MDMA (Ecstasy) can cause over-heating. It is especially dangerous when combined with dancing in a warm atmosphere.

action

HEAT EXHAUSTION

1 MOVE THE CASUALTY INTO SHADE Help him into a cooler, shady place – inside if possible. Lay him down and loosen any tight clothing. Raise his legs to help increase blood flow to the brain.

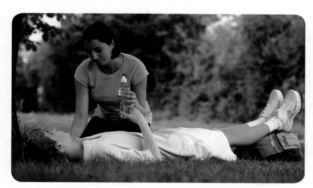

2 GIVE WATER Give the casualty sips of water – do not let him drink too much too quickly (see page 51). You can give him water containing oral rehydration salts or isotonic drinks to help replace some of the salts he has lost through sweating. Do not add salt to the water. Cool his skin with cold water.

3 MONITOR THE CASUALTY Check and make a note of his level of consciousness, breathing, pulse (see page 30) and body temperature (see page 62). Recheck regularly until he recovers. Advise him to stay in the shade and to see his doctor, even if he appears to recover quickly.

⚠ WARNING

● If the casualty with a heat-related illness does not improve quickly and you notice any of the signs of heatstroke, call for emergency help straightaway.
● If the casualty becomes unconscious, open the airway and check breathing (see page 14). Be prepared to begin CPR (see pages 16–17).

HEATSTROKE

1 GET HELP Call the emergency services. Move the casualty to a cool room and help him to sit down and remove as much clothing as you can.

2 COOL THE CASUALTY Soak a large sheet or towel in cool water and wrap it around the casualty. Pour more cool water over the sheet or towel to keep it cool. An alternative to this method is to shower or sponge the casualty with cool water. Fan his face if possible and open a window to ensure a supply of fresh cool air.

3 CHECK TEMPERATURE Cool the casualty until his body temperature has fallen below 37.5°C (99.5°F), then wrap him in a dry sheet if you have one.

4 MONITOR THE CASUALTY Check and make a note of his level of consciousness, breathing, pulse (see page 30) and body temperature (see page 62). Recheck regularly until medical help arrives. If his body temperature begins to rise again, restart the cooling process. Provided the casualty is fully conscious, give him water to drink.

what next?

Most people who suffer from heatstroke make a full recovery with prompt treatment. The very young and the elderly are more likely to suffer complications. Medical treatment aims to continue the cooling process.

▶▶See also: **UNCONSCIOUS ADULT/CHILD/BABY** pp14–19 • **DEHYDRATION** pp50–51

dehydration

This condition develops when a person does not drink enough water to replace body fluids lost through sweating or through vomiting and diarrhoea. It is important to help the casualty to rehydrate as soon as possible to avoid severe dehydration.

WATCHPOINT A person who is unwell and is vomiting and/or has diarrhoea may become dehydrated. Give him plenty to drink. Give water, or water containing rehydration salts.

assessment

Symptoms of dehydration start to become apparent when the body loses only about one per cent of its fluid. For mild to moderate dehydration, you may notice some or all of the following:

Feels unusually tired

Urine darker and/or smaller quantities and less frequent than normal

Mouth, lips and eyes feel dry

Headache

Feels thirsty

Dizzy or light-headed on standing up

Muscle weakness and possible cramps

If fluid loss is five per cent or greater:

- Heat-related illness
- Increasing thirst and irritability
- Decreased sweating
- Urination may cease
- Pulse and breathing rate increases, but gradually weakens
- If untreated, the casualty may develop seizures, and could lose consciousness

⚠ WARNING

In addition to the above symptoms, in babies and children the skin may be very pale. In a young baby, the fontanelle (soft area of the scalp) will be sunken and the baby will shed few or no tears when it cries.

Staying hydrated

Water is lost mainly through sweating and urinating. The amount of water in the body is regulated to control the levels of compounds, such as salts, in the blood.

● **MAKE SURE YOU DRINK ENOUGH** There is no set amount of water you should drink each day. Drink water to satisfy your thirst and drink more in hot weather, or if you are exercising or working in extreme heat and/or humidity for long periods. The amount needed depends on your body weight,

the temperature around you and the type of activity you are undertaking. You should consume enough fluids to produce clear urine.

● **DRINKING TOO MUCH WATER** Drinking too much water too quickly can lead to water intoxication as the body salts become too diluted (known as hyponatraemia). **This can cause the brain to swell, leading to confusion or collapse.** Even someone resting in extreme heat risks water intoxication if he drinks a large amount of water over a short period.

1 GIVE FLUIDS Sit the casualty down. Give her plenty of water to drink and tell her to drink it **slowly**. Water is sufficient, but you can also give her water containing oral rehydration salts, or isotonic drinks. Do not give her anything to eat as this may dehydrate her even more.

2 TREAT MUSCLE CRAMPS Stretch and massage the affected muscles to relieve the cramp (see below).

3 MONITOR THE CASUALTY Advise the casualty to rest, and monitor her condition. She should start to feel better. If she does not improve, or if she deteriorates, get medical advice.

⚠ WARNING
- Do not add salt to the casualty's water.
- If the casualty becomes unconscious, open the airway and check breathing (see page 14). Be prepared to begin CPR (see pages 16–17).

Treating muscle cramp

Muscles may go into spasm or jerk involuntarily as a result of exercise, dehydration and/or heat exhaustion. Muscle cramps can be very painful. The aim of treatment is to stretch the muscles to reverse the effect and relieve the cramp.

- **CRAMP IN THE CALF MUSCLES** Sit the person down. Hold his foot and flex his ankle, pointing his toes upwards to stretch the calf muscles. Massage the back of the calf.

- **CRAMP IN THE FOOT** Help him to stand on the foot and lean forward to stretch the affected muscles on the underside of the foot. Massage the foot firmly.

- **CRAMP IN THE THIGH MUSCLES** Help the person to lie down. If the cramp is in the front of the thigh, bend the knee to stretch the muscles, then rub the front of the leg. If the cramp is in the back of the thigh, straighten the leg, then massage the back of the leg.

sunburn

Damage (burning) caused by over-exposure to the ultraviolet (UV) rays in sunlight is called sunburn. Two main types of UV rays cause damage to skin: UVB rays are responsible for the majority of sunburn and can lead to skin cancer; UVA rays penetrate deeper into the skin causing ageing, but contribute much less towards sunburn.

assessment

Most sunburn is caused by exposure to bright sunlight, but it can also occur on overcast days, especially at high altitudes, or from sitting under a sun lamp. Watch for the following signs:

Skin is red and tender; feels hot even after initial cooling

MILD SUNBURN
● Itchy skin, especially in the days after the initial exposure, which eventually peels
● Skin very sore to touch, and may feel 'tight' as it begins to heal

SEVERE SUNBURN
● Possible fever
● Blisters
● Swelling
● There may also be symptoms of heat-related illness (see pages 48–49), such as headaches, dizziness and nausea

Sun protection

When skin is exposed to sunlight, it produces a pigment called melanin to provide some protection from UV rays. The less melanin in the skin, the less the skin is protected. People with fair skin naturally have lower levels of melanin than those with darker hair or skin.

● **COVER UP** Wear clothes that cover your arms and legs (sun-proof clothing is ideal), a hat that protects the neck and sunglasses.
● **STAY IN THE SHADE** Do this as much as possible, but always when the sun is at its peak – between 11am and 3pm.
● **ALWAYS USE SUNSCREEN** Use cream with a sun protection factor (SPF) of at least 30 and reapply it at least every 2 hours and immediately after swimming. For very pale skin, use SPF 50. Make sure children are well protected as their skin is more delicate than an adult's.

GET HELP Severe sunburn in which the skin has blistered needs hospital treatment. Take the casualty to hospital or call the emergency services if the blistering is extensive.

WATCHPOINT Over-exposure to the sun may also result in heat exhaustion or heatstroke (see pages 48–49). Seek medical advice for dizziness, headache, confusion or nausea.

TIME TO ACT To test whether your skin is burning, press a patch of skin on your arm until it is white. Normally the colour returns immediately. If it stays white, your skin may be burning.

action

1 MOVE THE CASUALTY TO THE SHADE Give the casualty a towel or light cotton clothing to cover affected areas and help him into the shade.

2 COOL THE BURNED AREA Tell the casualty to cool his skin by sponging it with lukewarm water or by having a tepid shower. For a large area of skin, he may want to cool the area by soaking in a cool bath.

what next?

● Mild sunburn can be treated at home. Advise the person to stay out of the sun, either inside or in the shade, and to keep the area covered with light (preferably cotton) clothing until the skin has healed. The casualty's skin may also flake or peel after a few days. This is the body's way of protecting itself: the skin cells have been damaged and are at risk of becoming cancerous, so the body sheds them.
● Adults may take one of their usual painkillers such as paracetamol or ibuprofen to relieve discomfort. A child can be given appropriate doses of children's paracetamol or children's ibuprofen.
● A casualty with severe burns will need to be assessed at a hospital. As with any burn, there is a risk of fluid loss and infection (see pages 112–113).

3 DRINK WATER AND FLUIDS Make sure the casualty drinks plenty of fluids to replace the fluid lost through sweating and to cool down. Do not let him drink alcohol because it will dehydrate him further.

4 APPLY CREAMS
For mild sunburn, tell the casualty to apply a moisturising lotion or aftersun lotion. Aftersun lotions help to cool and moisturise the skin, which helps prevent the 'tight' feeling that can develop as the skin heals, but they do not provide protection from the sun. Calamine lotion may also relieve itching and soreness.

 TAKE CARE
Do not touch blisters caused by sunburn – treat as for burns. Cool the burned area with water until the pain eases. Cover the blister with kitchen film or a non-fluffy dressing and take the casualty to hospital.

Check for moles

Regularly check your skin for moles. They are formed by a collection of skin pigment cells called melanocytes. Most are normal and harmless, but in a few cases they can develop into malignant melanoma, an aggressive form of skin cancer. Look out for the ABCD (Asymmetry, Border irregularity, Colour variation, Diameter greater than 6mm) and see your doctor.

▶▶See also: **VISION PROBLEMS** pp68–69 • **BURNS AND SCALDS** pp112–113 **53**

allergic reaction

Any allergic reaction, including the most extreme form, occurs because the body's immune system reacts inappropriately in response to the presence of a substance that it wrongly perceives as a threat. There may only be mild itching, a skin rash, wheezing or sneezing, or, more rarely, a whole-body reaction known as anaphylaxis.

assessment

Symptoms of allergy are commonly mild, but **a severe allergic reaction is life-threatening** and occurs within seconds or minutes of exposure to the allergen. In a severe allergy, many of the features of mild allergy are present, but more pronounced. Look out for the following signs or symptoms:

MILD ALLERGIC REACTION

- Red, itchy rash, possibly blotchy with raised red areas of skin (hives)
- Swollen, puffy hands and feet
- Sneezing and possible wheezing
- History of mild allergy
- Possible abdominal pain and/or vomiting
- Itchy, watery eyes, often reddened

SEVERE ALLERGIC REACTION

- Initially, generalised flushed appearance to the skin, possibly all over the body
- Swelling of the mouth and throat
- Difficulty breathing and possible asthma attack in a susceptible casualty, who may gasp for air
- Difficulty swallowing, which gradually worsens
- The casualty feels a sense of impending doom and may become very agitated, confused and frightened
- Casualty feels weak as blood pressure drops, and skin becomes pale; possible collapse

Understanding anaphylaxis

Also known as anaphylactic shock, anaphylaxis is an extreme and severe allergic reaction that affects the entire body. The reaction between the allergic antibody (IgE) and the allergen triggers the sudden release of body chemicals, including histamine, from cells in the blood and tissues. These chemicals act on blood vessels, causing swelling anywhere in the body, especially the lungs, which results in breathing difficulties. Blood pressure falls and the circulatory system can fail, leading to shock (see pages 38–39).

- **ADRENALINE** If given quickly, a drug called adrenaline (also known as epinephrine) can reverse the effects of anaphylaxis by constricting the blood vessels, relaxing the smooth muscles in the lungs, improving breathing, stimulating the heartbeat and reducing the swelling.

- **AUTOINJECTOR** Anyone who is susceptible to having a severe allergic reaction should carry an autoinjector (such as Epipen) – a preloaded syringe containing adrenaline. There are different types, and the person will normally know how to use it. If the casualty is unable to deliver the medication, follow the instructions on the autoinjector. The technique is shown opposite.

GET HELP A severe allergic reaction is life-threatening. Occasionally a serious reaction to a known allergen takes several hours to develop. If in doubt, call for emergency help.

TIME TO ACT Asthma attacks are often triggered by an allergic reaction. If a casualty does not have her asthma medication with her, call for emergency help immediately.

WATCHPOINT Common triggers of mild allergy are dust, pollen, pet fur and foods. Regular doses of antihistamine can help reduce symptoms. Seek medical advice.

action

MILD ALLERGY

1 ASSESS THE CASUALTY Ask the casualty about any known allergy. Ask if she normally carries medication such as an asthma puffer.

2 REMOVE THE TRIGGER If possible, remove the casualty from the trigger – for example, take her inside if she is allergic to pollen or remove a bee stinger immediately (see page 322).

3 TREAT SYMPTOMS If she is carrying medication, let her take it. Seek medical advice if you are in any doubt about her condition.

 WARNING

If the casualty becomes pale and weak, treat for shock (see pages 38–39). Help her to lie down then raise and support her legs.

Managing serious allergy

● **ALWAYS CARRY MEDICATION** Anyone susceptible to severe allergic reactions should carry a preloaded adrenaline injection kit (see opposite).
● **CARRY MEDICAL ID** Wear an ID tag or bracelet and, if possible, carry a card.
● **AVOID KNOWN TRIGGERS** Common allergens include foods, such as peanuts, tree nuts (almonds, walnuts, cashews, Brazils), sesame seeds or oil, fish, shellfish, dairy products and eggs. Non-food causes include wasp or bee stings, latex, penicillin and other drugs.

SEVERE ALLERGIC REACTION

1 CALL FOR HELP Call for emergency help immediately, explaining that the casualty is suffering from a severe allergic reaction and stating the cause, if known. If there is a bee stinger, remove it immediately (see page 322).

2 GIVE MEDICATION Find the casualty's adrenaline (epinephrine) autoinjector and give it to him. If he cannot use it, you can help him. Hold it with your fist, remove the safety cap and press the end firmly against the casualty's thigh until you hear a click; hold in place for 10 seconds (see right). You can apply the medication through clothing. Rub the area.

3 MAKE THE CASUALTY COMFORTABLE Help the casualty to sit down in whatever position he finds most comfortable for breathing. The best position is sitting upright with his back straight. Do not lie him down. His condition should start to improve.

4 MONITOR THE CASUALTY Check his level of consciousness, breathing and pulse (see page 30) while waiting for emergency help. Note any change and tell the emergency services. If he starts to deteriorate, treat as for shock (see pages 38–39). Lay him down with his head low, and raise and support his legs.

5 REPEAT MEDICATION If his symptoms return, give adrenaline (epinephrine) again every 5 minutes, until medical help arrives.

▶▶See also: **UNCONSCIOUS ADULT/CHILD/BABY** pp14–19 • **SHOCK** pp38–39 • **ASTHMA** pp42–43

drug and alcohol poisoning

Poisoning can result from an excess intake of alcohol or overdose of prescription, over-the-counter or recreational drugs. The effect will vary according to the drug. Some trigger hyperactivity and/or hallucinations in which the casualty starts to 'see things'; others depress the bodily functions, in particular the nervous system, so carry a risk of unconsciousness.

assessment

Drugs act on the brain and nervous system and change a person's level of consciousness. A casualty may take more than one type of drug, which can complicate symptoms. Look for:

Sleeping tablets are a common cause of drug overdose.

- Evidence of alcohol or drug near the casualty, or from people nearby
- Drowsiness
- Enlarged or unequal-sized pupils (the black part of the eye)
- Nausea and/or vomiting
- Reduced level of response
- Loss of consciousness

TYPES OF DRUGS

DRUG GROUP	POSSIBLE EFFECTS
Alcohol	Depresses the central nervous system, causing a flushed, moist face, deep and noisy breathing, strong pulse; later, shallow breathing and a weak, fast pulse. Possible unconsciousness.
Anaesthetics, such as the recreational drug ketamine	High doses suppress normal brain and breathing functions, causing drowsiness, shallow breathing, hallucinations and possible unconsciousness.
Depressants and sedatives, such as sleeping tablets, barbiturates and tranquillisers	Casualty is sedated and becomes increasingly drowsy; breathing is shallow with a weak, irregular or an abnormally fast pulse; drowsiness leads to unconsciousness and the heart may stop.
Narcotics, such as heroin and morphine	Drowsiness, leading to unconsciousness; shallow breathing with weak, irregular or fast pulse; the heart may stop.
Hallucinogens, such as LSD and mushrooms	Agitation if the casualty has a 'bad trip', excitability, shaking hands, profuse sweating and possible unconsciousness.
Pain relievers	Nausea and vomiting, abdominal pain, drowsiness and possible unconsciousness. In addition, for aspirin overdose – rapid breathing, ringing in the ears, fever, sweating, disorientation and seizures. Paracetamol overdose symptoms develop gradually – jaundice and serious liver damage can develop days later.
Solvents, such as cleaning fluids that give off fumes	Headaches, ringing in the ears, hallucinations, nausea and vomiting, possible unconsciousness.
Stimulants, such as amphetamines (Ecstasy/MDMA) and cocaine	Excitability and/or irrational behaviour, hands may be shaking, dilated pupils, profuse sweating, possible symptoms of heatstroke.

GET HELP If the casualty is losing consciousness, call for emergency help as soon as possible. Ideally, get someone else to make the call while you look after the casualty.

TIME TO ACT If you are unsure what drugs the casualty has taken, look for containers nearby to help you identify the drugs or ask any witnesses.

WATCHPOINT Do not touch needles found near the casualty as there is a risk of infection; they must be disposed of safely. Inform the ambulance officers

action

ALCOHOL POISONING

1 MAKE THE CASUALTY COMFORTABLE If the casualty is fully conscious, help him into a comfortable position. Wrap him in a blanket to protect him from the cold. Alcohol dilates the blood vessels so there is a risk of hypothermia (see page 46).

2 TREAT ANY INJURIES Check the casualty for injuries, treating anything you find. If he has fallen, look for signs of head injury (see pages 82–83).

3 MONITOR THE CASUALTY If the casualty is conscious, monitor him until you are certain he has recovered. **If he loses consciousness, call for emergency help.** Check his level of consciousness, breathing and pulse (see page 30) while waiting for help. Make a note of any change.

Possible complications

Symptoms and signs of drug or alcohol misuse can mask other conditions such as head injury (see pages 82–83), stroke (see pages 34–35) or hypoglycaemia (see pages 58–59).

- **HYPOTHERMIA** If a casualty is outside in the cold, there is a risk of hypothermia, especially after drinking alcohol.
- **HEAT-RELATED ILLNESS** A casualty who has taken stimulant drugs and collapsed after dancing in a hot atmosphere is at risk of heatstroke (see pages 48–49).
- **HIDDEN INJURY** If he has fallen, he may have a head injury. Look for signs of bleeding, especially if there has been a fight.

DRUG POISONING

1 MAKE THE CASUALTY COMFORTABLE If the casualty is fully conscious, help him into a comfortable position. Ask him what he has taken; bear in mind that he could become unconscious at any point.

2 CALL FOR EMERGENCY HELP Explain that you suspect drug poisoning, and give as much information as you can.

3 TREAT INJURIES If a casualty has had a fall, assess and treat any injuries.

4 MONITOR THE CASUALTY Check his level of consciousness, breathing and pulse (see page 30) while waiting for emergency help. Note any changes.

5 KEEP SAMPLES If a casualty vomits, try to preserve a sample or show the ambulance officers when they arrive as this can help the medical team to identify what the casualty has taken.

 WARNING

- If the casualty becomes unconscious, open the airway and check breathing (see page 14). Be prepared to begin CPR (see pages 16–17). If he is breathing, place him in the recovery position (see page 15) as he may vomit, and monitor him closely.
- Never try to make a person vomit in an attempt to clear the drug out of his system.

 TAKE CARE

Any casualty who is intoxicated may become belligerent and difficult to treat. In this case call the emergency services. Watch from a safe distance until he allows you to help.

▶▶See also: **HEAT-RELATED ILLNESS** pp48–49 • **BLOW TO THE HEAD** pp82–83

diabetic emergency

People with diabetes can develop hyperglycaemia (raised blood sugar/glucose) or hypoglycaemia (low blood sugar/glucose). Giving sugar will be life-saving if blood sugar is low, and is unlikely to do harm if sugar levels are raised. Patients usually know how to control their condition, but even experienced people with diabetes may be susceptible to an attack.

assessment

Suspect low blood sugar/glucose if a casualty known to have diabetes has missed a meal, been vomiting or has recently taken a lot of exercise. Some or all of the symptoms may be present.

RAISED BLOOD SUGAR (HYPERGLYCAEMIA)

This is more likely to develop over several days or even weeks. Symptoms may include:

- Extreme thirst
- Frequent urination, especially at night
- Weight loss
- Itchy skin
- Abdominal pain
- In the later stages, the casualty will become very drowsy, **which will lead to unconsciousness – this is an emergency**

 WARNING

If you know that the casualty has diabetes and he fails to respond to sugar, or his condition begins to deteriorate, call the emergency services straightaway.

LOW BLOOD SUGAR (HYPOGLYCAEMIA)

This can occur if the blood sugar–insulin balance is incorrect. A person with diabetes often recognises the warning signs:

- Feels shaky and weak
- Skin is pale and feels cold and clammy
- Confused, irritable and behaving irrationally
- Rapid, but full and bounding pulse; casualty may tell you that his heart is pounding
- Casualty will quickly lose consciousness if he is not given some sugar

 TAKE CARE

A person who has recently been diagnosed with diabetes is more susceptible to a 'hypo' attack, especially while he is becoming used to balancing his sugar–insulin levels.

Understanding diabetes

Diabetes is a condition in which the body cannot control the level of glucose (sugar) in the blood. Insulin helps to remove glucose from the blood so it can be converted into energy. Diabetes develops either because an organ called the pancreas does not produce insulin (Type 1 diabetes), or because the body's cells are unable to use it (Type 2 diabetes). Diabetes can result in raised blood sugar levels (hyperglycaemia) and treatment can cause low blood sugar (hypoglycaemia), both of which are serious.

- **TYPE 1 DIABETES** This is a life-long condition that usually begins in childhood or early adulthood. People with Type 1 diabetes need to have insulin every day, normally via a syringe or an insulin pen.
- **TYPE 2 DIABETES** This is the most common type. It is associated with obesity, and is more common in the over 40s, but can develop in much younger people. Type 2 diabetes is controlled by monitoring a person's diet, controlling weight and exercising. Oral tablet medication is often needed and eventually people also need insulin.

action

HYPERGLYCAEMIA

1 **CALL FOR HELP** If a casualty collapses and you suspect hyperglycaemia, open the airway and check breathing (see page 14). Call for emergency help.

2 **MONITOR THE CASUALTY** If he is breathing, place him in the recovery position (see page 15). Check and note his level of consciousness, breathing and pulse (see page 30).

3 **RECHECK THE CASUALTY** Continue to recheck the casualty regularly while you are waiting for medical help to arrive.

what next?

● A person with suspected diabetes will be given a full medical examination at the hospital to assess his general state of health.

● If diabetes is confirmed, a medical team will work with him to plan a care program, which will include advice on diet and exercise. A diabetes specialist nurse will demonstrate any equipment needed to help manage the condition.

HYPOGLYCAEMIA

1 **SIT THE CASUALTY DOWN** Reassure the casualty and help him to sit down on a chair or on the floor if he is feeling faint.

2 **GIVE SUGAR** Provided the casualty is fully conscious and alert, give him a sugary drink, such as fruit juice, or some glucose tablets. People who have diabetes often carry a dose of glucose concentrate or have some sugary food in their pocket as a precaution. If he is not fully conscious, call the emergency services immediately.

3 **CHECK RESPONSE** If the casualty improves quickly after eating or drinking something, follow this with some slower-release carbohydrate food, such as a cereal bar, a sandwich, piece of fruit, biscuits and milk or the next meal if it is due.

4 **FIND MEDICATION** Help the casualty to find his glucose testing kit and medication, and let him check his glucose levels and take his insulin if required. Stay with him until he recovers completely. It is important to seek medical advice if you are at all concerned about the casualty.

▶▶See also: **UNCONSCIOUS ADULT/CHILD/BABY** pp14–19

seizures

A seizure is caused by a burst of excess electrical activity in the brain, which results in a brief disruption in the messages that pass between brain cells. Seizures can result from epilepsy, but in young children they can be triggered by a fever.

GET HELP If a seizure lasts 5 minutes or more, or a casualty has a series of seizures without regaining consciousness, get help. This is a medical emergency.

assessment

Seizures range from brief absences to episodes of convulsing and losing consciousness. The pattern is similar whatever the trigger.

FEBRILE SEIZURE IN YOUNG CHILD
A young child's temperature control system is not fully developed. Fever can trigger a febrile seizure.
- Child has a raised temperature
- Collapse followed by seizure
- History of febrile seizures with previous illness

MAJOR SEIZURE
Symptoms typically follow this pattern:
- Sudden collapse
- Casualty becomes rigid and may arch her back
- Convulsive movements begin – these may affect one or both sides of the body
- Breathing becomes difficult – casualty may clench her jaw. Blood or blood-stained saliva may appear at the mouth (she has probably bitten her lips or tongue). Do not be tempted to put anything in her mouth. There may also be signs of lost bowel or bladder control
- Eventually, the muscles relax and breathing returns to normal
- Casualty will wake up, but may be dazed
- Casualty is likely to fall into a deep sleep, after which she may not be aware of anything that has happened

ABSENCE SEIZURE
- The person may appear to be daydreaming or switching off. **She will be briefly unconscious** and totally unaware of what is happening around her
- Possible unexplained actions, such as lip smacking or rubbing hands

action

FEBRILE SEIZURE IN YOUNG CHILD

1 PROTECT THE CHILD Do not restrain the child. Place padding such as pillows around her to prevent her injuring herself.

2 COOL THE CHILD Seizures result from a raised body temperature. Cool the child by removing the bedclothes. Remove clothing, although you may have to wait for convulsive movements to stop before you can do this. Open a window if possible, but do not let the child get too cold.

3 CALL FOR HELP Call the emergency services. Place the child in the recovery position (see page 15) when the seizure stops. Check and note the level of consciousness, breathing and pulse (see page 30). Recheck regularly until help arrives.

 TAKE CARE
- Do not cool a child by sponging with water. This can make surface blood vessels contract and conserve body heat, causing temperature to rise.
- If a child has had a febrile seizure, she is likely to have another one if she has a fever again; this does not mean she will develop epilepsy.

MAJOR SEIZURE

1 CLEAR A SPACE Try to break the casualty's fall. Remove any objects or furniture from around the casualty, or place padding against her so that she cannot injure herself.

2 PROTECT THE CASUALTY'S HEAD Place cushions or rolled towels or blankets around the casualty's head to protect her further.

3 CHECK FOR EPILEPSY INFORMATION Once the convulsive movements have stopped, check the casualty's arms, neck or pockets as she may be wearing a medical ID bracelet (see page 55) or necklace or have a card that describes her condition and normal seizure pattern.

4 PLACE IN RECOVERY POSITION If she falls asleep, open the airway and check her breathing. Place her in the recovery position (see page 15). Make a note of how long the convulsions lasted.

5 MONITOR THE CASUALTY Check and make a note of her level of consciousness, breathing and pulse (see page 30) and recheck regularly. Stay with her until she wakes up. Call the emergency services if you are in any doubt about the casualty.

When to call for help

Call the emergency services if:

- You know that it is the casualty's first seizure
- The seizure continues for longer than 5 minutes
- She remains unconscious for longer than 10 minutes after the convulsions
- One seizure follows another without her regaining consciousness in between
- The person is injured during the seizure
- You are concerned about the casualty's condition and believe that she needs urgent medical attention.

 TAKE CARE

If a person is having a seizure:
- Do not restrain her or attempt to 'bring her round'
- Do not try to put anything in the casualty's mouth during the seizure
- Stay calm, and do not frighten her by making abrupt movements or shouting
- Assume the casualty is unaware of what is happening, or what has happened
- Do not give her anything to eat or drink until she has fully recovered.

ABSENCE SEIZURE

1 HELP THE CASUALTY TO SAFETY Sit the casualty down somewhere quiet. Make sure she cannot hurt herself – for example, by walking into a road. If she is inside, clear a space around her.

2 CHECK FOR EPILEPSY INFORMATION The casualty may be carrying a card or wearing a bracelet (see page 55) that describes her condition.

3 REASSURE THE CASUALTY Stay with the casualty until you are certain that she has fully recovered – be aware that an absence seizure can be followed by a major seizure. Calmly reassure her and explain anything that she has missed.

fever

A fever is defined as a body temperature that rises above 38.5°C (101°F) for any length of time. It is one of the mechanisms the body uses to fight infection. Most fevers are caused by minor infections, such as colds and flu, and resolve as the cause disappears. In some instances, a fever is a sign of a more serious illness.

assessment

A fever can normally be treated at home with fever medication, such as paracetamol, and rest, but there are some instances where medical advice is necessary. Symptoms of fever include:

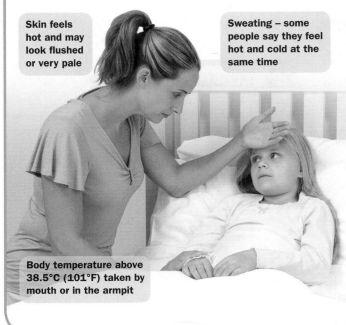

Skin feels hot and may look flushed or very pale

Sweating – some people say they feel hot and cold at the same time

Body temperature above 38.5°C (101°F) taken by mouth or in the armpit

ADDITIONAL SYMPTOMS
● Casualty feels generally unwell and may complain of aches and pains
● Headache

WHEN TO SEEK MEDICAL ADVICE
● For an adult or child who is coughing up green, brown, grey or rusty-coloured phlegm (spit or catarrh); develops breathing difficulties; becomes confused; or develops symptoms of meningitis (see pages 64–65)
● If a person is elderly, or less than eight weeks old
● If the patient is a child and has lower back pain; pain or difficulty when passing urine; has been vomiting or had diarrhoea for more than 24 hours (sooner if both); has had a vaccination in the last 10 days and/or has a very high temperature and is prone to febrile seizures (see page 60)

Fever warning signs in a baby

SEEK MEDICAL ADVICE IF A BABY:
● Has a raised temperature
● Has a seizure (see page 60)
● Becomes very pale, especially if the skin is blotchy (see pages 64–65)
● Has breathing difficulties – quick, difficult or grunting breathing, or unusual breathing patterns
● Is very hard to wake or unusually drowsy
● Is coughing up green, brown, grey or rusty-coloured phlegm (spit or catarrh)
● Refuses feeds, keeps vomiting up feeds or has watery diarrhoea for more than eight hours. If the

baby has both vomiting and diarrhoea, seek medical advice sooner.

CALL EMERGENCY SERVICES IF A BABY:
● **Has a hoarse cough with noisy breathing,** is wheezing or cannot breathe through the nose
● Is unusually hot, cold or floppy
● Cries in an unusual way, or for an unusually long time, or seems to be in pain
● If a newborn baby develops jaundice (looks yellow) when she is more than a week old, or develops jaundice over two weeks after birth.

GET HELP Raised body temperature can also be a sign of heatstroke (see page 49), a life-threatening condition that can occur in hot weather.

TIME TO ACT If a fever develops after travelling to a country with a high risk of infectious disease, seek urgent medical advice.

WATCHPOINT If an elderly person with a fever becomes confused, it can be a sign that a pre-existing condition has worsened, so seek urgent medical advice.

action

1 KEEP THE CASUALTY COOL Advise the casualty to rest and avoid strenuous activity. Keep her cool. She should not wear too many clothes or use too many bedclothes. It is important to keep the room at a comfortable temperature, and make sure that fresh air is circulating.

2 OFFER MEDICATION Let the casualty take the recommended dose of her usual fever medication, such as paracetamol. Give a young child the recommended dose of paracetamol or ibuprofen syrup. Do not give paracetamol to a baby less than one month old, or ibuprofen if less than three months old, unless advised to do so by your doctor.

3 GIVE DRINKS Make sure that the casualty drinks enough fluid to replace fluid lost through sweating and to prevent dehydration. To keep her hydrated, water is best but warm drinks can be soothing.

4 MONITOR CASUALTY Check her temperature every few hours. Seek medical advice if her condition deteriorates, she develops new symptoms and/or the fever lasts for 4 days or more.

 WARNING

● Don't give aspirin to a child who is less than 16 years old as it can trigger a rare but life-threatening condition called Reye's syndrome.
● A sudden raised temperature in a child aged under four can result in a seizure (see page 60).
● Seek urgent medical advice if body temperature remains very high **and the person becomes lethargic and delirious**.
● Do not give ibuprofen to pregnant or breastfeeding women, and use with caution and on medical advice for anyone with asthma, a history of stomach ulcers, indigestion, kidney disease or anyone who is taking blood-thinning medication, such as warfarin.

Measuring body temperature

You can assess whether a person's skin is hot or cold by putting your hand against an exposed area, commonly the forehead. But to obtain an accurate reading use a thermometer.

● **DIGITAL THERMOMETER**
For an adult, or a child over the age of seven, place the thermometer under the tongue and leave it in place until it beeps; it takes about a minute. The reading will appear in the window. For a younger child, put the thermometer under the armpit.

● **EAR SENSOR THERMOMETER**
Place the disposable cover over the sensor, tug the ear backwards to straighten the ear canal, and put the tip of the thermometer in the ear. It will give a reading in about a second. This thermometer can be used while a person is asleep, although it is not as reliable as an oral thermometer.

▶▶See also: HEATSTROKE p49 • FEBRILE SEIZURES p60 • MENINGITIS pp64–65

suspected **meningitis**

Meningitis is the term for inflammation of the meninges, the membranes around the brain and spinal cord. Meningitis can be caused by a virus or bacteria. Bacterial meningitis is more serious as it can harm the brain or cause septicaemia (blood poisoning), which often occur simultaneously. Without immediate hospital treatment, it can be fatal.

assessment

Symptoms can appear in any order, and may not all be present. They can develop over one to two days, or in a matter of hours. Watch for symptoms that appear suddenly and worsen quickly:

INITIAL SYMPTOMS
- Flu-like illness with high temperature
- Hands and feet feel cold; pain in the limbs
- Pale, blotchy skin
- Vomiting

AS THE CONDITION DEVELOPS
- Headache, possibly severe, with neck stiffness (less common in the very young)
- Stomach cramps or diarrhoea
- Eyes may become especially sensitive to light (less common in very young children)
- Rapid breathing – possibly breathlessness
- The casualty may become difficult to wake
- A blank staring expression
- Casualty may be confused and delirious
- Meningococcal rash (see below)
- Possible seizures

IN BABIES AND TODDLERS
The following symptoms may also be present:
- Refusing to eat or feed
- Dislike of being handled
- High-pitched, whimpering cry
- Floppy, listless and unable to stand
- Unresponsive with a blank, staring expression
- Tense or bulging fontanelle (the soft spot on top of the head)

⚠ WARNING
The organisms responsible for bacterial meningitis also cause septicaemia (blood poisoning), an even more dangerous condition.
This condition can appear with or without meningitis. Seek medical advice immediately if you notice any of the following symptoms:
- Fever; cold hands and feet
- Limb, joint and muscle pain
- Pale, blotchy skin
- A rash (but do not wait for this to appear).

Checking for a rash

A meningococcal rash starts as red or brown pinprick marks, which can develop into larger red or purple blotches, or blood blisters, as the condition worsens. To confirm a meningococcal rash, press a glass against the rash: you will see the marks through the glass (all other rashes fade when pressed).

action

1 MONITOR THE SYMPTOMS Treat a fever (see pages 62–63). Watch the casualty carefully – it is easy to think that non-specific symptoms such as fever and vomiting are due to less dangerous illnesses.

2 SEEK MEDICAL ADVICE If the casualty has a flu-like illness plus any of the symptoms opposite, such as a headache, stiff neck, or his eyes are sensitive to light, seek medical advice. Do not wait for a rash to appear.

3 DO THE GLASS TEST If you see any sign of a rash, check it by pressing the side of a clear drinking glass firmly against the skin (see box, opposite). If the spots do not fade, it could be a sign of septicaemia. On darker skin, check for the rash on lighter areas, such as the palms of the hands, the fingertips or the soles of the feet. The spots or rash may fade at first, so keep checking.

4 CALL FOR HELP If someone is very ill, obviously getting worse and/or has a rash, call the emergency services immediately, even if you have already spoken to a doctor. If there is likely to be a delay, take the casualty to hospital yourself.

5 MONITOR THE CASUALTY Keep the casualty cool and reassure him – do not let him get too cold. Reassure him and check and make a note of any change in his level of consciousness, breathing and pulse (see page 30) while you are waiting for help.

what next?

• If a person has suspected bacterial meningitis and/or septicaemia, he will be admitted to hospital for treatment with antibiotics. The diagnosis will be confirmed by blood tests and an analysis of cerebrospinal fluid taken via a lumbar puncture.
• Anyone who has been in direct, prolonged close contact with the infected person may be given a short course of antibiotics as a precaution.

Understanding meningitis

Meningitis is caused by different organisms including bacteria, viruses and fungi.

• **BACTERIAL MENINGITIS** Most cases of bacterial meningitis and septicaemia are caused by germs that live naturally – and in most people harmlessly – at the back of the throat. Septicaemia (blood poisoning) is caused when the bacteria enter the bloodstream and multiply uncontrollably. The bacteria that cause meningitis and pneumonia are the most common in the developed world. They survive outside the body for only a few seconds and are spread by prolonged close contact, sneezing and kissing.
• **VIRAL MENINGITIS** This is more common than bacterial meningitis. It can make a person very ill, but most recover in two weeks. It can be caused by a number of viruses, including *Herpes simplex*, chickenpox and mumps.
• **PROTECTION WITH IMMUNISATION** Children can be vaccinated against most types of bacterial meningitis. However, although the vaccinations give excellent protection, they do not prevent all forms of the disease. There is as yet no vaccine for one of the most serious – meningitis B.

infected wound

Infection occurs when disease-causing micro-organisms (germs) enter the body and multiply. Any break in the skin allows bacteria to enter the body, increasing the chance of infection. Check daily for signs of infection; any wound that does not start to heal within 48 hours is at risk. Early diagnosis can reduce any danger to the injured person's overall health.

assessment

Suspect infection if you notice any of the following symptoms or signs:

- The wound and surrounding skin feels hot
- The area around the injury is swollen
- Yellow pus in the wound and/or redness around the wound – there may be red 'trails' leading away from the wound
- Swollen lymph glands in the armpit or groin
- Raised temperature (see pages 62–63); the casualty may feel generally unwell

action

1 REMOVE OLD DRESSINGS Take off the old dressings and dispose of them hygienically. Carefully clean around the wound with soap and water or alcohol-free antiseptic wipes.

2 COVER THE WOUND Place a sterile dressing over the infected wound and secure it with a bandage. Raise and support the injury, for example in a sling (see pages 90–91) if necessary.

3 SEEK MEDICAL ADVICE Tell the person to arrange an appointment with his doctor as a course of antibiotics may be needed, or take him to hospital.

Understanding infection

- **INFECTION SOURCES** Germs can enter the body via the cause of injury – for example, a dirty knife. Alternatively, they can come from a person's clothing, hands or breath. There may also be tiny particles of dirt or dead tissue in a wound.

- **WOUND CARE** Good hygiene reduces risk. Wash your hands thoroughly with soap and water before treating a casualty. If water is unavailable, use alcohol gel. Wear disposable gloves – ideally non-latex gloves as many people are allergic to latex. Bleeding naturally flushes out most, if not all, the dirt but you should always carefully wash around the wound to remove dirt from the surrounding skin.
- **TETANUS IMMUNISATION** Tetanus is a very serious disease resulting from micro-organisms found in soil and manure. It is rare in countries where most people are protected against this infection through immunisation (see page 101).

 WARNING

If an injured casualty becomes unwell, has a raised body temperature, is shivering and is becoming weak and lethargic, take him to hospital yourself or get emergency help.

sudden hearing loss

Most hearing loss is gradual and age-related but a number of conditions can result in sudden loss of hearing over a matter of days or even hours. In many cases, the cause is an ear infection or wax blockage that can be treated easily. Consult a doctor or hospital if sudden hearing loss in one or both ears occurs without an obvious cause.

assessment

Temporary hearing problems can result from:

- Blocked nose as a result of a severe cold or hay fever – this can cause a build-up of mucus against the eardrum, especially in children
- Pressure change during take-off and landing when flying
- Brief exposure to loud noise, such as music, which can leave a loud ringing in the ears for a few hours. A sudden, very loud noise such as an explosion can damage the ear-drum
- Infection of the outer or inner ear
- Build-up of wax in the ear canals
- Ménière's disease – a serious disorder in which excess fluid collects in the inner ear, resulting in severe dizziness
- Head injury

 WARNING

If sudden hearing loss follows a blow to the head, call for emergency help immediately.

Protecting hearing

Persistent exposure to loud noise can cause permanent hearing loss, but you can take steps to prevent damage to ears.

- **WEAR EAR PROTECTION** If you are exposed to sustained loud noises at work, wear ear plugs or ear defenders. Have regular hearing tests.
- **KEEP SOUND LEVELS LOW** Make sure the sound level of headphones is low enough to be able to hear a conversation above them.
- **LIMIT LISTENING TIME** Restrict listening to personal music players to no more than an hour at a time.

action

1 REASSURE THE CASUALTY If the deafness results from a change in pressure after flying, tell the casualty to hold his nose and blow through his nose until he feels his ears 'pop'. If he has a cold or hay fever, hearing will return when he recovers. Ringing in the ears after exposure to loud noise should stop in a few hours.

2 SEEK MEDICAL ADVICE Arrange for the casualty to see his doctor for any other cause. If he cannot contact his doctor, take him to hospital.

3 TREAT EARACHE If the casualty is in pain, suggest he takes a dose of paracetamol. Give him a hot-water bottle wrapped in a towel to hold against his ear. It will help to soothe the pain.

what next?

- The casualty's doctor may prescribe a course of antibiotics as treatment for an ear infection or burst eardrum. The doctor will arrange a follow-up appointment to check that the infection has responded. A burst eardrum will normally heal by itself.
- If the cause cannot be identified, a casualty will be referred to a specialist for tests to assess the cause and measure the degree of hearing loss.

▶▶See also: **BLOW TO THE HEAD** pp82–83

sudden **vision problems**

Vision problems can develop following an injury to the eye or head. They can also result from disorders of the nervous system or the eyes. Age-related deterioration is the most likely cause of vision problems, and these can develop gradually or suddenly. Any sudden change should be investigated, as early treatment can prevent permanent loss of sight.

assessment

If a person is suffering from sudden vision problems, there may also be evidence of injury. As well as a reduction of vision, a person may experience the following symptoms:

Sudden blurred or distorted vision

Pain in and around one or both eyes, possibly with nausea and vomiting

Redness and watering

ADDITIONAL SYMPTOMS
- Difficulty focusing or colours may appear faded
- Burning or gritty sensation in the eyes
- Sudden appearance of 'floaters' in the eye – these are spots that appear to be 'on' the eye
- Partial loss of field of vision
- Obvious eye injury

SYMPTOM FINDER

SYMPTOMS	POSSIBLE CAUSES
Red itchy eyes, with yellow pus-like discharge	If vision is restored when the discharge is cleaned away, it may be conjunctivitis, an infection of the conjunctiva (the membrane that covers the eyes). Seek medical advice as treatment may be needed.
Sudden onset of double vision	Bleeding into the brain from a stroke or head injury; a symptom of a disorder of the nervous system. Call for emergency help.
Flashing lights and spots in front of the eyes	If this precedes a headache, it could be a migraine (see page 74). If it occurs with no warning, it could be a detached retina at the back of the eye (see box, opposite). Call for emergency help.
Blurred or double vision	Vision can be affected by diabetes-related disorders, some prescription drugs, ingestion of poisons and clouding of the eye lens (cataracts). if severe, seek medical advice or take the casualty to hospital.
Blurred or distorted vision with pain in one or both eyes	Glaucoma, a condition caused by excess fluid in the eye that results in a build-up of pressure in the eyeball, or iritis (an inflamed iris, the coloured part of the eye). Seek medical advice.

GET HELP If the casualty experiences problems with his vision after a blow to the head, call the emergency services without delay.

TIME TO ACT Call for emergency help immediately if the casualty (adult or child) complains of sudden loss of sight in one or both eyes.

WATCHPOINT Regular eye tests for adults and children can detect early signs of deterioration before more general symptoms of vision problems appear.

action

1 REASSURE THE CASUALTY If there is loss of vision, the casualty is likely to be very frightened.

2 TREAT ANY INJURY If the eye is injured, help her to lie down and support her head. Give her a pad to hold over the injured eye. If the casualty has splashed chemicals in her eye, see page 117.

3 SEEK MEDICAL ADVICE Advise the casualty to call her doctor, or make the call for her. If you are in any doubt about her condition, take her to hospital or call the emergency services.

Detached retina

The retina is the innermost layer at the back of the eye. It contains millions of light receptors that convert the image formed by the eye's optical system into impulses that are carried along the optic nerve to the brain. The retina can become detached from its underlying layer and may be torn. This causes sudden full or partial loss of vision, rather like a curtain falling over part of the eye.

● **TAKE THE CASUALTY TO HOSPITAL This is a serious condition that can lead to blindness** if it is not diagnosed and treated very quickly. The tear can be repaired surgically, which can restore vision and prevent further deterioration.

Snow blindness

The surface of the eyes can be damaged by over-exposure to ultraviolet (UV) light. This can be caused by the glare of sunlight on snow, concrete or water and can be prevented by wearing UV-protecting sunglasses.

1 ASSESS SYMPTOMS The casualty will experience a gritty feeling and excruciating pain in the eye. His eyes may be red and watering.

2 TAKE THE CASUALTY TO HOSPITAL Give him clean pads to hold against his eyes if there is likely to be any delay.

3 REST THE EYES The casualty will be advised to wear sunglasses and stay out of the sun until his eyes have healed.

what next?

● The casualty will be assessed at the hospital by a medical team. The tests that are carried out will depend on the symptoms.
● A basic sight test, known as a Snellen test, is used to assess a person's vision. The test involves reading a chart with rows of letters that become progressively smaller on each line.
● The casualty may be referred to a specialist for additional eye tests. If a head injury is suspected, imaging tests, such as an MRI scan, may also be given to ascertain the underlying cause.
● Treatment depends on the findings. Some conditions such as glaucoma may respond to drug therapy. Other conditions, such as vision problems following a head injury, may require surgery.

▶▶See also: **CHEMICAL IN EYE** p117 ● **EYE INJURY** p118

severe **abdominal** pain

Most abdominal pain is short-lived and caused by a minor ailment such as indigestion or mild food poisoning. Severe abdominal pain can result from injury or be a sign of a more serious disorder affecting the digestive system, urinary system, aorta or, in women, the reproductive system. Persistent or severe abdominal pain needs prompt medical attention.

assessment

Pain anywhere in the abdomen may be localised or general. Find out as much detail as you can as it helps the medical team. Ask the casualty when she last ate or drank something.

SYMPTOMS

- Possible fever and/or generally feeling unwell
- Bleeding (internal or external) if pain results from an injury or ruptured aorta
- Bloating or distended abdomen
- Vomiting and/or diarrhoea – which may be prolonged and/or severe
- Urinary problems
- Signs of **shock** (see pages 38–39)

IS IT SERIOUS?

SIGNS	QUESTIONS TO ASK
Pain	Has this happened before? Where is the pain (see right)? Is it concentrated in one area or has it spread? If so, where? Is it mild, moderate or severe – ask the casualty to give it a score out of 10. Is the pain continuous or intermittent, and has it changed or moved? When and where did it start? Does movement, breathing or coughing make it worse (or better)? Does it shoot through to anywhere else?
Bleeding	Where is the bleeding? Is blood loss slight or severe? Are there signs of internal bleeding (see page 38)?
Vomiting	How many times has the casualty vomited and when did it start? Does she feel better after vomiting? What does the vomit look like? Does it contain dark reddish blood that looks like coffee grounds (see page 38)?
Diarrhoea	How often do the bouts of diarrhoea occur? Does the casualty feel better after going to the toilet? Is there blood or mucus in the faeces?
Urine	When did the casualty last urinate and was it normal? Was it painful? Is the urine normal or cloudy? Does it smell unusual and/or contain blood?
Additional symptoms	Does the casualty have a fever (see pages 62–63)? Is she restless or tired, or is she too weak to move? Could she have food poisoning, or could she have gastroenteritis? Is the casualty a woman of child-bearing age? Does she have a history of menstrual pain? Could she be pregnant?

Top
Upper right
Upper left
Middle
Lower right
Lower left
Lower centre

GET HELP If a child is in severe, constant pain that lasts for an hour or more and/or her abdomen is distended (bloated) call the emergency services.

TIME TO ACT If the casualty's pain is severe, he is vomiting and has a fever, call the emergency services. Treat for shock (see pages 38–39) and monitor him until help arrives.

WATCHPOINT If you suspect serious illness or injury, do not give the casualty anything to eat or drink (including pain-relief medication) as he may need an anaesthetic later.

action

1 MAKE THE CASUALTY COMFORTABLE Sit or lie her down. She may be most comfortable if she is propped up with pillows. Give her a bowl if she is feeling sick.

2 GIVE A HOT WATER BOTTLE Wrap a hot water bottle in a towel and give it to the casualty to hold against her stomach.

3 SEEK MEDICAL ADVICE If you are in any doubt about the casualty's condition, seek medical advice. Make a note of her level of consciousness, breathing and pulse (see page 30). If her condition deteriorates, call the emergency services.

 WARNING

Call the emergency services immediately if there is an obvious abdominal wound or if the pain lasts more than 4 hours in an adult (one hour in a child) or is accompanied by ANY of the following:
- Severe vomiting and/or diarrhoea
- Blood-stained vomit
- Swollen and tender abdomen
- Swelling in the groin or scrotum
- Casualty feels faint and confused
- Fresh, bright red blood from the anus or dark, tarry stools
- Blood in the urine.

Severe pain and heavy bleeding in early pregnancy could be a sign of miscarriage or a life-threatening ectopic pregnancy in which the fetus develops outside the womb (see page 78) and requires urgent medical treatment.

Appendicitis

Appendicitis is an inflamed appendix. The appendix is a small blind-ended tube attached to the first section of the large intestine. It is situated on the lower right-hand side of the abdomen.

● **IS APPENDICITIS SERIOUS?** Appendicitis can be serious. It is a common cause of abdominal pain, especially in children. The appendix can become inflamed, swollen and infected. This can lead to gangrene (tissue death) in the wall of the appendix, which may burst as a result.
● **DIAGNOSIS AND TREATMENT** The pain usually begins in the centre of the abdomen. Over a period of hours it worsens and becomes most intense in the lower right-hand side. The casualty needs to be admitted to hospital for surgery. **If the appendix bursts, the pain may suddenly stop, but this can lead to the life-threatening infection peritonitis** (inflammation of the membranes lining the abdominal cavity and covering the organs).

what next?

● A doctor will conduct a physical examination and ask the casualty about the pain. Blood tests and ultrasound or other imaging tests may be carried out to confirm a diagnosis.
● If the cause of the abdominal pain is still uncertain, exploratory surgery may be needed. Further treatment will depend on the findings.
● Some casualties will need to be admitted to hospital for further investigation and, depending on the findings, may require surgery.

▶▶See also: **SHOCK** pp38–39 • **VOMITING** p72 • **DIARRHOEA** p73 • **WOUNDS AND BLEEDING** pp96–97

vomiting

Caused by irritation of the digestive system, vomiting can result from a viral or bacterial infection or parasites. If prolonged, it can cause dehydration. The risk is greater when diarrhoea and vomiting occur together.

WATCHPOINT Good hygiene is especially important. Wash your hands before and after attending a casualty who is vomiting or has diarrhoea.

assessment

Most cases of vomiting are mild, but if symptoms are severe, the person is young, elderly or has another illness, hospital treatment may be needed. Any of the following symptoms can occur:

- Feeling of nausea
- Vomiting, possibly with diarrhoea
- Stomach pains
- Fever
- Known history of eating or drinking a poisonous or contaminated substance (see pages 114–115)

 TAKE CARE

- Nausea, vomiting and tiredness are common during early pregnancy.
- Infections such as gastroenteritis can be highly infectious, so personal hygiene is very important.
- If you are concerned, tell the casualty to seek medical advice, as some infections need treatment with antibiotics.
- Tell the casualty to avoid alcohol.
- Anyone whose work involves handling or preparing food must take leave until he is free of symptoms.

 WARNING

- Call for emergency help if the casualty begins to show signs of dehydration (see pages 50–51).
- If dehydration is severe, there is a risk of shock developing (see pages 38–39).

Vulnerable people

For elderly people, young children and babies, the effects of prolonged vomiting and diarrhoea can have serious health consequences. They are at a greater risk of becoming dehydrated than young, healthy adults.

- If the vomiting in an elderly person is severe, prolonged and/or accompanied by diarrhoea, call for medical advice. **If the casualty shows signs of dehydration, he may need to be taken to hospital for treatment.**

ELDERLY PEOPLE

- Most elderly people can be treated at home. Make the casualty comfortable and treat as opposite, but monitor the casualty for signs of dehydration as this can be fatal.
- Give the casualty plenty of water to drink, on its own or with rehydration salts. Some types of rehydration salts are not suitable for people with a kidney condition. Always check the packet instructions.

BABIES AND YOUNG CHILDREN

- If a baby is breastfed, advise the mother to keep breastfeeding to replace lost fluid. A baby who is bottle-fed should be given water, or water with rehydration salts. Give frequent, small feeds.
- Call for medical advice if a baby or young child keeps vomiting most of his feeds or has watery stools; vomiting or diarrhoea lasts more than 8 hours in a baby (or 24 hours in a young child); or there are signs of dehydration, such as sunken eyes and/or fontanelle in a baby. If a baby or young child is vomiting and has diarrhoea, call for medical advice even sooner as the risk of dehydration is greater.

action

1 MAKE COMFORTABLE Reassure the casualty and make him as comfortable as possible. Give him a cloth so he can wipe his face.

2 GIVE SIPS OF WATER Give the casualty water after he has been sick. Tell him to sip the water slowly as he may vomit again.

3 BUILD UP FLUIDS Gradually build up the amount of fluid he drinks. Water is sufficient, but you can give him water containing rehydration salts (follow the packet instructions) or unsweetened fruit juice.

4 INTRODUCE FOOD GRADUALLY When the casualty is beginning to feel hungry again, give him small amounts of easily digested foods. Try plain pasta, rice or bread for the first 24 hours. If vomiting persists or recurs or there are other symptoms, such as diarrhoea, seek medical advice.

Food poisoning

Eating food or drink that is contaminated with bacteria, or the toxins they produce, can cause food poisoning. Some bacteria, commonly Campylobacter, *E. coli* and Salmonella, multiply fast in food in warm, damp conditions. The more bacteria present, the higher the chance of infection and illness. Most bacteria are destroyed by thorough cooking; food poisoning can result from eating undercooked foods.

● **REPORTING INCIDENTS** Food poisoning can affect a whole group if they have all eaten the same contaminated food. Severe cases should be reported to the local health authority so that the source can be identified.
● **WHEN TO SEEK ADVICE** Most cases of food poisoning clear up within a few days without medical treatment. Seek medical advice if the vomiting or diarrhoea lasts for more than a few days or the condition worsens, there is blood in the stools, the diarrhoea contains yellowish or greenish mucus, or the affected person is elderly, pregnant, or a baby or young child.

diarrhoea

If a casualty passes watery stools more than three times a day, he has diarrhoea. As with vomiting, it is generally a symptom of an infection, such as food poisoning.

assessment

Diarrhoea usually clears up in a couple of days and is not serious. There is a risk of dehydration if diarrhoea persists.

● Acute diarrhoea comes on suddenly, and can last for 1–10 days. It is most likely to be the result of an infection – such as food poisoning or gastroenteritis
● If a casualty has chronic diarrhoea that lasts for more than 2 weeks, it is most likely to be the symptom of a long-term condition such as irritable bowel syndrome
● Diarrhoea may accompany vomiting or it may occur on its own

action

1 GIVE SIPS OF WATER Give the casualty water to drink to replace some of the lost fluids and tell him to sip it slowly. He should aim to drink about 200ml of fluid after every loose stool.

2 BUILD UP FLUIDS Gradually build up the amount of fluid that he drinks. Water is sufficient, but you can give him water containing rehydration salts. Avoid sports drinks or sugary drinks as the sugar content can make diarrhoea worse.

3 INTRODUCE FOOD GRADUALLY When the casualty is beginning to feel hungry again, give him small amounts of easily digested foods. Offer foods such as plain pasta, rice or bread for the first 24 hours. If diarrhoea persists or recurs or there is blood in the stools, seek medical advice.

severe headache

A headache is a common complaint, often due to stress or tension, but a sudden severe headache following a blow to the head can indicate a potentially life-threatening injury (see page 82). It can be a sign of serious illness such as stroke (see page 34), of meningitis (see page 64), of carbon monoxide poisoning (see page 45) or of a condition such as migraine.

assessment

When a casualty has a sudden severe headache, establish the cause to eliminate serious injury or illness. Any or all of the following symptoms may indicate a potentially serious condition:

Sudden headache – especially after a blow to the head

Possible abdominal pain and vomiting

Sensitivity to light

Stiff neck

Fever

⚠ WARNING
A headache can appear hours or days after a blow to the head.

action

1 FOR A SUDDEN 'THUNDERCLAP' HEADACHE Get medical advice as soon as possible. Such headaches can be caused by bleeding into the brain.

2 USE A COLD COMPRESS Sit the casualty down and give her a cold pad to hold against her head. This can soothe a headache and should reduce swelling and bruising if she has had a blow to the head.

3 GIVE PAIN RELIEF If the casualty is prone to tension headaches or suffers from migraine, let her take her usual pain relief or migraine medication. Don't ever give aspirin to a child under 16 years old, as it can trigger Reye's syndrome, a rare but potentially life-threatening condition.

4 MONITOR THE CASUALTY Signs of serious head injury may not be immediately apparent. Monitor her condition. Get emergency help if you notice any of the symptoms above or she begins to deteriorate.

Understanding migraine

A migraine is a severe headache that is often accompanied by other symptoms. The person may experience an 'aura' comprising flashes of light or blind spots, difficulty in focusing and seeing things as if through a broken mirror. Attacks can be triggered by emotional, physical, dietary, environmental and medicinal factors. A migraine attack can last from 4 hours to 3 days. Some people experience migraine attacks several times a week, others only occasionally. The casualty may be more comfortable in a darkened room.

 WARNING
If the casualty becomes unconscious, open the airway and check breathing (see page 14). Be prepared to begin CPR (see pages 16–17).

panic attack

This is a sudden bout of extreme anxiety that can be brought on by a strong fear of something (phobia) or an emotional upset. Some people have a history of panic attacks, but in others an attack can come on with no apparent warning. A panic attack is often accompanied by hyperventilation and/or an abnormally fast heart rate.

assessment

Panic attacks can cause concern, but they usually subside fairly quickly. You may notice that the casualty has some or all of the following symptoms:

- Unnaturally fast breathing, possibly with tingling around the mouth or in the hands
- A very fast pulse rate
- Feeling of tension that causes a headache or feeling of chest tightness
- The casualty may be very apprehensive and may even have a fear of dying

 TAKE CARE

Do not restrain someone who is having a panic attack, and **never attempt to slap the person to 'snap her out of it'**.

action

1 REMOVE THE CAUSE Try to find out the cause of the casualty's fear and separate her from it. Either remove it from her or move her away from it.

2 BE FIRM Try to calm the casualty by talking firmly but kindly and calmly to her. Explain that she is having a panic attack and keep others away.

3 ENCOURAGE THE CASUALTY TO BREATHE CALMLY
Breathing more slowly will help to calm her and will stop her hyperventilating (see right). Try to encourage her to copy your breathing pattern.

4 MONITOR THE CASUALTY Stay with her until she has recovered. If she has a history of panic attacks, advise her to seek help to learn how to control them.

 WARNING

Do not ask a casualty to rebreathe her air from a paper bag as this can cause low blood oxygen levels.

Hyperventilation

A panic attack may be accompanied by hyperventilation – a state in which a casualty is overbreathing (breathing unnaturally fast). If it persists, the casualty breathes in too much oxygen and exhales carbon dioxide too quickly before the body can use it to regulate breathing.

- **HELP CASUALTY TO BREATHE SLOWLY** Help her regain control of her breathing. The out-breath should be longer than the in-breath. Ask her to copy your breathing pattern.
- **LONG-TERM HELP** If a person is susceptible to panic attacks and overbreathing, advise her to talk to her doctor as this is treatable.

unexpected childbirth

Childbirth is a completely natural process that can be lengthy, especially with a first baby. There is usually plenty of time to get a woman to hospital, or for help to arrive. It generally happens around the 40th week of pregnancy, but about 2 weeks either side is normal. A pregnant woman is likely to be very anxious if labour starts unexpectedly.

assessment

If a woman goes into labour, offer her reassurance while you wait for the emergency services or help to deliver the baby.

- Find out the expected delivery date
- Ask if she has her maternity notes – these will have important contact details and medical notes

There are signs to look for that will tell you how far labour has progressed:
- Possible contractions – these last up to a minute and initially come at intervals of

5–20 minutes, becoming closer as the labour progresses. Note the length of each contraction and the time taken between the beginning of one contraction and the start of the next
- Rupture of the membrane around the baby can cause fluid to gush out (the waters breaking). Once this happens, there is an increased risk of infection as the baby's protective layer has gone

The stages of labour

Labour has three distinct stages. The first prepares the woman's body for the birth. The baby is born in the second stage. The afterbirth (placenta) is delivered in the third stage.

Cervix fully dilated

Placenta

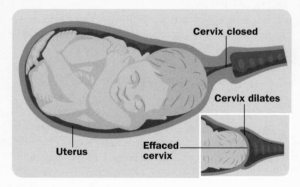

Cervix closed

Cervix dilates

Uterus

Effaced cervix

- **FIRST STAGE** This stage of labour can last several hours, although it may be shorter in second and later pregnancies. The uterus begins contractions, which help to press the baby's head against the cervix. The cervix gradually opens and 'thins' until it is 10cm in diameter. During this stage, a plug of mucus will be expelled. In addition, the water around the baby (amniotic fluid) may gush out.

- **SECOND STAGE** When the cervix is fully dilated (open) the woman's contractions change and she will feel a desire to push the baby out – this is a sign that the baby is about to be born. This stage normally lasts anything from 10 minutes to an hour, but can be longer.

- **THIRD STAGE** Ten minutes to half an hour after the baby is born, the third stage begins. The uterus contracts again. The placenta, known as the afterbirth, comes away from the wall of the uterus and is expelled from the body along with the umbilical cord.

GET HELP Call the emergency services, giving them any details you can find in the woman's maternity notes. Ask the woman who else she would like you to call.

TIME TO ACT If the labour is premature, tell the emergency services so they can arrange to take the woman to a hospital that has neonatal facilities for the baby.

action

1 CALL FOR EMERGENCY HELP Give the mother's due date, the place where she was expecting to give birth and the stage of labour she has reached.

2 DURING FIRST STAGE Listen to the woman and reassure her. She may be very worried, especially if the labour is earlier than expected. Help her to walk around or get into a comfortable position and encourage her to breathe slowly and steadily.

3 TIME HER CONTRACTIONS Make a note of the length and the frequency of her contractions. These will get stronger and more frequent. If she is uncomfortable, she may ask you to massage her back with the heel of your hands. If she is very hot, cool her face and neck with a damp cloth or sponge.

4 DURING SECOND STAGE If the woman tells you that she wants to push, this is a sign that the second stage has started. Ask her to remove any clothes that could interfere with the birth. Find a sheet to put underneath her and keep the area clean. Support her, but do not interfere with the birth.

5 WRAP THE BABY As soon as the baby is born, give her to her mother. Wrap them both in a towel and/or blanket. The baby will be very slippery, so handle her carefully. Do not cut the cord. Monitor both the mother and baby while you wait for help.

6 DURING THIRD STAGE Soon after the birth, contractions will recommence and the mother will deliver the afterbirth. Let this happen naturally (it can take up to 30 minutes). Do not interfere and do not cut the cord. The doctor and midwife will need to check that the afterbirth is complete.

Premature labour

Some babies are born before the 37th week of pregnancy. If it is close to 37 weeks, the birth may proceed as normal, **but it is vital to get the mother to hospital**. Some labours start earlier for a number of reasons. If contractions begin well before the baby is due, it may be possible for doctors to stop them with drugs. The mother will also be given steroid injections to help the baby's lungs, so the baby can breathe properly after the birth.

 WARNING

● If the umbilical cord is around the baby's neck as she emerges, try to ease it over the head to prevent strangulation. Do not pull on the cord.
● If the baby does not cry or make a sound after being born, do not slap her. Stimulate her by drying her face and chest with a towel. Open the airway and check breathing (see page 14). Be prepared to begin CPR if she is not breathing (see pages 16–17).
● If the bleeding is profuse after the third stage, or the mother is in any pain, keep her warm and lie her down with her legs raised and supported as there is a risk of shock developing (see pages 38–39).

▶▶See also: **UNCONSCIOUS BABY** p19 • **SHOCK** pp38–39

suspected **miscarriage**

Most miscarriages occur within the first 12 weeks of pregnancy. As a miscarriage can happen without warning, and may result in serious blood loss, treat it as an emergency. Bleeding in pregnancy does not always lead to miscarriage, but medical attention should always be sought. The woman will need reassurance and emotional support.

assessment

Miscarriage is very common, especially in the first 12 weeks of pregnancy. Symptoms may be similar to a normal menstrual period:

Vaginal bleeding – occasionally severe

Abdominal pain and low backache – similar to period pain

Possible severe cramping pains – similar to labour pains

ADDITIONAL SYMPTOMS

- In some cases, bleeding may be slight and develop over a few days
- Blood clots may be passed
- **If blood loss is severe or has been prolonged, symptoms of shock may be evident** (see pages 38–39)
- The casualty may say she has passed some tissue during the bleeding
- The casualty may become very distressed

action

1 REASSURE THE CASUALTY If you suspect that a pregnant woman is having a miscarriage, arrange for some privacy. Help her to lie down in a comfortable position. Make sure she has a sanitary towel, or a small, clean towel, if she needs one. Do not give her a tampon. Assess the level of bleeding.

2 CALL FOR HELP If bleeding is slight, advise her to call her doctor or midwife. If bleeding is severe, call the emergency services or take her to hospital.

3 MONITOR THE CASUALTY Check and make a note of her level of consciousness, breathing and pulse (see page 30). Check regularly until help arrives. If the woman becomes very weak and/or collapses, treat as for shock (see pages 38–39). Raise her legs and cover her with a blanket to keep her warm.

 TAKE CARE

- Preserve any tissue that a woman passes and give it to the medical team attending her.
- All bleeding in pregnancy should be assessed by a midwife or doctor. Bleeding does not necessarily indicate a miscarriage. Occasional light bleeding in the first 12 weeks of pregnancy is not uncommon; many women go on to have a healthy pregnancy.
- If a woman's blood type is rhesus negative she may need an anti-D injection. Ask a doctor.

WARNING

If a newly pregnant woman complains of very severe abdominal pain, particularly if it is one-sided, call the emergency services, or take her straight to the hospital. This could be an ectopic pregnancy (when the fetus is developing outside the womb), which is a medical emergency.

ACCIDENTS AND INJURIES

choking

If a small object 'goes down the wrong way', it can block the airway and cause muscle spasm. This can be life-threatening as the air passages that lead to the lungs become partially or totally blocked. Elderly people are at particular risk as they often have difficulty chewing food. Young children are also apt to put small objects in their mouths.

assessment

If the casualty can still cough, do not intervene as there is a risk that the obstruction could get into the lungs. There may be another cause for the cough, so ask the casualty if choking is the reason. Look out for the following symptoms of breathing difficulty:

- Casualty suddenly starts coughing, gasping for breath and has difficulty talking
- Skin becomes grey-blue (known as cyanosis). This is especially noticeable at the ears, lips, fingertips and inside the mouth (see page 40)

 WARNING

Act quickly to clear the obstruction or the casualty will lose consciousness. If the casualty becomes unconscious, open the airway and check breathing (see page 14). The throat will relax, which may free the blockage or open up the airway for rescue breaths.

ADULT AND CHILD (AGED 1 TO PUBERTY)
- If the airway is partially blocked, the casualty will be able to speak, cough and breathe
- If the airway is completely blocked, the casualty will not be able to talk, cough or breathe

BABY (0–12 MONTHS)
- If the airway is partially blocked, the baby can cough but will find it difficult to cry or even make a noise
- If the airway is completely blocked, the baby will not make a sound and will stop breathing

 SAFETY FIRST WITH YOUNG CHILDREN

- Keep toys with small pieces out of reach of very young children – check the label for suitability.
- Do not give a young child small, hard or chewy sweets or nuts.
- Stay with your child while he is eating.
- Make sure your child is sitting down whenever he is eating and/or drinking.
- Purée or mash food for a baby until he learns to chew properly.
- When a young child starts wanting to feed himself, give him soft or well-cooked foods to eat.
- Remove fruit pips.
- Do not leave a baby alone with his bottle or drink.

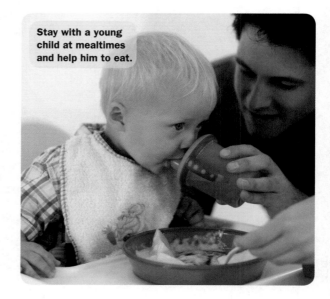

Stay with a young child at mealtimes and help him to eat.

 TAKE CARE

Elderly people who are infirm need special attention at mealtimes. Make sure that they are seated, give them small spoonfuls of food and check that their mouth is completely clear when the meal is finished.

action

ADULT/CHILD

1 CLEAR A PARTIALLY OBSTRUCTED AIRWAY Tell her to cough and clear an obstruction herself if she can.

2 GIVE BACK BLOWS If the airway is completely blocked, help her to bend forward and support her upper body. Give up to five sharp back blows between the shoulder blades with the heel of your hand, checking her between blows.

3 GIVE CHEST THRUSTS Put a hand on her back for support and put the heel of your other hand in the CPR position on her chest (see page 16) and give up to five thrusts, checking her between thrusts.

4 CALL FOR HELP
If necessary, repeat steps 2 and 3 up to three times. If the obstruction has not been cleared, call the emergency services. Continue with the back blows and chest thrusts until help arrives. If the casualty loses consciousness, give CPR (see pages 16–18).

 WARNING
● Check the casualty's mouth after every back slap or chest thrust. Pick out anything obvious. **Don't sweep a finger around the mouth** to look for an object as you may push it further down the throat or damage the throat tissues.
● Anyone who has been given chest thrusts must be seen by a doctor.

BABY

1 GIVE BACK BLOWS If a baby cannot breathe, lay her face down along your forearm, supporting her head. Using the heel of one hand, give her five firm blows between her shoulder blades.

2 CHECK MOUTH
Turn the baby over onto your other arm. Cradle her head with your hand and keep it as low as possible. Look inside her mouth. If the mouth is not clear, go to step 3.

3 GIVE CHEST THRUSTS Keeping the baby along your forearm, support your arm along or across your thigh. Place two fingers a finger's breadth below the nipple line and press sharply inward up to five times, checking after each thrust.

4 CALL FOR HELP Repeat steps 1 to 3 up to three times. If the mouth is still not clear, take the baby with you and call the emergency services. Continue back blows and chest thrusts until help arrives. If the baby loses consciousness, prepare to give CPR (see page 19).

▶▶See also: **UNCONSCIOUS ADULT/CHILD/BABY** pp14–19

blow to the head

Any blow to the head is potentially serious. A comparatively minor bump could affect a person's level of consciousness. Brain tissue or blood vessels inside the skull could also be damaged but the effects may not be apparent. A person may appear to be fine, then develop a headache or collapse later on. Anyone with a head injury may also have a spine injury.

assessment

Stay with a casualty who has sustained a head injury. Assess her carefully. In particular, watch for any change in her condition. Signs of potentially serious injury to look out for include:

Mild headache initially that becomes progressively worse, or sudden severe headache

No recollection of the incident or events shortly beforehand or afterwards

ADDITIONAL SYMPTOMS
- A brief period of unconsciousness after a blow to the head
- Serious wound to any part of the face or head
- Depressed area of the skull following an injury indicates a possible skull fracture. There may also be watery blood leaking from the nose or ear
- Breathing becomes noisy and/or slow
- Slow, but strong pulse
- Pupils (the black part of the eyes) become unequal in size
- Persistent vomiting
- Casualty becomes drowsy; **she may become unconscious**

Confusion and uncharacteristic behaviour; she may become very irritable

⚠ **TAKE CARE**
- Do not let a casualty go home on her own after a head injury.
- Do not give any alcohol. Seek medical advice if the casualty needs to take prescription medication.

The risks of head injury

- **CONCUSSION** A blow to the head can cause the brain to be shaken within the skull – known as concussion. This shaking causes a temporary disturbance in the brain, which can result in the casualty becoming unconscious for a short time. The casualty normally recovers completely but may not remember what happened. However, a more serious brain injury – compression (see right) – could develop later.

- **COMPRESSION** Compression injury results when there is a build-up of pressure against the brain within the skull. This can follow a severe blow to the head that results in skull fracture. However, it can also be caused by bleeding between the brain and the skull after an apparently minor blow, swelling within the brain, a stroke or a brain tumour. Symptoms may be apparent immediately, or may develop hours or even days later. It is life-threatening; the casualty will deteriorate and almost always need surgery.

GET HELP It is always better to be safe – seek medical advice, even if the casualty appears to be unharmed by the blow to the head.

 TIME TO ACT A person who is injured on the sports field should rest and must not be allowed to 'play on', even if he claims to have recovered.

WATCHPOINT If the casualty needs medical treatment, do not give him anything to eat or drink as he may need an anaesthetic. If he is thirsty, moisten his lips with water.

action

1 SIT THE CASUALTY DOWN Assess the casualty's level of consciousness. If he is fully conscious, help him to sit down, ideally on the floor, so that he cannot fall. Make him comfortable.

2 PLACE COLD PACK ON INJURY Give him a pack of ice (wrapped in a cloth) to place against the injury. If the person was knocked out, even if only for a very short time, seek medical advice.

3 MONITOR THE CASUALTY Tell the casualty to rest quietly. Stay with him. If he does not recover completely within half an hour, or begins to deteriorate at any point (see opposite), call the emergency services at once. If a casualty remains conscious, make sure that someone stays with him for at least 24 hours after the injury.

 WARNING
If the casualty is not fully conscious, help him to lie down and place him in the recovery position. Call the emergency services. Check for likely back or neck injury (see pages 84–85). Monitor him closely.

If there is a scalp wound

● **APPLY DIRECT PRESSURE** Place a sterile pad on the wound and apply pressure directly over it. Help the casualty onto the floor into a half-sitting position so that her head is positioned above her heart.
● **BANDAGE** Secure the pad with a bandage wrapped around the head to maintain pressure on the wound (see pages 96–97). Take the casualty to hospital or call for emergency help.

what next?

Severe head injuries always require treatment in hospital. The casualty will be assessed by the medical team and diagnosis will be confirmed with brain scans. Surgery may be required. Further treatment will depend on the severity of the injury.

 TAKE CARE
● To protect against head injuries when cycling, always wear a cycle helmet.
● People who have had a blow to the head should take precautions, such as avoiding contact sports for 2 months after the accident.

back and neck injury

The column of bones (vertebrae) in the back and neck supports the body and protects the delicate spinal cord. A back or neck injury can fracture one or more of the vertebrae or injure the muscles. Serious injury can damage the spinal cord, which could result in permanent loss of movement to any part of the body below that point.

assessment

If a person falls awkwardly onto his head, back or neck, suspect spine injury until you are told otherwise. **It is safer to immobilise him than risk permanent injury by moving him.** Look for:

Fall from a height – for example, off a ladder, down the stairs or from a horse

Severe pain in the neck or back

Signs of head injury

ADDITIONAL SYMPTOMS
- Feeling of heaviness in the limbs, or inability to move or feel them
- Inability to move or feel any part of the body
- Signs of loss of bladder control
- Possible irregularity along spine

⚠ **WARNING**
- Do not move the casualty unless his life is in immediate danger.
- If the person is unconscious, do not tilt the head to open the airway, use the jaw thrust (see box, opposite). Then check his breathing.

After a traffic accident

- **ASSUME THERE IS A NECK INJURY** The type of incident will give you an indication of the likely injury. In a car accident, the force of the collision may have propelled the casualty's body forwards and then back, resulting in a whiplash injury.
- **SUPPORT THE HEAD** Sit behind the casualty if possible and place a hand on each side of her head, without covering her ears (see right). Maintain this support until help arrives.
- **GET HELP** Ask someone to call the emergency services while you stay with the casualty.

GET HELP If you suspect a serious spine injury, do not move the casualty as you could cause permanent damage. The emergency services will bring special equipment.

WATCHPOINT Do not give the casualty anything to eat or drink as she may need an anaesthetic when she reaches hospital. If she is thirsty, moisten her lips with water.

action

1 CALL FOR HELP Reassure the casualty and ideally ask someone else to call the emergency services while you support the head.

2 IMMOBILISE THE CASUALTY Kneel or lie behind her head, place your elbows on your knees or on the ground. Leaving her head in the position you found her, place your hands on either side of her head to support it. Be careful not to cover her ears as she needs to hear you talking to her.

3 GET EXTRA SUPPORT Ask someone to get some rolled blankets, towels or coats and place them on either side of the casualty's head for additional support until the emergency services arrive.

4 MONITOR THE CASUALTY Stay at her head and ask your helper to check and make a note of her level of consciousness, breathing and pulse (see page 30). Recheck regularly until medical help arrives.

Opening the airway of a neck injury casualty

If a casualty with suspected back or neck injury is not breathing, do not tilt the head to open the airway, as it is important to keep her back and neck in a straight line. Instead, use a technique called the jaw thrust:

● **SUPPORT THE CASUALTY'S HEAD** Resting your elbows on your knees or on the ground, place your hands on either side of her head and keep it in line with her body.

● **PUSH THE JAW UPWARDS** Place your fingertips on either side at the angle of the lower jaw and 'push' it upwards (towards the ceiling) and forwards.
● **CHECK BREATHING** Look, listen and feel for signs of breathing for no more than 10 seconds (see page 14). Be prepared to begin CPR (see pages 16–17).

injured **lower limb**

An injury to the pelvis or lower limb – thigh, knee and lower leg – is most commonly caused by a fall on a hard surface. Sprains and broken bones are most common, while an injury to the pelvis or thighbone may lead to internal bleeding and shock.

WATCHPOINT Do not give the casualty anything to eat or drink as he may need an anaesthetic when he reaches hospital. If he is thirsty, moisten his lips with water.

assessment

Always compare the injured and the uninjured legs when assessing the severity of an injury. It is always safer to treat the injury as a break. Signs and symptoms to look out for include:

Deformity or swelling at site of injury

One leg turned outwards

Severe pain at site of injury

Casualty unable to walk on injured leg

ADDITIONAL SYMPTOMS
● One leg may be shorter than the other; this is most likely following a fractured thigh as the large muscles contract around the bone ends
● Possible shock if the pelvis is broken (see pages 38–39)

⚠ WARNING
● Do not allow a casualty with a lower limb injury to walk. He must be taken to hospital on a stretcher. Call the emergency services as soon as possible.
● Avoid unnecessary movement as the broken bone ends can damage any blood vessels or nerves alongside the injured area.

Folding triangular bandages

Folded lengthwise, these bandages can be used to provide support to an injured lower or upper limb. Narrow-fold bandages can also be used to help maintain pressure to control bleeding if you do not have a roller bandage. Open triangular bandages are used as slings, but do not exert enough pressure to control bleeding.

1 LAY BANDAGE FLAT
Lay the bandage out on a flat surface with the longest edge facing you. Bring the top point down to touch the base.

2 BROAD-FOLD BANDAGE
Fold the bandage in half again to make a broad-fold bandage used to 'splint' an injured limb to an uninjured part of the body.

3 NARROW-FOLD BANDAGE Fold the bandage in half again. This narrow bandage is used to tie the feet and ankles together.

action

LEG INJURY

1 SUPPORT INJURED LEG
Do not let the casualty walk. Hold the joints above and below the site of the injury. Ask a helper to put rolled blankets or towels on either side of the injured leg.

2 CALL FOR HELP Ideally ask someone else to call the emergncy services while you reassure the casualty and support the injured leg.

3 WHEN HELP IS DELAYED Provide extra support to the injured leg by immobilising it. Place soft padding between the legs and bring the uninjured leg to the injured one. Secure the feet and ankles using a narrow-fold bandage (see box, opposite) tied

securely in a figure of eight to prevent further movement. If you have help, ask the other person to do this while you support the joints.

4 ADD THREE MORE BANDAGES Slide three broad-fold bandages (see box, opposite) under the natural hollows of the knees and ankles. Move the bandages into position: the first **A** around the knees, the second **B** above the fracture site and the third

C below it. You must avoid the fracture site. The photograph above shows a fractured lower leg. Tie reef knots (see box, right) against the uninjured leg or over the padding in the centre.

WARNING

● If there is a wound at the site of the break, or a bone is exposed, cover it with a piece of gauze, then build up padding on either side of the bone until it is higher than the bone. Secure with a bandage.
● If the injury is near the ankle, instead of a figure-of-eight bandage, use two narrow-fold bandages – one around the leg and one around the feet.
● If the injury is near the upper thigh, position the bandage above the injury so that it is around the hips, avoiding the fracture site.
● Stop bandaging if doing so causes the casualty discomfort. Immobilise the limb with rolled coats, blankets or cushions and wait for medical help.
● Check the circulation in the limb beyond the bandages (see page 93). If it is restricted, loosen the bandages and reapply or support as above.

Tying a reef knot

A reef knot is used for tying bandages. It lies flat so that it is comfortable as well as secure.

1 RIGHT OVER LEFT
Take the right-hand end over the left-hand end and pass it underneath.

2 LEFT OVER RIGHT
Then pass what is now the left-hand end over the right-hand end and under.

3 PULL TIGHT Pull the ends gently to tighten the knot.

4 TO UNDO THE KNOT
Hold the strands on one side of the knot (either both of the blue or both orange). Sharply pull both ends

away from each other at the same time. Slide the straight section out of the knot.

PELVIC INJURY

1 HELP THE CASUALTY TO LIE DOWN **Do not let the casualty walk.** Help him to lie down on his back if he is not lying down already. Carefully slide some folded towels, a cushion or a rolled coat under his knees to raise them slightly. Stop if this causes the casualty any discomfort.

2 IMMOBILISE LEGS Place soft padding between the knees and ankles. For extra comfort, slide a folded triangular bandage (see narrow-fold bandage, page 86) under his ankles. Tie the bandage in a figure of eight around his feet and ankles to immobilise the legs and secure with a reef knot (see page 87) tied against the soles of his shoes. Tie a second triangular bandage (see broad-fold bandage, page 86) around the knees for additional support.

3 IMMOBILISE PELVIS Tie a towel around his pelvis.

4 CALL FOR HELP The casualty needs to be transported in the treatment position on a stretcher. Call the emergency services as soon as possible. Monitor him while you are waiting. Keep his head low to minimise the risk of shock as there may be severe internal bleeding following a pelvic injury.

 TAKE CARE
Do not move the casualty unless his life is in immediate danger. Even then his legs must be immobilised and supported beforehand.

KNEE INJURY

1 HELP THE CASUALTY TO LIE DOWN **Do not let the casualty walk.** Help her to lie down on her back with her knee in a comfortable position, probably slightly bent. She is likely to be in severe pain. Support the knee with pillows or rolled coats.

2 FOR EXTRA SUPPORT Wrap some soft padding, such as cotton wool, around the knee and, if possible, secure it with a roller bandage that extends from mid calf to mid thigh. Stop immediately if this causes further pain.

3 CALL FOR HELP The casualty needs to be carried on a stretcher in the treatment position. Call the emergency services. Monitor the casualty while you are waiting for help to arrive.

Additional support

Occasionally it may be necessary to provide additional support to a casualty who has a leg injury – if, for example, you have to wait a long time for help. In this instance it can help to place a splint along the outside of the body.

● **SUITABLE MATERIALS** Use something sturdy but not too bulky – a fence post, broom handle or walking stick is ideal. The splint needs to extend from the casualty's armpits to the feet. For additional comfort, place padding between the object and the limb before securing it.

● **SECURING THE SPLINT** Place the padding against the injured side and position the splint. Secure it using seven folded triangular bandages. Slide them under the natural hollows of the body and move them into position. Tie the first, a narrow-fold bandage (see page 86) around the feet and ankles, then tie six broad-fold bandages as follows: the first around the knees, then around the chest, pelvis, above and below the fracture site, and, finally, a bandage around the lower legs.

injured **upper limb**

Usually, considerable force is needed to break a bone, but force can also pull a joint out of place (dislocation), injure the bands of tissue, called ligaments, that hold a joint together (sprain) or tear or strain a muscle. If in doubt, treat this kind of injury as a break, as broken bone ends can damage surrounding tissues.

assessment

Unless you can see a bone end in a wound, it is impossible to know if a bone is broken without an X-ray. If any of the following symptoms are present, immobilise the injured limb and take or send the person to hospital:

- Deformity or swelling at the site of injury; compare injured and uninjured arms
- Pain increased by movement
- Casualty may be unable to bend his arm
- If the casualty is supporting the arm and leaning towards the injured side, suspect injury to the collarbone or shoulder
- If one shoulder looks flatter when compared with the opposite one, the joint may be dislocated
- Possible wound near the broken bone
- Bone end may be protruding

 TAKE CARE

- If there is a wound, cover it with a dressing to protect it from infection, and control bleeding by applying direct pressure (see pages 96–97). If the bone is visible, press either side of the wound. Immobilise the joints above and below the wound, then raise and support the arm.
- Always immobilise the injury before transporting a casualty to minimise the risk of further injury.

Improvising slings

A sling can be improvised by using a scarf folded in half diagonally. Depending on the site of the injury, you may also be able to use the casualty's clothing.

- **JACKET 'SLING'** If the casualty is wearing a jacket, undo the fastenings. Ask the casualty to support the injured arm and fold the lower half of the jacket up over the injured arm, making sure the elbow is supported. Secure the hem of the jacket to the top half with a safety pin. This is ideal for an injured forearm, wrist or hand as it provides the most support. If the casualty has an upper arm injury, partially unbutton or unzip the jacket and slide the hand into the jacket opening. Secure the zip with a safety pin. Do not use this 'sling' for a casualty who has a forearm or wrist injury as it does not provide sufficient support.

- **SLEEVE 'SLING'** Help the casualty to support the arm on the injured side in the most comfortable position, across the chest. Pin the sleeve cuff to the opposite side of the shirt or jacket. This can be useful for a shoulder or upper arm injury – do not use it if the casualty has a wrist injury.

- **BELT 'SLING'** Use a belt or long scarf folded into a thin strip. Fasten or tie into a loop, slip over the casualty's head and twist once to form a figure of eight. Slip the lower loop over the casualty's wrist. Do not use if the casualty has a wrist injury.

▶▶See also: **SHOCK** pp38–39 • **WOUNDS AND BLEEDING** pp96–97

action

SHOULDER/COLLARBONE

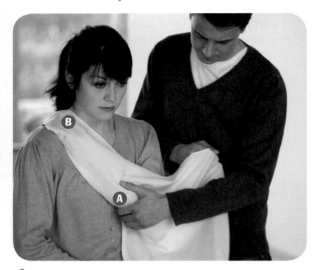

3 **SECURE THE CORNER**
Twist the corner of the bandage at the elbow **D** until it fits the elbow snugly, and tuck in the end to secure the sling.

4 **TAKE TO HOSPITAL** If possible take the casualty to hospital yourself, or call the emergency services if you have no transport.

⚠ TAKE CARE

- For comfort, place a broad-fold bandage (see page 86) around the injured arm and upper body. Tie the knot against the chest on the uninjured side.
- Check the circulation in the thumb (see page 93) after securing the sling. If it is restricted, loosen the sling and reapply, or simply support by hand.
- Do not give the casualty anything to eat or drink as he may need an anaesthetic later.

1 **SUPPORT ARM WITH AN ELEVATION SLING** Help the casualty to support the injured arm so that her fingers are touching the opposite shoulder. Place a triangular bandage over the arm with the longest edge parallel to her uninjured side **A** and the top point at her shoulder **B**. Tuck the longest edge under her injured arm.

2 **SECURE SLING AT THE SHOULDER** Carry the lower point around the casualty's back and up to the shoulder to meet the other point **C**. Tie the ends in a reef knot (see page 87) just in front of the collarbone.

⚠ WARNING

- Any casualty with a suspected fracture or a dislocated joint must be taken to hospital for treatment. You can take the casualty yourself if you have transport.
- Always immobilise the injury before transporting the casualty. This minimises the risk of further injury and is more comfortable for the casualty.

Children and the elderly

- **CHILDREN AND BABIES** Children's bones are still growing so they are softer than an adult's. As a result, the force that might cause a sprain in an adult may cause a child's bone to partially break on one side and bend on the other, like a twig. This is known as a greenstick fracture. The injury needs to be treated in the same way as any other break.
- **ELDERLY PEOPLE** Conversely, the bones of an elderly person are more fragile and it can take comparatively little force to break a bone.

ARM INJURY

1 **SUPPORT ARM** Gently place the casualty's arm across her body. Encourage her to support it herself, and help her if necessary. Help her to sit down.

2 **IMMOBILISE WITH AN ARM SLING** Carefully slide a triangular bandage between the casualty's arm and her chest so that the longest side is along the uninjured side **A**. Take the top corner around the back of the casualty's neck to the front of the shoulder on the injured side **B**.

3 **PROTECT INJURY** Wrap soft padding – a small towel, for example – around the site of the injury for extra support. Bring the lower part of the triangular bandage **C** up over the arm and tie a reef knot (see page 87) over the hollow in front of the shoulder.

4 **SECURE** Twist the excess fabric **D** at the elbow so that the sling fits around it, then tuck the end into the fabric. The weight of the arm in the sling will hold it in place.

5 **TAKE TO HOSPITAL** If possible take the casualty to hospital yourself, or call the emergency services if you have no transport.

INJURY NEAR ELBOW

1 **SUPPORT ARM** If the injury is near the elbow, the casualty will not be able to bend his arm. Help him to sit down and support his arm in the position that feels most comfortable. Tell him to avoid unnecessary movement. If one or more bones are broken, the jagged ends could damage the blood vessels or nerves around the joint.

2 **PROTECT ARM** Wrap soft padding around the outside of the joint – a small towel is ideal.

3 **IMMOBILISE THE INJURY** For additional comfort, tie two broad-fold bandages (see page 86) or large scarves around the arm and body. Place one bandage above the elbow and the other around the forearm.

4 **CHECK THE CIRCULATION** Check the pulse at the wrist and loosen the bandages if there is no pulse.

5 **TAKE TO HOSPITAL** If possible take the casualty to hospital yourself or call the emergency services if you have no transport.

⚠ WARNING

If there is a wound, cover it with a dressing to minimise the risk of infection and bandage it in place. If there is a bone sticking out of the wound, loosely drape a piece of gauze over the top. Place padding on either side and bandage over the top.

wrist and hand injury

A typical wrist and hand injury results from a fall onto an outstretched hand, when a bone in the forearm is broken at the wrist. Known as a Colles fracture, it is most common in the elderly. Wrists may also be sprained, and the small bones in the wrist, hand or fingers may be injured.

assessment

It is difficult to tell whether the wrist is sprained or a bone is broken without an X-ray. **If in doubt, always take the casualty to hospital.** Look for:

- Severe pain at the site of injury, increased by movement
- Swelling, and later bruising, around the injured area
- Open wound and bleeding following a crush injury (see pages 102–103)

⚠ TAKE CARE

- Cover a wound with a sterile dressing to protect it from infection and control bleeding by applying direct pressure (see pages 96–97). If the bone is visible, press on either side of the wound.
- If the casualty's hand has been crushed and is still trapped, free it only if you know the incident happened recently (see page 102).

action

1 SUPPORT ARM Gently place the casualty's arm across her body. Encourage her to support it herself. Help her to sit down. If the casualty has injured her hand, treat any wounds (see pages 96–97).

2 IMMOBILISE FOREARM IN AN ARM SLING Slide a triangular bandage between the casualty's arm and her chest so that the longest side is parallel with the uninjured side. Take the top corner around the casualty's neck to the front of the shoulder on the other side.

3 PROTECT INJURY Place soft padding around the site of injury for extra support. Bring the lower part of the bandage up over the arm and secure the sling in front of the shoulder (see page 91).

4 TAKE TO HOSPITAL If the casualty is uncomfortable, provide extra support by securing the arm to the body with a broad-fold bandage (see page 86). You can take the casualty to hospital or call the emergency services if you have no transport.

⚠ WARNING

- If there is a wound on the hand, treat any bleeding (see page 96), raise the hand and support it with an elevation sling (see page 90).
- After immobilising the arm, check for a pulse at the wrist. If there is no pulse, remove the sling and support the injury by hand and/or with cushions.

sprained ankle

A sprain occurs when the joint capsule or one or more ligaments have been stretched, twisted or torn – it is the most common ankle injury. In a minor sprain, some of the fibres within the ligament are stretched. In more serious sprains, the ligament may be torn. Minor sprains can be treated at home. Serious sprains need medical attention.

assessment

A sprained ankle is a common injury and the pain can be excruciating. If in doubt, take a casualty to hospital. Look for these signs:

● The casualty may not be able to bear weight on the leg
● Pain in and around the joint – the casualty may feel faint with the pain
● Swelling, and later bruising, around the joint

 TAKE CARE

Use **RICE** to remember treatment steps
R – Rest
I – Ice
C – Compression
E – Elevation

action

1 **REST LEG** The casualty should stop the activity that caused the injury. Help her to sit down and rest the ankle. Support it in a raised position.

2 **COOL WITH ICE** Cool the injury to reduce pain and swelling. Make a cold compress (see page 108). Ideally wrap a bag of ice or frozen peas in a cloth and place it on the ankle. Do not put ice straight onto the skin as it will cause a cold burn. Leave the ice in place for about 20 minutes.

3 **COMPRESSION** If the compress is small, leave it in place or wrap a layer of soft padding, such as a roll of cotton wool, around the ankle. Apply pressure with a compression support or compression bandage to help limit the swelling. This should extend from the toes to the knee.

4 **ELEVATE ANKLE** Raise and support the ankle so that it is higher than the hip to prevent swelling. Advise the casualty to rest the ankle. **If you suspect serious injury, take the casualty to hospital.**

5 **CHECK CIRCULATION** Make sure that the bandage is not too tight. Press on a toenail until it turns white, then let go: the colour should return quickly. If it does not return, the bandage is too tight; remove it and reapply. Recheck every 10 minutes.

⚠ **TAKE CARE**
Reapply the cold compress over the bandage every 2–3 hours. Remove the bandage at night and do not sleep with an ice pack on the injury.

▶▶See also: INJURIED LOWER LIMB pp86–88 • SEVERE BRUISING pp108–109

chest injury

A framework of bones called the ribcage surrounds and protects the organs of the chest as well as major blood vessels. The chest may be injured by an external force from a fall or traffic incident or even during an assault. It is important to immobilise the injured side – if a rib is broken, the bone end could pierce a lung, blood vessel or the chest wall.

assessment

Anyone with a suspected rib injury should be assessed at hospital. Sometimes the ribs are not broken, but there is bruising of ribs or nearby muscles. Rib fractures may (but not always) show on a chest X-ray. If a rib fracture is suspected, the main purpose of the X-ray is to look for complications rather than to diagnose the fracture itself.

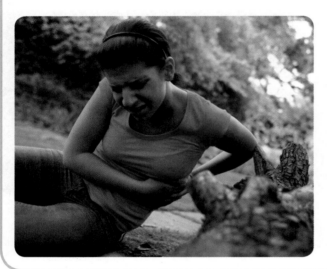

SYMPTOMS AND SIGNS OF CHEST INJURY
● Possible chest wound near site of injury
● Pain in one or both sides of the chest worsened by movement, breathing or coughing
● Swelling and deformity at site of injury suggests a fractured rib
● Wound on the chest caused by fractured rib or injury that pierces chest wall, such as stabbing
● Evidence of bruising on injured side

Is it serious?

A chest injury is potentially serious as it can cause breathing difficulties. If a wound penetrates the chest wall, a lung could collapse. The following should be treated as emergencies:

● **GASPING FOR BREATH** Symptoms of breathing difficulty (see page 40): person may be coughing, gasping for breath and find it difficult to talk. Skin becomes grey-blue (known as cyanosis). This is especially noticeable at the ears, lips, inside the mouth and at the fingertips.
● **FLAIL CHEST** Normal chest movement may be reversed over the damaged area on the injured side. This is known as flail chest.

● **RAPID BREATHING** Breathing may become fast and shallow; the casualty appears frightened, while struggling to breathe.
● **WOUND TO CHEST WALL** This can be caused by a broken rib or an injury that pierces the chest wall.
● **COUGHING UP BLOOD** If a lung is injured, the casualty may cough up bright red frothy blood and tell you there is a crackling sound. You may see blood bubbling from a wound and hear air being sucked in and out of it.
● **GOES INTO SHOCK** Symptoms and signs of shock may be evident (see pages 38–39).

action

IF THERE IS A WOUND

1 PLACE IN HALF-SITTING POSITION Help the casualty to sit on the floor. Place a sterile pad against the wound and ask the casualty to hold it against him. Lean him towards the injured side and support him with cushions.

2 COVER WOUND Place a sterile dressing over the wound. Cover the dressing with a sheet of plastic wrap or kitchen foil, secured with tape on three sides only. This allows air to escape from the chest but also prevents more from being sucked into the wound. The covering should be taut.

3 CALL FOR HELP Call the emergency services. Check and make a note of the casualty's level of consciousness, breathing and pulse (see page 30). Recheck regularly until medical help arrives. If the person needs to be put in the recovery position, place him on his injured side as this helps to stabilise the chest wall.

NO EXTERNAL WOUND

1 SUPPORT ARM ON INJURED SIDE Tell the casualty to support the arm on the injured side; help him if necessary. Encourage him to sit down. Support the arm in a sling (see page 91) to stabilise the chest wall and minimise the risk of further damage.

2 TAKE TO HOSPITAL You can take the casualty to hospital yourself or call the emergency services if you have no transport.

 TAKE CARE

If there is a wound, protect yourself and the casualty by wearing non-latex disposable gloves.

 WARNING

If the casualty becomes unconscious, open the airway and check breathing (see page 14).
If he needs to be placed in the recovery position, roll him onto his injured side as this helps to stabilise the injured chest wall and enables the uninjured lung to work normally.

wounds and bleeding

A wound is a break in the skin that allows blood to escape from the body. Bleeding is potentially serious as fluid is lost from the circulatory system. Bleeding from the smallest blood vessels – the capillaries – is usually minor. However, if the larger vessels, the arteries and veins, are damaged, significant life-threatening blood loss can result very quickly.

assessment

The principles of first aid are the same whatever the site of blood loss. Blood loss is faster when a larger vessel is damaged.

● Blood loss from an artery is often bright red and, if a major vessel is damaged, blood may be spurting from the wound in time with the heart beat
● Blood loss from a vein will be darker red and, if a larger vein is damaged, may gush profusely
● In some parts of the body, nerves and tendons can run very close to blood vessels and may be damaged. As a result the casualty may experience loss of movement or feeling

⚠ TAKE CARE

● **Always wear non-latex disposable gloves if you have them** to protect yourself and the casualty from infection.
● Always seek medical advice if a person who is taking a blood-thinning medication (anticoagulant) for a medical condition has a minor injury as he will bleed more profusely.
● Apply pressure directly over an injury or on either side if there is an object stuck in the wound (see page 100). Never use indirect pressure as it will cut off the blood supply.

⚠ WARNING

● If signs of shock appear (see pages 38–39), call the emergency services immediately. Make a note of the casualty's level of consciousness, breathing and pulse (see page 30). Recheck regularly until medical help arrives.
● If blood seeps through a dressing, cover it with another one, secured with a second bandage. If blood comes through the second bandage, you may not be applying pressure at the right point. Take off both dressings and apply a new one.

action

SEVERE BLEEDING

1 APPLY DIRECT PRESSURE Place a sterile wound dressing or clean pad against the wound and press firmly. Remove or cut away clothing to expose the wound if necessary.

2 RAISE AND SUPPORT INJURY Raise the injured part so that it is higher than the casualty's heart. This will slow down the blood flow to the area.

3 TREAT FOR SHOCK Help the casualty to lie down, while keeping the injured area raised and supported. Raise and support her legs above the level of her heart, on a chair for example. This reduces the risk of shock (see pages 38–39). Keep the legs straight and rest her ankles or heels on the chair to prevent blood pooling in her legs.

4 BANDAGE Tie a bandage around the dressing. Support an arm in a sling (see pages 90–91) for extra support. Call the emergency services.

WOUND ON THE PALM

1 **COVER WOUND WITH DRESSING PAD** Place a large sterile dressing pad in the palm of the casualty's hand, preferably the type with a bandage attached. Ask her to clench her fist tightly over the pad to apply pressure. Raise and support her hand.

2 **SECURE DRESSING** Wind the bandage around the casualty's clenched fist, leaving the thumb exposed. Secure the bandage over the top of the fingers to maintain pressure. Check the circulation in the thumb (see page 93).

AT INNER ELBOW OR KNEE

1 **BEND ARM OR LEG** Place a sterile dressing pad over the injury and bend the arm or leg over it to apply pressure. Raise the injured part to slow down the blood flow further.

2 **CHECK CIRCULATION** As raising the affected limb and applying pressure to the wound can severely reduce the blood supply to the rest of the limb, check the circulation in the lower arm or leg every 10 minutes, releasing the pressure if necessary.

⚠️ **WARNING**
● If the casualty becomes unconscious, open the airway and check breathing (see page 14). Be prepared to begin CPR (see pages 16–17).
● Do not give the casualty anything to eat or drink as he may need an anaesthetic later.

Varicose veins

Veins in the legs have one-way valves that prevent back flow of blood as it returns from the tissues to the heart. If these valves fail, blood pools in the veins, resulting in varicose veins. The veins are often near the surface and can burst following a relatively minor knock, causing life-threatening profuse bleeding.

BLEEDING FROM VARICOSE VEINS

1 **RAISE INJURED LEG** Help the casualty to lie down on the floor and raise his leg as high as you can – this will immediately slow down the bleeding. Ideally, rest the leg on your shoulder.

2 **APPLY DIRECT PRESSURE** Keeping the leg raised, place a sterile dressing pad over the wound and press firmly until the bleeding is under control.

3 **SECURE DRESSING** If necessary, place another dressing over the first one. Bandage firmly in place. To ensure the bandage is not too tight, check circulation in the foot (see page 93). If necessary, loosen the bandages and reapply.

4 **CALL FOR HELP** Call the emergency services as the casualty needs to be taken to hospital in the treatment position. Keep the leg raised until the medical team arrives.

⚠️ **TAKE CARE**
If the casualty is wearing elastic-topped stockings, remove them. Releasing the grip stops the bleeding.

gunshot wound

A gunshot can cause a life-threatening puncture wound. In addition to the entry wound, there may be an exit wound. A bullet can also bounce around inside the body, resulting in a deep pathway of damage within the body.

WATCHPOINT Do not give the casualty anything to eat or drink as he may need treatment that requires an anaesthetic. If he is thirsty, moisten his lips with water.

assessment

An entry wound on one side of the body that lines up with an exit wound on the other side does not mean that the bullet followed a straight path: the internal damage could be erratic. Look for the following effects of a gunshot wound:

● Possible entry wound and exit wound if a bullet passes through the body – it can be difficult to tell which is which, but this does not affect treatment
● Internal bleeding along the path of the bullet
● Severe external bleeding
● Sign of penetrating chest wound (see page 95)
● Internal organs may be damaged and protruding from the abdomen (see opposite)
● Signs and symptoms of shock may be evident (see pages 38–39)
● Possible breathing difficulties, especially if the lungs are affected

 TAKE CARE
● Do not risk your own safety (see box, below).
● Wear non-latex disposable gloves if you have them to protect yourself and the casualty.

 WARNING
If the casualty becomes unconscious, open the airway and check breathing (see page 14). Be prepared to begin CPR (see pages 16–17).

action

1 CALL FOR HELP Ask a helper to call the emergency services and tell them that the casualty has a gunshot wound.

2 CONTROL BLEEDING Apply direct pressure over a sterile dressing to control the bleeding (see pages 96–97); bear in mind that there might be a second wound. Raise and support the affected part. If the wound is on the abdomen, position the casualty as shown in steps 2 and 3, opposite.

3 TREAT FOR SHOCK Help the casualty to lie down, keep his head low, and raise and support his legs. If the wound is to the abdomen, position as in step 3, opposite. Reassure him and make him as comfortable as possible.

4 SEAL CHEST WOUND If there is a chest wound, seal it on three sides with a dressing and kitchen foil or plastic wrap (see page 95) to prevent air from being sucked into the wound.

5 MONITOR THE CASUALTY Check and make a note of the level of consciousness, breathing and pulse (see page 30). Keep checking until help arrives.

Safety at a crime scene

● **STAY SAFE** Any situation that involves a gun or stabbing is potentially dangerous. Do not approach the casualty unless you are certain that you are not putting your own life at risk. If you are not sure, call the emergency services and move to a safe distance. If possible, stay nearby as you may be needed as a witness.
● **PRESERVE ANY EVIDENCE This is a crime scene.** It is important that it is preserved so that the police can gather the evidence they need. If you have to move anything to help the casualty, tell the emergency services what you have done when they arrive.

stab wound

Stabbing causes a deep puncture wound. A knife wound can pierce vital internal organs and damage major blood vessels. A casualty needs urgent medical help as these injuries can be life-threatening.

WATCHPOINT Do not give the casualty anything to eat or drink as he may need treatment that requires an anaesthetic. If he is thirsty, moisten his lips with water.

assessment

Your aim is to arrange to get the casualty to hospital as soon as possible, but if you are at a crime scene, **remember that your own safety is paramount.** The effects of a stab wound are:

- Severe internal and external bleeding
- Penetrating chest wound (see page 95)
- Internal organs may be damaged and protruding from the abdomen
- Signs and symptoms of shock may be evident (see pages 38–39)

 TAKE CARE

Wear non-latex disposable gloves if you have them to protect yourself and the casualty.

⚠ **WARNING**

- Do not risk your own safety (see box, opposite).
- If the casualty becomes unconscious, open the airway and check breathing (see page 14). Be prepared to begin CPR (see pages 16–17).
- If the casualty's abdominal contents are visible, do not touch them. If possible, cover them to prevent them becoming dry. Use plastic wrap or, if not available, a sterile wound dressing or clean pad of cloth.

action

1 CALL FOR HELP If possible, stay with the casualty while a helper calls the emergency services and tells them that a person has been stabbed.

2 CONTROL BLEEDING Apply direct pressure and, if possible, raise the affected part to help control the bleeding (see page 96). If the wound is on the abdomen, help the casualty to lie down with his head low. Place a sterile dressing on the wound and press firmly against it.

3 RAISE THE CASUALTY'S KNEES To ease the strain on the abdomen, bend his knees slightly and place towels, cushions or rolled-up coats underneath them.

4 TREAT FOR SHOCK Keep the casualty calm and treat for shock (see pages 38–39). Tell him help is on its way.

5 MONITOR THE CASUALTY Check and make a note of the level of consciousness, breathing and pulse (see page 30). Recheck often until help arrives.

▶▶See also: **SHOCK** pp38–39 • **CHEST INJURY** pp94–95 • **WOUNDS AND BLEEDING** pp96–97

glass wound

Broken glass causes incised wounds with clean-cut edges. This type of wound can bleed profusely. By acting quickly to give first aid you can reduce the amount of blood loss before taking the casualty to hospital.

WATCHPOINT Do not give the casualty anything to eat or drink as she may later need an anaesthetic. If she is thirsty, moisten her lips with water.

assessment

The wound will need prompt attention, as well as stitches to help healing. Expect to find the following signs if there is a glass wound:

● There could be several wounds – treat the most severe first
● Possible bright red arterial bleeding at the wrist if a person has put an arm through the glass
● Symptoms of shock (see pages 38–39)
● Shards of glass on, or embedded in, a wound

 WARNING

Do not remove anything that is embedded in the wound as it could be plugging the wound and preventing additional blood loss.

 TAKE CARE

● Wear non-latex disposable gloves if you have them to protect yourself and the casualty.
● Do not press down on the object as it will worsen the injury.
● After attending to the casualty, sweep up any broken glass to prevent further injury.
● Dispose of the glass safely: wrap it in layers of newspaper and tape up the parcel.

action

1 MOVE THE CASUALTY Take the casualty away from the broken glass. Pick off any loose shards of glass.

2 CONTROL BLEEDING AND TREAT FOR SHOCK Apply direct pressure over a sterile dressing or clean pad and raise the injured area to control the bleeding (see page 96). Help the casualty to sit up or lie down and raise the limb above the level of her heart.

3 IF GLASS IS EMBEDDED Do not remove the glass from the wound. Press either side of the piece of glass, pushing the edges of the wound together.

4 PROTECT WOUND Drape a piece of gauze loosely over the glass. Place padding on either side of the piece of glass (roller bandages make excellent padding). If possible, build up the padding until it is higher than the glass.

5 SECURE PADDING Use another bandage to secure the padding. If you can build the padding up high enough, bandage over the top of the object, as shown here. If not, bandage securely on either side of the object.

6 TAKE TO HOSPITAL You can take the casualty to hospital yourself or call the emergency services if you have no transport or if a stretcher is required.

gravel **graze**

The greatest danger from this type of wound is infection from bacteria in the gravel and soil. Bleeding may be controlled easily with direct pressure and elevation. Medical attention will be needed for a large or small graze where dirt has become embedded in the wound. There is a risk of tetanus infection with any dirty wound.

assessment

Points to note when checking the casualty:

- The wound may be extensive and/or the bleeding severe
- The wound may be very dirty. Dirt may be plugging the bleeding, which may start only after all the dirt has been washed off

 WARNING

Do not try to remove anything embedded in the wound (see opposite). Seek medical advice.

The danger of tetanus

Tetanus is a potentially fatal bacterial infection that can develop when a particular bacterium (germ) found in soil enters your body via a wound or an animal bite. The risk is greatest if the wound is deep or there is manure in the soil, but even small wounds, such as a prick from a thorn, can cause tetanus.

Tetanus infection is rare in countries where most people are vaccinated against it as part of a national immunisation program. If the wound is dirty, seek medical advice if the casualty has never been immunised or is unsure how many vaccinations have been given in the past.

 TAKE CARE

Tell the casualty to seek medical advice if a fever develops, the wound fails to heal, swelling or redness develops, or it feels hot, as this may mean that the wound has become infected (see page 66).

action

1 CONTROL BLEEDING Apply direct pressure over a sterile wound dressing or clean pad and raise the injured area to control the bleeding.

2 WASH WOUND Once the bleeding stops, remove the pad. Keep the injured area raised and rinse the wound under cold running water to wash away any loose dirt. If there is no running water, use alcohol-free antiseptic wipes. Pat the area dry.

3 CLEAN AROUND WOUND Gently place a fresh sterile dressing over the wound. Carefully wipe dirt from around the wound – you can use clean gauze pads. Use a separate pad for each stroke. Pat the area dry.

4 DRESS WOUND Cover the affected area with a plaster or a sterile wound dressing if the injury is extensive. If it has been thoroughly cleaned, the graze should heal on its own.

5 TAKE TO HOSPITAL All large wounds need medical attention, as does any wound with gravel embedded in it. Carefully cleaned minor injuries should heal naturally. Ask the casualty whether she has been immunised against tetanus (see box, left); if not, she should tell the hospital team or her own doctor.

crush injury

A crush injury occurs when a body part is squeezed between two heavy objects. It can follow an earthquake or explosion, or a traffic accident, and the casualty may suffer internal and external bleeding, broken bones and shock.

GET HELP If the casualty is trapped, call the emergency services immediately. Tell them what has happened; they will bring specialist cutting and lifting equipment.

assessment

Your approach will depend on the cause of the crushing and how long the casualty has been trapped. Do not guess when the incident took place – ask the casualty and bystanders.

⚠ WARNING

Do not attempt to remove the weight from the casualty if you do not know how long ago the crushing incident occurred. Call for emergency help immediately.

⚠ TAKE CARE

● **Make sure that you are not putting yourself in any danger by approaching the casualty.**
● If you are releasing the casualty, ensure that you can lift the cause of crushing without injuring yourself or putting yourself in danger.
● Protect yourself and the casualty with non-latex disposable gloves if you have them.

Signs and symptoms of shock

Casualty unable to move

Severe external bleeding

Signs of severe bruising or internal bleeding

Pain at site of injury, indicating possible broken bone

Dangers of crush injury

If a person is trapped for any length of time, there are two serious risks:

● **SUDDEN ONSET OF SHOCK** When a limb is crushed, circulation beyond the point of impact is likely to be completely cut off. If the weight is removed, fluid floods into the area, which can overwhelm the circulatory system, causing shock to develop (see pages 38–39).

● **CRUSH SYNDROME** While circulation to an area is restricted by crushing, toxic substances can collect in the affected tissues. If the weight is removed, these substances are suddenly released back into the circulatory system, which can cause a cardiac arrest.

action

YOU KNOW THE INCIDENT OCCURRED RECENTLY

1 RELEASE CAUSE OF CRUSHING Release the affected part of the body if you can and if it is safe to do so.

2 TREAT ANY INJURY Support any suspected broken bones. If there is a wound, apply pressure over a sterile dressing or clean pad, and raise and support the area to control the bleeding. Then, to minimise the risk of shock developing, help the casualty to lie down with her legs raised and supported.

3 CALL FOR HELP Call the emergency services. Check and make a note of the casualty's level of consciousness, breathing and pulse (see page 30). Recheck often until medical help arrives.

YOU DO NOT KNOW WHEN THE INCIDENT OCCURRED

1 CALL FOR HELP Do not remove the object that is crushing the casualty. Leave her in the position in which you found her and call for emergency help.

2 REASSURE THE CASUALTY Talk to the casualty and make her as comfortable as you can.

3 MONITOR THE CASUALTY Check and note her level of consciousness, breathing and pulse (see page 30). In addition, check the pulse in the trapped limb if you can reach it safely.

impalement

If a person becomes impaled on an object, moving the casualty (or the object) can worsen the injury and cause increased pain.

assessment

Find out how and when the person became impaled and which body part is affected. Look out for:

- Signs of external or internal bleeding
- Symptoms and signs of shock

 TAKE CARE
- Make sure that you are not putting yourself in any danger by approaching the casualty.
- Protect yourself and the casualty by wearing non-latex disposable gloves if you have them.

action

1 CALL FOR HELP Do not move the casualty or attempt to remove the object. Ask someone to call the emergency services. Provide as much information as possible.

2 SUPPORT THE CASUALTY Make the casualty as comfortable as you can; support his body by hand or with cushions, if possible, to ease discomfort.

3 REASSURE THE CASUALTY Tell him that help is on the way. Check and make a note of his level of consciousness, breathing and pulse (see page 30). Recheck regularly until medical help arrives.

 WARNING
- Do not give the casualty anything to eat or drink as an anaesthetic may be needed later in hospital.
- If the casualty becomes unconscious, open the airway and check breathing (see page 14). If he is breathing, and placing him in the recovery position is difficult, maintain the head tilt and chin lift position (see page 14) to keep his airway open.

amputation

Fingers and toes – and even larger body parts such as arms – that are partially or completely severed in an accident can sometimes be reattached. It is vital to preserve the amputated part. The medical team will assess the extent of the damage.

WATCHPOINT Do not give the casualty anything to eat or drink as he will need an anaesthetic later in hospital. If he is thirsty, moisten his lips with water.

assessment

There are various complications associated with amputation of a body part, depending on the extent of the injury. The first-aid treatment is always the same – check for:

- Severe external bleeding (see page 96) and possibly internal bleeding (see page 38)
- Signs of shock (see pages 38–39)

 TAKE CARE
- Wear non-latex disposable gloves if you have them to protect yourself and the casualty.
- Tell the medical team if the casualty is taking a blood-thinning medication (anticoagulant) as he will bleed more profusely.

Care of severed part

- **WRAP IT UP** Do not wash or rinse the part. Put the part in a polythene bag or wrap it in plastic wrap to keep it clean and prevent it from drying out. Wrap a clean soft cloth or towel around it.
- **PUT IT IN ICE** Place the wrapped part in a container full of ice (crushed is ideal). Make sure that the ice does not touch the surface of the part. Mark the package with the casualty's name and time of the incident. Give the package to the emergency services.

action

1 CONTROL BLEEDING
Place a sterile wound dressing or clean pad on the wound, apply direct pressure and raise the affected area. Secure the pad with a bandage.

2 TREAT FOR SHOCK Keeping the injured area elevated, help the casualty to lie down on the ground. Raise and support his legs.

3 CALL FOR HELP Ask a helper to call emergency services and **tell them that it is an amputation.**

4 MONITOR THE CASUALTY Check and make a note of his level of consciousness, breathing and pulse (see page 30). Recheck regularly until help arrives.

5 PRESERVE THE PART Keep the part clean. Wrap it and place it in ice if possible (see box, left).

 ▶▶See also: SHOCK pp38–39 • WOUNDS AND BLEEDING pp96–97

mouth wound

Wounds in the mouth are mostly minor and look worse than they are because they bleed profusely. They are often the result of a casualty biting her own tongue and/or lip during a fall. In some cases, a tooth may be knocked out. Prompt first aid can prevent a casualty inhaling blood, which could cause breathing difficulties.

assessment

Most mouth wounds can be treated at home, although those that are more severe may need the attention of a doctor or dentist. These are indicated by:

- Severe bleeding from lips or inside the mouth
- History of recent tooth extraction or any other facial injury
- Loss of tooth

 WARNING
- If bleeding has not stopped after half an hour, or it restarts, take the casualty to hospital.
- If a casualty has suffered a blow to the head, watch for signs of serious injury (see pages 82–83).

 TAKE CARE
Wear non-latex disposable gloves if you have them to protect yourself and the casualty.

action

1 SIT THE CASUALTY DOWN Help her to lean forward so that she does not inhale blood accidentally.

2 PLACE PAD AGAINST INJURY Give the casualty a pad to hold against the injury. If the wound is on the lips or inside the cheek, tell her to pinch the pad over the injury between her finger and thumb.

3 FOR BLEEDING TOOTH SOCKET Roll up a small piece of gauze and place it in the gap. Tell the casualty to apply pressure by biting on the pad.

4 CHECK THE MOUTH After 10 minutes, check her mouth. If the injury is still bleeding, tell her to reapply pressure for another 10 minutes. Advise her to spit out any blood in her mouth.

5 CHECK TOOTH If a tooth has been knocked out, preserve it (see box, right). Take the casualty to a dentist or hospital for possible re-implantation.

Care of knocked-out tooth

An adult, or second, tooth can often be re-implanted if it is not damaged. Do not wash the tooth however dirty it appears to be. Take the casualty to a dentist or hospital where they can check the bone and gums for damage and assess the possibility of re-implantion.

- **KEEPING THE TOOTH SAFE** Once bleeding has stopped and as long as the person is fully conscious, tell her to put the tooth in the empty socket. If she cannot do this, tell her to put it in the side of her mouth against her cheek, taking care not to swallow it.
- **PRESERVE IN MILK** If it is not safe to put the tooth in the casualty's mouth, put it in a container of milk – not water.
- **CHILDREN'S TEETH** A child's milk (first) tooth cannot be replaced, but second teeth can be re-implanted. Preserve the tooth as described above and take the child to the dentist with the preserved tooth.

animal or human bite

Bites carry a serious risk of infection as mouths are full of bacteria. The force of the bite can cause bruising, crush injuries and lacerated wounds, and can carry germs deep into the tissues. If the wound is small, you can clean it yourself. Large, severe or deep bites may require surgery as underlying structures, such as tendons or nerves, may be damaged.

assessment

Seek medical advice for all but the most minor bites, especially bites to a hand. Symptoms and signs include:

- Bruising caused by crushing from the teeth
- Puncture wounds in the pattern of the teeth
- Severe lacerations
- Symptoms and signs of shock (see pages 38–39) if the blood loss is severe
- Tingling or loss of feeling and movement if the tendons or nerves are damaged

⚠ WARNING

Animal bites (particularly dog and bat bites) carry the risk of rabies, which can be passed to humans. Anti-rabies treatment may need to be given immediately.

Safety with dogs

- **CHILDREN AND DOGS** Children are often the victims of dog bites. Never leave a young child alone with a dog. The defensive reaction of an irritated dog is to bite, even when the child bothers it unintentionally. A loved family pet can be as serious a threat to a child as an unknown dog.
- **DEALING WITH AN AGGRESSIVE DOG** Do not run away from the dog. Use anything at hand, such as a stick, to protect yourself and others. Back away slowly until you can get to safety.
- **WARD OFF AN ATTACKING DOG** Do whatever you can to stop an attack (see pages 304–305).
- **REPORTING A DOG BITE TO THE POLICE** You should report an incident with an aggressive dog to the police, who may prosecute the owner.

action

1 MOVE THE CASUALTY TO SAFETY If the casualty is bitten by an animal, move to a safe place away from the animal. If it is a dog, shut it in a separate room.

2 CONTROL BLEEDING Place a sterile wound dressing or clean pad on the wound, apply direct pressure and raise the affected area.

3 WASH SMALL BITES If the bite is small, wash the area thoroughly with soap and water if available, or alcohol-free cleansing wipes. Gently pat dry with gauze swabs, then cover with a sterile dressing secured with a bandage (see page 96).

4 TAKE TO HOSPITAL If the wound is severe or deep, take the casualty to hospital or call the emergency services. The casualty may need surgery. A course of antibiotics may be prescribed to prevent infection.

5 MONITOR THE CASUALTY If she becomes generally unwell with a high temperature within a week of a bite, advise her to seek medical advice urgently, especially if the wound was treated at home. Find out if the casualty has been immunised against tetanus (see page 101).

⚠ TAKE CARE

Wear non-latex disposable gloves if you have them to protect yourself and the casualty.

severe **nosebleed**

Nosebleeds are fairly common, especially in children. They usually happen in cold, dry air, or as a result of a minor injury, nose picking or blowing too hard. Very occasionally, nosebleeds can be a sign of underlying illness or injury.

WATCHPOINT If a nosebleed continues for more than 30 minutes or follows a blow to the head, seek medical advice. Monitor the casualty for any change in her condition.

assessment

Very rarely a nosebleed can be life-threatening, especially in older people. Seek medical advice if you notice any of the following:

- Frequent nosebleeds (more than one a week); this can be a symptom of high blood pressure
- Persistent nosebleeds in a person who is on blood-thinning medication such as warfarin
- Thin watery blood from the nose following a blow to the head (see pages 82–83), which can indicate a possible skull fracture

- Frequent nosebleeds accompanied by bleeding gums as well as bruises that develop for no apparent reason
- Nosebleed within a week of surgery to the nose
- Nosebleed in a person with very high blood pressure

action

1 SIT THE CASUALTY DOWN Help the casualty to sit down. Tell her to lean forward (she should not lean back) so that the blood can drain.

2 PINCH THE NOSE Tell the casualty to breathe through her mouth and pinch the soft part of her nose to help reduce the blood flow. She can lean over a sink or a bowl so that she can spit out any blood; swallowing it can make her sick. Advise her not to sniff, swallow or cough as these actions can disturb the clots that are forming.

3 CHECK NOSE After 10 minutes release the pressure and check the nose. If it is still bleeding, pinch the nose for another 10 minutes.

4 OFFER A COLD COMPRESS Give the casualty an ice or cold pack (see page 108) to hold against the bridge of her nose to help reduce the blood flow, or give her an ice cube to suck.

5 CHECK NOSE AGAIN Once the bleeding has stopped, let the casualty clean around her nose with a damp cloth. Tell her not to blow her nose, and to avoid strenuous activity for up to 12 hours.

Helping a young child

A very young child may not be able to pinch her nose for long enough. Help her to sit forward, and pinch her nose for her. Reassure her, get her to spit into a bowl and wipe her face.

▶▶See also: **BLOW TO THE HEAD** pp82–83

severe **bruising**

A bruise is a closed wound in which bleeding from damaged blood vessels is trapped in the tissues, causing bluish-black discoloration. Depending on the force of the blow, there may be additional injuries. Bruising may not appear immediately.

GET HELP Call the emergency services if you suspect serious internal injury. Internal bleeding may be identified only by signs of shock (see pages 38–39) with no visible bleeding.

assessment

Bruising is most commonly the result of bleeding from the smallest blood vessels (the capillaries) and in some instances appears a few days after an injury. If a large blood vessel is damaged, swelling will be more severe. Signs of severe bruising include:

Redness and/or bluish discoloration at the site of injury

Swelling and discomfort

ADDITIONAL SYMPTOMS
● Possible signs of bleeding from the body openings if there is serious underlying damage (see page 38)
● Symptoms of shock if internal injury is severe (see pages 38–39)
● Possible underlying fracture

Severe pain at site of injury

 WARNING

● If unexplained bruises occur easily or for no apparent reason, especially if accompanied by frequent nosebleeds or bleeding gums, seek medical advice.

● A person taking a blood-thinning medication (anticoagulant) such as warfarin for a medical condition is at risk of severe bruising because the medication can prevent clotting.

Making a cold compress

Cooling an injury with ice slows down the metabolism within the tissue, reducing bleeding, muscle spasm and inflammation (and therefore pain), so aiding recovery. Place a cold compress on an injury for 10–20 minutes at a time – don't leave it for any longer. Repeat this procedure every 2–3 hours; it is most effective in the first 48 hours after injury. Never put ice directly onto the skin because it can cause a cold burn.

● **MAKING AN ICE PACK** Fill a plastic bag with ice cubes or crushed ice. Seal the bag, then wrap it in a hand towel or dishcloth. Alternatively, you can use a bag of frozen peas or sweetcorn as it will mould well to the shape of the body.
● **MAKING A COLD PACK** If you do not have any ice, soak a small towel in cold water and wring it out, then place it over the injury. Keep it cool by dripping cold water over it at regular intervals.

action

1 **REST THE INJURY** Tell the casualty to stop his current activity and rest. Raise the injury, as this reduces blood flow to the area.

2 **COOL THE INJURY**
Place a cold compress (see box, opposite) over the injury. Leave it in place for up to 20 minutes.

3 **COMFORTABLE SUPPORT** Tell the casualty to keep the injury raised and to rest the affected part. Wrap padding around the injury and apply a compression bandage if the pain is severe (see page 93).

4 **ELEVATE THE INJURY** Rest and support the injury in a raised position to minimise swelling. Apply a sling to an arm injury if necessary (see page 91).

⚠ WARNING
● If several small bruises subsequently form around a large one, and the casualty has not had any other accidents, he should seek medical advice immediately to find out whether his blood is clotting as it should.
● Seek medical advice if the bruise is accompanied by swelling and severe pain and the person is taking a blood-thinning medication (anticoagulant).

black eye

A black eye develops when blood and other fluids collect in the space around the eye, resulting in swelling and the typical dark discoloration.

assessment

Most black eyes heal on their own and the eye itself is not injured. Sometimes the bruising signifies a more serious eye injury and there is a risk of long-term damage. Signs that cause concern are:

● Fluid leaking from the eye
● **Casualty complains of blurred vision** in the affected eye
● The affected eyeball, iris or pupil appears to be a different shape from the other one

action

1 **SIT CASUALTY DOWN** Tell the casualty to stop her current activity and rest.

2 **COOL THE INJURY**
Give the casualty a cold compress (see box, opposite) to hold against the affected area for 10–20 minutes.

3 **MONITOR THE CASUALTY** Check and make a note of her level of consciousness, breathing and pulse (see page 30). Make a note of any change in her condition.

4 **TAKE TO HOSPITAL** If the casualty's condition deteriorates, or there is serious injury to the eye, take her to hospital or call the emergency services.

▶▶See also: EYE INJURY p118

electrical injury

Contact with domestic low-voltage electricity or lightning is often the cause of an electrical injury, usually a burn. The electrical current must be broken before help can be given. If the casualty has been thrown by the current, there may be a fracture; if unconscious, the heart may stop. An incident with high-voltage electricity, such as power cables, is often fatal.

assessment

Assess the extent of the casualty's injuries – in particular, check to see if there is more than one burn. Symptoms to note are:

● Superficial, partial or full-thickness burns (see pages 112–113). There may be a second burn (an exit burn) where the electric current left the body
● Internal injury along the path of the electricity
● Symptoms and signs of shock if burns are severe (see pages 38–39)
● Signs of upper and lower limb injury (see pages 86–91) or possibly back and neck injury (see pages 84–85) if the casualty was thrown by the electrical current
● Casualty may be unconscious

 WARNING

● **Do not touch a casualty who remains in contact with the source of electricity.**
● Do not touch a casualty with wet hands.
● Do not go within 18m of a person who has been struck by high-voltage electricity unless the authorities have officially told you that the supply has been switched off and you have seen them test it yourself.
● Do not approach a casualty who is found near a high-voltage power line or overhead cable. Call the emergency services and keep any bystanders away.

 TAKE CARE

Wear nonlatex disposable gloves if you have them to protect yourself and the casualty.

How to break the contact with electricity

If a casualty is still in contact with the cause of the injury, you too will sustain an electric shock if you touch him. Low-voltage alternating current (AC) can cause muscle spasm, so the casualty will still be grasping the appliance that caused the electric shock.

● **TURN OFF THE MAINS SUPPLY** First, try to turn off the electric current. This can normally be done by switching the supply off at the mains. If successful, you can approach the casualty.

● **MOVE THE SOURCE AWAY FROM THE CASUALTY** If you cannot find the mains switch, remove the source from the casualty using a length of wood, which is non-conductive. Stand on a thick book, such as a telephone directory, a stack of newspapers or some similar dry insulating material. Use the wood to push the object away from contact with the casualty.
● **PULL THE CASUALTY AWAY** If neither of the first options is successful, stand on the insulating material. Loop a rope around the casualty's legs and attempt to pull him clear.

TIME TO ACT Electric current can cause a casualty's breathing and heartbeat to stop. If the casualty is unconscious, be prepared to begin CPR (see pages 16–17).

WATCHPOINT Check electrical appliances regularly; this is especially important in an elderly person's home. Old appliances can be a fire risk.

action

1 BREAK ELECTRICAL CONTACT Assess the area carefully before you approach to make sure the casualty is no longer touching the electrical appliance (see box, opposite).

2 COOL BURNS Stop the burning process. Hold the injury under cool running water for at least 10 minutes, or until the pain eases. Remove the casualty's watch, jewellery or any tight clothing that might restrict swelling. Do not remove anything that is stuck to the wounds.

3 COVER BURNS Cover the burns to protect them from infection and further fluid loss. Use plastic wrap, laid along the burn – do not wrap it around a limb. Cover a hand or foot with a plastic bag. Tape it closed, making sure the tape is on the plastic, not the skin. If you do not have either of these, use a sterile wound dressing or clean, non-fluffy cloth, such as a cotton pillowcase.

4 TREAT ANY OTHER INJURIES Attend to any other injuries, such as fractures, that the casualty has sustained in the accident. Watch the casualty for signs of shock and treat as necessary.

5 CALL FOR HELP Call the emergency services. Monitor the casualty while you are waiting. Check and make a note of the casualty's level of consciousness, breathing and pulse (see page 30). Recheck regularly until help arrives.

 WARNING

If the casualty becomes unconscious, open the airway and check breathing (see page 14). Be prepared to begin CPR (see pages 16–17).

 TAKE CARE

● If you have young children in the home, put safety covers into unused electrical sockets.
● Do not overload sockets or extension leads.
● Use extension leads with a multiple socket adapter rather than single socket adapters to reduce the risk of overloading a socket.
● Always use adapters and extension leads that have circuit breakers.
● Fix wires to the skirting board; never let them trail across the floor.
● Check wiring regularly; throw away appliances with cracked or damaged flexes.
● Make sure that appliances have sealed plugs.
● Keep electrical appliances away from water. Never touch appliances with wet hands.
● If a plug becomes warm when an appliance is switched on, it is faulty and should be replaced.
● Have a professional, qualified electrician install a safety switch and circuit breakers in your fuse box (consumer unit or mains box).

▶▶See also: **UNCONSCIOUS ADULT/CHILD/BABY** pp14–19 ● **SHOCK** pp38–39 ● **BURNS AND SCALDS** pp112–113

burns and scalds

Burns are caused by dry heat (fire or smoke), chemicals or electricity and scalds by wet heat (hot water or steam). The skin is the body's natural infection barrier and is made up of several layers. Any break in the skin allows fluid to escape and germs to enter. As burns may affect large areas and/or several layers of skin, serious fluid loss and infection can result.

assessment

Assess the extent and depth of the burn (see box, below). While you examine the casualty, start to cool the injury to stop the burning. Check for:

Redness and swelling around the site of the injury

Severe pain, although deep burns can be painless

Fluid-filled blisters

Raw patches of skin

ADDITIONAL SYMPTOMS
- Pale waxy-looking skin – this indicates a deep burn
- Soot around the mouth and burned nose hairs if the casualty has inhaled hot smoke
- Breathing difficulties (see pages 40–41)
- Symptoms and signs of shock (see pages 38–39)

 TAKE CARE
- Wear non-latex gloves if you have them to protect yourself and the casualty.
- Never put ice, iced water or any creams or greasy substances, such as butter, on a burn.
- **If you don't have cool water, you can use a cool liquid such as milk.**
- Do not let the person become too cold as there is a risk of hypothermia (see page 46).
- Do not use adhesive dressings on a burn as the injury may be larger than you think.

 WARNING
If the casualty becomes unconscious, open the airway and check for breathing (see page 14). Be prepared to begin CPR (see pages 16–17).

Depth of burns

- **SUPERFICIAL BURNS** These are burns characterised by redness and swelling that affect only the surface of the skin. Sunburn is a prime example.
- **PARTIAL-THICKNESS BURNS** These are burns to the top layer of the skin, and fluid (plasma) will escape from the body. Also, if the skin is not broken, blisters form. The skin will be raw and the burns are very painful.
- **FULL-THICKNESS BURNS** The damage affects all the layers of the skin. These burns may be relatively pain-free as the nerves in the skin may be damaged. Blood vessels, muscle and fat beneath the skin will also be damaged.

GET HELP For all serious burns, ask someone to call the emergency services while you cool the burn. The ambulance officers carry specialist burn dressings in their medical kit.

TIME TO ACT Call the emergency services immediately if there is any sign of burns to the mouth or air passages – this can be life-threatening.

WATCHPOINT If the casualty needs hospital treatment, do not give her anything to eat or drink as she may need an anaesthetic. If she is thirsty, moisten her lips with water.

action

1 COOL THE BURN Stop the burning process by running cool water over the burn for at least 10 minutes, or until the pain eases. If possible, sit the casualty down and keep the injured area raised.

2 CALL FOR HELP Make the casualty as comfortable as possible. Call for emergency medical help if required (see box, right).

3 REMOVE CONSTRICTIONS Skin damaged by burning swells very quickly, so remove or cut away any clothing or jewellery from the affected area while you are cooling it. Do not remove anything that is stuck to the burned area.

4 COVER BURN Cover the burn to protect it from infection and further fluid loss. Ideally, cover it with plastic wrap or a plastic bag. If these are not available, use a sterile dressing or clean, lint-free cloth, such as a cotton pillowcase. Lay the film along the burn rather than wrapping it around a limb. Cover a hand or foot with a plastic bag. Tape it shut, with the tape on the plastic and not the skin.

5 TREAT FOR SHOCK Help the casualty to lie down while keeping the injured area raised and supported. Raise his legs above heart level and support them on a chair. Cover with a blanket to keep him warm.

6 MONITOR THE CASUALTY Check and note the casualty's level of consciousness, breathing and pulse (see page 30). Keep checking regularly until the emergency services arrive.

When to seek medical help

- **BABY OR YOUNG CHILD** For any burn on a baby or young child.
- **LARGE AREA OF BURNS** For partial-thickness burns that are larger than the casualty's hand.
- **BLISTERING** For burns with blisters.
- **FULL-THICKNESS BURNS** All deep burns need medical treatment, however small.
- **BURNS TO THE AIRWAY** For burns in the airway following inhalation of fumes of smoke. The tissues of the mouth and throat swell quickly, blocking the airway and preventing breathing.
- **BURNS AROUND A LIMB** Any burn that extends all the way round a limb, even if superficial.
- **ELECTRICAL OR CHEMICAL BURNS** See electrical injury (pages 110–111) or chemical burns (pages 116–117).
- **OTHER INJURIES** If there are other injuries that need attention, or if the person feels unwell.
- **PRE-EXISTING CONDITION** If the person has a pre-existing medical condition or is pregnant.
- **BURNS ON A HAND OR GENITALS**

If in doubt, seek medical advice, and always if a burn is larger than 2.5cm.

accidental poisoning

The most common method of poisoning is by swallowing (ingestion). Many cases occur as a result of swallowing poisonous household products, which also cause burns. Most casualties are children, but the elderly are also at risk. Poisoning can also result from an accidental or, occasionally, deliberate overdose of over-the-counter, prescription or recreational drugs.

assessment

Symptoms and signs will depend on what the person has swallowed, so it is important to establish the cause. Look for:

Burns or blisters at the mouth if the poison is a corrosive substance

Abdominal pains – these can be severe

Empty containers, berries or leaves near the casualty

ADDITIONAL SYMPTOMS

● Vomiting and/or diarrhoea – this may be bloodstained
● Signs of breathing difficulties
● Possible seizures (see page 60)
● Casualty may not be fully conscious, and **may lose consciousness at any time**

⚠️ TAKE CARE

● If the victim has swallowed a chemical, protect yourself from contact with it by wearing rubber gloves and protective clothing.
● Use a protective mask if an unconscious casualty has burns on the lips and you have to give rescue breaths.

POISONOUS SUBSTANCES

TYPE	WHAT TO WATCH OUT FOR
Cosmetics and creams	Make-up, creams and cleansers can be poisonous if swallowed.
Medicines	Overdoses of prescription drugs and over-the-counter medications, such as cough medicines, paracetamol, aspirin and ibuprofen (see pages 56–57).
Household chemicals	Bleach, carpet-cleaning products and dishwasher detergent can cause burns; soap, furniture polish and other household products are also poisonous.
Plants	Many plants are harmful, especially deadly nightshade, wild arum lily berries, yew, hemlock, lupins, daphne, delphiniums and foxgloves (see page 271).
Garden chemicals	Weedkiller can cause burns; slug pellets and fertilisers are also poisonous.

▶▶See also: UNCONSCIOUS ADULT/CHILD/BABY pp14–19 ● INHALING FUMES pp44–45

GET HELP Call the emergency services if you suspect someone has been poisoned. You can also call your regional Poison Control Centre, see page 341 for contact details.

TIME TO ACT Never attempt to induce vomiting, especially if the substance is corrosive. Anything that burned the gullet on the way down will burn it again on the way back up.

WATCHPOINT If you are not sure what the casualty has swallowed, give samples of vomit to the attending medical team; this can help to identify the substance.

action

1 IDENTIFY POISON If your region has a poison control centre (see page 341), call it. If the casualty is conscious and able to talk, ask her what she took. If she is not fully conscious, look around for clues. Try to rouse the person and then encourage her to spit out anything that is in her mouth.

2 CALL FOR HELP Call the emergency services. Tell them what the casualty has swallowed, when she took it and how much you think she took. Give them the container that the substance came in.

3 SOOTHE BURNED LIPS If the casualty has swallowed a corrosive poison, it may have burned her lips. Let her take small sips of cool milk or water to soothe the burns, but get her to spit it out.

4 WIPE AWAY VOMIT If the casualty vomits, wipe her mouth clean, but do not give her anything to eat or drink. Help her to lean forward so that fluid can drain from her mouth safely.

5 MONITOR THE CASUALTY Monitor the casualty's condition. Make a note of any change in her level of consciousness, breathing and pulse (see page 30) while you are waiting for help to arrive.

Safety with poisons

● **POISONOUS PLANTS** A surprising number of garden plants have poisonous berries, leaves or roots. If you have young children, consider fencing the plants off or even digging them up.

● **MEDICATION** Keep all medicines out of reach of children, preferably in a locked cabinet. Make sure that bottles have child-resistant caps. If a person is on regular medication but finds it difficult to remember which tablet to take and when to do so, consider putting pills in an automatic dispenser box to reduce the risk of an accidental overdose.

what next?

Treatment will depend on what the casualty has swallowed. Blood tests may be needed to identify the poison. Medical staff will want to know the person's age, estimated weight, whether she has any existing medical conditions and if she is on medication.

 WARNING

If the casualty becomes unconscious, open the airway and check breathing (see page 14) and be prepared to begin CPR (see pages 16–17).

▶▶See also: **DRUG AND ALCOHOL POISONING** pp56–57 ● **CHEMICAL ON SKIN** pp116–117

chemical on skin

Contact with chemicals can result in very severe burns, which need urgent medical attention. Try to determine which chemical has caused the injury – the information will help the medical team to decide on the most appropriate treatment.

 GET HELP Some chemicals give off dangerous fumes, which can cause breathing difficulties, so do not put yourself in any danger. Call the emergency services.

assessment

Assess the injury while you wash the chemical. Some burns may not be immediately apparent. Check for:

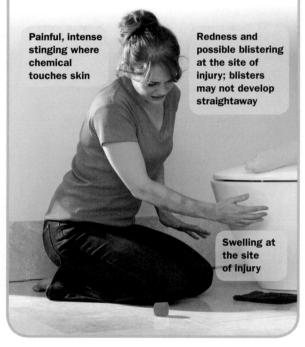

Painful, intense stinging where chemical touches skin

Redness and possible blistering at the site of injury; blisters may not develop straightaway

Swelling at the site of injury

⚠ TAKE CARE

- Protect yourself from contact with the chemical by wearing rubber gloves and protective clothing.
- Check the label on the chemical. Some spills need to be reported to the local authority.

⚠ WARNING

- The casualty may develop breathing difficulties (see pages 40–41).
- If the casualty becomes unconscious, open the airway and check for breathing (see page 14) and be prepared to begin CPR (see pages 16–17).

action

1 MOVE THE CASUALTY TO SAFETY If the casualty is inside, move her to safety. Make sure that the area is well ventilated and any fumes are dispersed.

2 RINSE AFFECTED AREA Pour water onto the burn for 20 minutes or longer – time this to ensure that you treat the injury for long enough. Pour the water away from yourself so that no chemical is washed onto your skin.

3 ALLOW WATER TO DRAIN SAFELY Make sure that the contaminated water can drain away safely; raise a casualty's foot if necessary so that the water does not run over unaffected areas.

4 REMOVE CONTAMINATED CLOTHES Help the casualty to remove any clothing that has become contaminated with the chemical while you are washing the area.

5 COVER BURN Cover the burn to protect it from infection and further fluid loss. Ideally cover it with plastic wrap or a plastic bag. Lay the plastic along the burn rather than wrapping it around a limb. If you do not have either of these, use a sterile wound dressing or lint-free cloth, such as a cotton pillowcase.

6 TAKE TO HOSPITAL Take the casualty yourself or call the emergency services, depending on the extent of the injury. Treat her for shock if necessary (see pages 38–39). Monitor the casualty's condition. Check and make a note of her level of consciousness, breathing and pulse (see page 30).

Safety at home

- **STORING CHEMICALS** Keep cleaning chemicals, dishwasher detergent and washing powder out of reach of children – do not keep them under the sink.
- **USE SAFETY CATCHES** Put safety catches on all cupboards containing chemicals. Choose chemicals with safety tops and leave them in their original bottles. Always keep garden chemicals in a locked shed.

- **USING CHEMICALS** Never combine chemicals (for example, toilet cleaner and bleach) when you are cleaning as they can give off dangerous fumes. Do not put down potentially toxic chemicals in the parts of the garden where children and pets are playing or where they might play.
- **POTENTIALLY DANGEROUS HOUSEHOLD CHEMICALS** Caustic chemicals, such as drain cleaner, some weed killers, bleach and paint stripper, need special care as they can cause burns. Many other chemicals, such as kitchen cleaner, polish, washing powders and conditioners, can cause an allergic reaction in some people. Always follow the instructions on the bottle, including the best course of action to follow in case of an accident.

what next?

- At hospital, the burn will be assessed, and treatment will depend on the chemical involved. If the burn is severe, the casualty will be referred to a specialist and may need to be admitted to hospital.
- The injury will be cleaned and dressed with a sterile gauze or dressing.
- The casualty will be offered pain relief.

chemical in eye

The severity of the burn depends on the substance involved and how long it was in contact with the eye. A casualty who cannot see is likely to panic.

assessment

Damage is usually limited to the front part of the eye, but internal damage can occur. Try to identify the chemical. Look for:

SYMPTOMS

- Pain – possibly severe – and redness
- Watering and irritation; it may feel like there is something in the eye
- Inability to open the affected eye; eyelids may go into spasm
- Swollen eyelids
- Blurred or lost vision is a sign of a serious burn. Glaucoma – increased pressure inside the eye – can occur, although its onset may be delayed by hours or days

action

1 PROTECT YOURSELF Put on protective gloves to protect yourself from contact with the chemical.

2 RINSE EYE Hold the casualty's eye under lukewarm running water for at least 30 minutes to wash out the chemical and prevent further damage. The affected eye should be lower than the good eye to prevent the chemical running into them both. If he cannot open his eye, gently hold the eyelids open.

3 COVER EYE Give the casualty a sterile or clean pad to hold over the injured eye.

4 TAKE TO HOSPITAL Take the casualty to hospital or call the emergency services. Tell the medical team what substance caused the injury.

▶▶See also: SHOCK pp38–39 • BURNS AND SCALDS pp112–113

eye injury

Eye injuries are usually the result of a scratch or graze caused by grit or a contact lens. Most injuries affect the transparent outer layer of the eye (cornea), which covers and protects the coloured part of the eye (iris) and lets light into the hole in the centre (pupil). These injuries need medical attention as they can result in temporary or permanent loss of sight.

assessment

Eye injuries are potentially serious as the casualty's sight can be damaged. Examine the eye very carefully. Small, loose pieces of dust can often be picked off by the casualty or rinsed off. The following are signs of serious injury:

- Severe pain in and around the eye
- An accident where the eye has been scratched by a thorn or small foreign body, such as a stone thrown up by a lawnmower
- Foreign object on the coloured part of the eye
- Obvious wound, especially if there is fluid leaking from the eye

⚠ **WARNING**

- Do not try to remove anything that is sticking to the coloured part of the eye.
- **Call the emergency services if the casualty experiences a sudden loss of vision** as a result of the injury.

action

1 SUPPORT THE CASUALTY'S HEAD Tell the casualty to keep her head as still as possible. Help her to lie down. Kneel behind her head and support her head on your lap to prevent unnecessary movement.

2 COVER THE EYE
Give the casualty a sterile wound dressing or clean pad to hold over the affected eye. Tell her not to move her eyes; if she moves the good eye, the injured one will also move.

5 BANDAGE THE EYE If you have to wait a while for transport, the casualty may be more comfortable if you secure the dressing with a bandage.

what next?

- A superficial eye injury that does not penetrate the eye membrane will usually take 24–72 hours to heal, depending on the size of the abrasion. The injury may be treated with eye drops to prevent infection.
- The casualty will be referred to an eye specialist if her vision is affected, if the eye socket or eyeball is injured, or if there is damage to the retina at the back of the eye.

3 REASSURE THE CASUALTY Keep the casualty as calm as you can. Do not give her anything to eat or drink as treatment requiring an anaesthetic may be needed when she reaches hospital.

4 TAKE TO HOSPITAL Try to keep the casualty in the treatment position (see steps 1 and 2 above) on the way to hospital. You can take her to hospital, or call the emergency services if you have no transport.

items in ear or nose

Children often put small objects into the nose or ear. Sharp items can easily damage the lining of the nose or structures of the ear, while the acid in small batteries can also cause burns. If an object is not removed, it could lead to internal injury and possible infection. A sharp object in the ear may pierce the eardrum, leading to possible deafness.

assessment

Look into the nose or ear with a torch (flashlight). If you see anything, take the casualty to hospital. You may also notice the following symptoms:

IF THE OBJECT IS IN THE EAR
- Temporary deafness
- Casualty feels movement if it is an insect and may be very frightened. You may be able to see the insect float out (see box, below)

IF THE OBJECT IS IN THE NOSE
- Pain if a sharp object is lodged in the nose
- Difficulty breathing through one nostril
- Swelling on one side of the nose
- Possible smelly discharge if the object has been there for some time

action

ITEM IN EAR

1 TAKE TO HOSPITAL If the person has an object in his ear or an insect is stuck, take him to hospital. Take him yourself if you have transport, or call the emergency services if you have no transport.

2 REASSURE THE CASUALTY Keep the casualty as calm as you can on your way to the hospital. Do not give him anything to eat or drink as treatment requiring an anaesthetic may be needed.

ITEM IN NOSE

1 REASSURE THE CASUALTY Tell the casualty to breathe through the other nostril or his mouth. Keep him as calm as possible. Do not let him poke inside his nose to try to release the object.

2 TAKE TO HOSPITAL You can take the casualty to hospital yourself, or call the emergency services if you have no transport. Do not give the casualty anything to eat or drink as an anaesthetic may be needed when he reaches hospital.

Insect stuck in the ear

If an insect flies or crawls into a person's ear, it may be possible to float it out. Put a towel around the casualty's shoulders, tilt his head so that the affected ear is uppermost and gently pour tepid water into the ear. As the ear is flooded, the insect should come to the surface. If this does not work, you should take the casualty to hospital.

what next?

Hospital staff will assess the injury and use special instruments to remove the object. This may need to be done under an anaesthetic, especially if the casualty is a child.

acute backache

Back pain can be very uncomfortable, but it is not usually serious. It is more common in people who are between 30 and 55 years of age. Lower back pain – a pain or ache on your back between the bottom of your ribs and the top of your legs – is the most common, and if it doesn't go away after a few days, it is a potential emergency.

assessment

Most back pain is caused by sprained ligaments or muscle strain, but it can result from a ruptured or prolapsed (slipped) disc.

Pain that spreads down into the buttocks and thigh (sciatica)

History of back problems

Sudden onset of pain after manual work, heavy lifting or bending awkwardly

action

1 **KEEP THE CASUALTY MOVING** Advise him to stay active and continue with his usual activities. While bed rest may provide some temporary relief from symptoms, it can actually make the injury worse. Keeping the injured area mobilised, on the other hand, normally promotes healing.

2 **GIVE PAIN RELIEF** The casualty can take the recommended dose of his usual pain relief medication, such as paracetamol. A cold compress may also provide some relief (see page 108).

3 **SEEK MEDICAL ADVICE** If back pain persists or recurs frequently, the casualty should seek medical advice so that a correct diagnosis can be made and the appropriate treatment given.

what next?

● Acute (short-term) back pain usually improves with physical activity. Recommended exercises for back pain include walking and gentle stretching.
● Chronic (long-term) back pain usually requires a combination of self-help techniques, medical treatment and manipulation therapies.

Encourage the casualty to see his doctor if he:
● Is elderly or has osteoporosis
● Has a history of concern
● Has a fever, chills or weight loss
● Has had a recent bacterial infection, is immune suppressed or uses injecting drugs.

 WARNING

Immobilise the casualty, treat as for back and neck injury (see pages 84–85) and seek urgent medical advice if:
● **The backache follows a fall or head injury**
● There is numbness or tingling in either leg
● You can feel any deformity along his back or neck
● There is loss of bladder and bowel control or he is unable to pass urine.

HOUSEHOLD EMERGENCIES

caught in a **blazing house**

Emergency fire services are called to thousands of house fires every year. Hundreds of people are killed and many more injured through burns or smoke inhalation. In a house fire there is no time to think about what to do and smoke fumes can be disorientating. Survival depends on split-second decisions, effective precautions and an escape plan that everyone knows by heart.

action

FIRE IN HOUSE

1 RAISE THE ALARM AND GET OUT If you smell smoke or your smoke alarm is activated, shout to alert all those in the house. Get everyone together and follow your escape plan (see page 125). If you do not have one, get everyone out of the building quickly by the safest route and tell them where to meet.

2 DO NOT DELAY Do not waste time investigating how the fire was started or attempting to rescue any valuables or personal treasures.

3 CHECK DOORS Before opening an internal door, check the top of the door and the handle with the back of your hand. If the door is warm, do not open it – there is fire on the other side.

⚠ WARNING

Do not stop to call the emergency services. You need to get out of the building first, then phone from a mobile, or neighbour's phone.

Many homes contain a lot of flammable materials that can fuel a fire and cause it to spread rapidly.

GET HELP The emergency fire service is there to help. Do not attempt to tackle the fire yourself. Get out, stay out and call the emergency services without delay.

 WATCHPOINT Keep door and window keys in an easily accessible place in the room where they are used. Everyone, including visitors, should know where the keys are located.

 TIME TO ACT Install smoke alarms and draw up your fire escape plan now (see page 125). If in doubt about how to do this, the fire service can advise you.

4 **OPEN CAREFULLY** If the door is cool, stand behind it and brace your foot against the bottom before opening it a crack to look out. Your foot will stop the door from being forced open by the pressure of any hot gases. Open the door slowly and make sure no smoke or fire blocks further progress. If you cannot move forward, take refuge (see right).

5 **CLOSE DOORS** As you leave, close all doors and open only the doors that you need to go through; then close them behind you. This will help to prevent the fire from spreading.

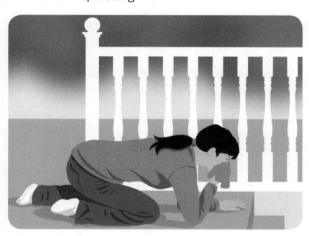

6 **KEEP LOW** If there is smoke, keep close to the ground where the air will be cooler and cleaner. Visibility will also be better. Cover your nose and mouth with a damp cloth if possible.

7 **DO NOT GO BACK** Once you and the other occupants are outside, check everyone is safe. Stay outside and phone for help – never go back.

 WARNING
Summon pets such as dogs and cats as you leave the building but do not search for them; never go back for them. Stay out of your home until the fire service tells you it is safe to return.

ESCAPE ROUTE BLOCKED

1 **GET INTO ONE ROOM** If you cannot get out of the house, get everyone into a refuge room. If possible, choose a room with a window that faces the road. Take a mobile phone or a landline handset with you.

2 **KEEP FIRE AND SMOKE OUT** Put bedding, rugs or a rolled-up carpet across the bottom of the door to block dangerous fumes.

3 **GET ATTENTION** Open a window and shout for help. Wave white or light-coloured fabric as a flag. If you have a phone, call the emergency services; if not, shout to someone outside to do it for you.

■ **TRAPPED IN AN ATTIC ROOM** If your attic room has a tight-fitting, solid door and has a skylight that can be accessed as a fire escape, then shut the door and put fabric across the base to block fumes. If there is a roll-out ladder, exit with the ladder immediately. If there is no ladder, remain in the room, but hang a flag out of the skylight and call for help, stating where you are.

■ **TRAPPED IN A HIGH-RISE** If you live in a high-rise apartment building, it is essential to be aware of escape routes. Follow the fire evacuation route. If the exit is blocked, remain in a refuge room and signal for help as above. If the window is sealed, break it at one corner, and push out the glass with a blunt instrument. Never use lifts in a fire, as you may get trapped.

▶▶See also: INHALING FUMES pp44–45

household emergencies

NO ACCESS TO DOORS

⚠ WARNING

If you cannot escape, it is highly recommended that you follow the 'Escape route blocked' action (see page 123). Only as a last resort should you attempt to escape through an upper floor window.

1 OPEN WINDOW Find a window with clear access from inside, and climb out. If you are on an upper storey, choose a window with a safe place to drop on to. If you are unable to open a window, use a heavy object to break the glass at a bottom corner. Knock out the glass and cover sharp edges with bedding to protect yourself as you climb through.

2 CUSHION THE GROUND Drop bedding and rugs out of the window to cushion your fall.

3 LOWER YOURSELF OUT
When leaving by an upper floor window, do not jump out. Lower yourself down over the windowsill to arm's length and drop to the ground. If you are alone with a child, lower her out first, holding her by her wrists then drop her to the ground. Do not leave first and expect to catch her, as she may be too scared to drop alone.

Lower a baby to the ground cradled in a duvet.

■ **FIT AN ESCAPE LADDER** For an isolated room or attic, a roll-out escape ladder can be a life saver. They are stored ready for use and can be fixed over a windowsill (see page 123).

⚠ TAKE CARE

Establish a bedtime routine so the house is safe overnight. Unless an appliance is designed to remain on permanently, such as a freezer, unplug it. Make sure all candles and smoking materials are extinguished, and place fireguards in front of open fires. Make sure exits are clear, and that door and window keys are accessible. Close all internal doors.

Smoke alarm

Install a smoke alarm on every storey of your home, positioned in hallways or on landings. Do not install in or directly outside the kitchen. You are twice as likely to die in a fire if you do not have a smoke alarm that works.

CHOOSING AN ALARM
● Ionisation alarms detect small fast-burning fires, such as stove-top fires. An optical alarm detects slow-burning fires, such as smouldering furniture. Install at least one of each type, or invest in a combined alarm. Interconnected alarms will raise the alarm at all other points if smoke is detected.
● Most smoke alarms use a 9V battery. Standard batteries should be replaced every 12 months. Mains-operated smoke alarms, with a battery back-up in case of power failure, must be fitted by a qualified electrician.
● A 'hush' facility desensitises the alarm if it is triggered accidentally. During the 8–10 minutes that this will last, the alarm is still able to detect a fire.
● Some alarms are fitted with a light which comes on as the alarm sounds, in case damage to electrical wiring affects the house lighting.
● A slowly pulsing small light is visible when the alarm is on, and will flash more rapidly when the alarm sounds.

MAINTAINING THE ALARM
● All smoke alarms have a manual test facility. Press the button weekly to check the alarm, or shine a torch (flashlight) beam over those with a torch test facility.
● Most alarms will 'chirp' for the last 30 days of battery life. Change the battery immediately.

 124

DRAW UP AN ESCAPE PLAN

1 **INVOLVE EVERYONE** Plan together as a household when drawing up your fire escape plan. Consider any special arrangements for the very young or elderly.

2 **PLAN ROUTE A** The best escape route is the one you normally use for getting in and out of the house. Keep it clear of obstructions.

3 **PLAN ROUTE B** An alternative escape route should be agreed and kept unobstructed, in case the first choice is blocked by the fire.

4 **CHOOSE THE REFUGE** In case both escape routes are blocked, decide which room is best for your 'refuge'. Ensure the room can be accessed by all members of the household, especially considering anyone with mobility difficulties, and has a window that opens, facing onto a road. You will need a telephone and spare blankets or rugs.

5 **MAKE KEYS ACCESSIBLE** Identify where door and window lock keys are to be kept and make sure everyone, including visitors, knows where they are.

6 **MEETING POINT** Ensure every member of the family is familiar with what should happen after they have escaped, such as meeting at a rendezvous point and contacting emergency services.

7 **DISTRIBUTE THE PLAN** Put the plan somewhere prominent, such as on the fridge door. Conduct a fire drill to walk through the plan.

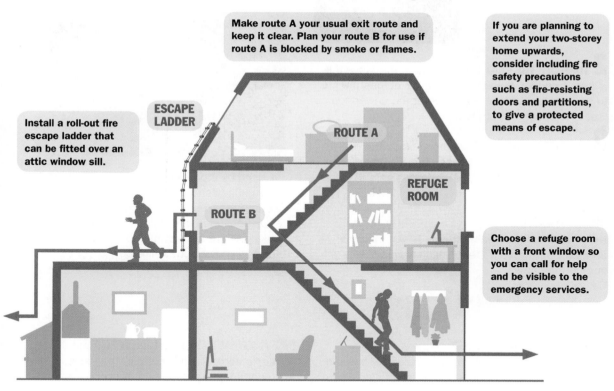

Make route A your usual exit route and keep it clear. Plan your route B for use if route A is blocked by smoke or flames.

If you are planning to extend your two-storey home upwards, consider including fire safety precautions such as fire-resisting doors and partitions, to give a protected means of escape.

Install a roll-out fire escape ladder that can be fitted over an attic window sill.

ESCAPE LADDER

ROUTE A

ROUTE B

REFUGE ROOM

Choose a refuge room with a front window so you can call for help and be visible to the emergency services.

■ **CHILDREN** Even small children should know that they must alert the household if they smell smoke or hear the smoke alarm. **All children old enough to understand should know how to contact the Fire and Rescue Service** and know their address by heart. Make sure they know what number to call in an emergency, and never in play.

■ **PLAN FOR RESTRICTED MOBILITY** If there are elderly people and people with disabilities in your home, consider them in your fire escape plan. You can ask the fire service to visit you to provide safety advice and fit specialised smoke alarms.

cooking fires

Many people are killed or injured by accidental household fires that have spread from the kitchen. The most common sort are fires caused by deep-fat frying, known generically as 'stove-top' fires. You can do much to prevent such fires taking hold by never leaving a cooking pan unattended and knowing what to do if a pan should catch alight.

action

DEEP-FAT PAN ON FIRE

1 LEAVE THE PAN ON THE STOVE TOP Do not attempt to move a pan of burning fat. You could accidentally spread the fire and injure yourself.

2 TURN OFF THE HEAT Only do this at the stove if it is safe to do so. If you have to reach across the fire to do this, turn off the appliance at the power source (see 'Watchpoint', opposite).

3 GET OUT Leave the kitchen and close the door. Get everyone out of the house, ring the emergency services and wait to be told when it is safe to return.

 WARNING

Never use water on an oil fire as it can cause a fireball. Do not use a fire extinguisher as it may spread the flames.

The tea towel technique

Serious injuries are caused every year by people attempting to put out a deep-fat pan fire, which is why the fire service advises you not to attempt to extinguish the flames, but to evacuate the area and call them.

As used by professionals, the correct technique is to extinguish the fire by covering the pan with a damp tea towel, rolling it over the flames away from yourself, to cut off the supply of oxygen. A fire blanket (see box, opposite) can be used to put out the fire.

precautions

SAFE DEEP-FAT FRYING

● Heat oil just enough to crisp a piece of bread or potato, or use a thermostatically controlled electric deep-fat frying pan. Overheated oil smokes, then ignites. Never leave a pan unattended.
● Only fill the pan one-third full of oil. Oil is a flammable liquid and can spontaneously ignite if it reaches a temperature of 350°C (660°F).
● Dry food on paper towel before frying to prevent it spattering oil onto a flame.

PREVENTING OTHER KITCHEN FIRES

● Keep electrical leads clear of the stove.
● Do not hang tea towels on or over the stove.
● Clean toasters regularly and keep them away from curtains.
● Turn off cooking appliances after use.
● Keep pets and small children at least 1m away from the stove top or oven.
● Take particular care if you are wearing loose clothing as it can easily catch fire.

GET HELP Do not hesitate to get out of the house if there is a fire in your kitchen that you cannot put out. Call the fire service as soon as possible once outside.

WATCHPOINT Gas appliances can be turned off at the control knob and electric at the power point, if it is safe to do so. Or switch off your electricity or gas supply at the mains.

TIME TO ACT Before starting to cook in an unfamiliar kitchen, when self-catering for example, check if the kitchen has a fire blanket. Do not wait until you need it to search for it.

Fire blanket

A fire blanket is a sheet of fire-resistant material used to cover a fire to cut off the supply of oxygen. It is unlikely that you will be able to retrieve the blanket from a fire to use it again, so learn how to use it correctly the first time. You will be able to use the fire blanket more effectively if you have read the instructions or, ideally, been trained in how to use it correctly.

● **MANY USES** A fire blanket is most useful in a kitchen on small, self-contained fires, especially burning oil. It can also be used on some electrical fires or to wrap around someone whose clothes are on fire.

● **BEST SIZE** Choose a blanket that is at least 1m square, made to a recognised standard such as BS EN 1869 or AS/NZS 3504. Draw-tapes allow you to access the blanket quickly and hold it safely between you and the fire.

● **CLOSE AT HAND** Keep the blanket accessible in a container on a wall, but not above a stove or a heater.

● **HOW TO USE** Cover the fire completely. Gaps allow air to get in and feed the flames. Leave the fire covered for at least 30 minutes to make sure it is fully extinguished. Discard the blanket after use and replace with a new one.

GRILL FIRE

■ **GRILL PAN ON STOVE** Keep your grill clean as a build-up of fat and residual food can catch fire spontaneously. Close the door if possible. Turn off the power, if it is safe to do so, but do not lean over the pan to reach the controls. Evacuate the area and call the fire service immediately.

■ **OUTDOOR CHARCOAL GRILL** Do not use flammable liquids to encourage poorly burning charcoal. If the flames get out of control, close the lid.

■ **OUTDOOR GAS GRILL** If a gas-fired barbecue catches fire, turn off the gas at the main cylinder immediately, if possible. If the gas cylinder is engulfed by flames, evacuate the area and call the fire service immediately.

MICROWAVE FIRE

1 KEEP THE OVEN DOOR CLOSED Opening the door will allow oxygen inside to feed the fire so keep the door closed. Switch off the power if it is safe to do so.

2 PREVENT FLAMES FROM SPREADING Throw a fire blanket over the microwave to contain and put out the flames.

 TAKE CARE

Most microwave fires are caused through misuse. Never use for drying clothes and do not place any metal objects inside the microwave or use metal containers to heat food.

electrical fires

Whenever electricity flows through a wire, the wire heats up: as occurs in an electric radiant heater. Fuses or circuit breakers protect household wiring from overheating. Misuse of fuses, poor maintenance of appliances and overloading of sockets can all lead to an electrical fire.

action

1 **TURN OFF THE ELECTRICITY** This needs to be done at the mains supply at the house powerboard (electrical panel). Do not touch or remove the plug or appliances until the electricity is turned off to avoid the possibility of an electric shock.

2 **EXTINGUISH THE FIRE** Use a fire blanket (see page 127) or a dry powder or carbon dioxide fire extinguisher (see below) on small electrical fires. Never use water as it could cause electrocution.

3 **GET HELP** If you cannot put out the fire get out of the property and call the emergency services immediately. Wait outside until you are told it is safe to return.

Extinguishers for electrical fires

You will be able to use a fire extinguisher more effectively if you have read the instructions or, ideally, been trained in how to use it correctly.

● **DRY POWDER** Containing dry powder, these are suitable for electrical fires, on burning solid materials and fires involving flammable liquids. Do not use on cooking oil. A 1kg extinguisher is adequate for home use.

● **CARBON DIOXIDE** For use on flammable liquids except cooking oil, and for electrical fires. They cause the least damage to electrical equipment, such as computers.

assessment

There are various signs of potential electrical problems. These include fuses that 'blow' frequently, flickering lights and scorch marks on sockets or plugs.

● Many homes have too few sockets, which causes the over-use of adaptors and trailing leads, both of which can result in fire.
● Badly wired plugs with visible loose wires can be a source of sparking.
● Electric flexes running underneath carpets can easily get worn and may overheat.

be aware

● Never overload an adaptor for single appliances or trailing adaptors with several socket outlets.
● Electrical appliances should be serviced once a year – especially those with heaters and motors.
● Electric blankets should be checked annually and not left on all night unless they are blankets designed for continuous running.

careless fires

Two common types of careless fires occurring in the home are fires started by unattended candles, and fires caused by cigarettes. Make sure that any lit candles are safely housed and kept away from curtains or other fabrics. Never leave a burning candle unattended. Smokers need to make sure that their butt ends are properly stubbed out.

action

CANDLE OR CIGARETTE FIRE

■ **ASSESS THE FIRE** If a cigarette, unextinguished butt or fallen candle causes a fire, ascertain what is on fire in order to take the appropriate action.

■ **BURNING PLASTIC Night-lights and tea-lights can get hot enough to melt plastic, which may then ignite.** Use a dry powder fire extinguisher (see box, opposite) to put out fires involving burning plastic.

■ **BURNING CURTAINS** Use water to extinguish burning curtains – throw water onto the fabric from a bucket, or for a smaller fire, pour water from a jug or kettle. Use a water extinguisher, if available.

■ **SMOULDERING UPHOLSTERY** Use water from a bucket or bowl to douse upholstery. Use a water extinguisher, if available. If the fire is small, and you can do so safely, take the furniture outside. This is a precaution against a deep-seated fire that may continue to smoulder and ignite later.

■ **GET OUT AND STAY OUT** If any fire takes hold and is no longer localised, get everyone out of the house and call the fire service. Stay out.

If your clothes catch fire

● **DO NOT RUN** Moving around will fan the flames and make them burn faster.
● **DROP AND ROLL** Dropping to the ground and rolling around will stop the fire from spreading and engulfing you. As flames will burn upward, lying down will also help to protect your face and head.

● **SMOTHER THE FLAMES** To be more effective, wrap yourself in a fire blanket, heavy coat or thick blanket.

be aware

USING CANDLES SAFELY
● Never leave a burning candle unattended.
● Use a snuffer or spoon to put it out. Blowing could spread sparks and hot wax. Do not move it.
● Keep candles out of draughts and away from curtains and other fabrics or furniture.
● Keep clothes and your hair away from the candle's flame.
● Do not drop anything, such as a matchstick, into hot wax, as the candle may flare up.

● Stand candles on a heat-resistant surface in a secure and stable holder so they do not fall over.

SMOKING PRECAUTIONS
● Never leave a burning cigarette unattended.
● Put out a cigarette properly – never discard a lit butt end. Cigarettes burn at 700°C (1290°F) and contain chemicals designed to keep them alight.
● Never smoke in bed or when drowsy.

▶▶See also: SEVERE BURNS AND SCALDS p23

chimney on fire

When deposits of soot or tar build up on the inside of a chimney, the heat from a lit fire below can cause them to ignite, with the resulting fire racing up the chimney. The fire can spread into the roof space or under floors and may cause extensive damage to the fabric of the whole house.

assessment

- One of the first indications of a chimney fire from inside the house is a roaring sound from the chimney. On the outside you will be able to see thick clouds of smoke and there may be flames coming out of the chimney.
- The chimney itself can reach temperatures that are high enough to ignite neighbouring timber in the roof space or under floorboards.
- The extreme heat makes the chimney expand, which can cause nearby plaster to crack and cause structural damage.

action

1 CONTACT THE FIRE SERVICE Ring the emergency services immediately.

2 REDUCE OXYGEN SUPPLY If you have an enclosed stove, shut all air vents and flue dampers to deprive the fire of oxygen.

3 MOVE FURNITURE To avoid further risk, move furniture away from the fireplace and from the chimney breast. This should be done in any room that shares the chimney.

4 ENSURE FREE ACCESS Make sure the fire service has access to the loft space.

5 HOSE DOWN ROOF Hose down the roof around the chimney with water, but avoid the chimney itself.

for next time...

- **Chimneys should be swept at least once a year – twice if you are burning wood.** Your insurance company may not pay out for chimney fire damage if this has not been done.
- Use a chimney-cleaning additive or a chimney-cleaning log to help dry out the accumulated tar so it flakes off. Do this a week or so before the chimney is swept.
- Only use well-seasoned wood for burning. Never burn cardboard or Christmas trees. Do not use your fire as a waste paper bin. Use only recommended fuels.
- Have small, frequent 'hot' fires that burn more completely and produce less smoke.
- Burning wood produces a lot of soot and tar, so if you have an enclosed fire, such as a wood-burning stove or kitchen stove, ensure it is connected to a properly insulated chimney liner. It needs a flue pipe connected to a double-skinned stainless steel liner or a lightweight concrete liner. Make sure flues are professionally installed for safety.

 ▶▶See also: **CHIMNEY COLLAPSES** p141

danger from lightning

If lightning strikes a house, it can wreck electrical and electronic equipment and start a major fire. The bolt will take the easiest route to earth, through cables, wires or water pipes. The chances of being killed by lightning are very small, but it is a myth that lightning will never strike twice.

action

 WARNING

You are in danger as soon as you hear thunder. Every 5 seconds that lapse between seeing lightning and hearing thunder represents 1.6km from the centre of a storm. Lightning can strike up to 16km from the centre.

1 UNPLUG APPLIANCES Unplug all non-essential appliances. TV sets and computers are especially at risk as lightning can cause power surges (see box, right). Do not unplug the TV aerial in case lightning strikes at that moment.

2 AVOID USING THE TELEPHONE Only use your landline in an emergency. Use a cordless handset – not the base station – or a mobile phone.

3 STAY AWAY FROM METAL OBJECTS Do not touch metal taps, pipes, radiators or sinks while the storm is in progress as they can conduct electricity.

4 STAY AWAY FROM WINDOWS Resist the temptation to watch a storm from a window in case it shatters.

5 STAY INDOORS Do not go outside until 30 minutes after the last thunder clap, as the greatest risk is to those outside.

Lightning will seek the best conductor – not necessarily the highest building.

for next time...

- If your house has been struck by lightning, it may be a good conductor and vulnerable to further strikes. Install a lightning conductor and earth the TV aerial and satellite dish.
- TV aerials can provide a path for lightning. In countries where lightning is more common, TV aerials and satellite dishes are usually earthed.

Surge protection

One of the effects of a lightning strike can be a sudden increase in voltage – or surge – in your electrical wiring, which can damage appliances. Anti-surge adaptors will regulate the voltage. Plug these in between the appliance and the socket to protect vulnerable equipment, such as computers, printers, hi-fi equipment and TV sets. Dishwashers, washing machines and tumble dryers are also at risk.

 TAKE CARE

If someone is struck by lightning, it is safe to administer first aid at once as the casualty will not carry an electrical charge. Check breathing and give CPR if necessary (see pages 16–17). Treat burns as you would those from any other source (see page 23).

▶▶See also: ELECTRICAL INJURY pp110–111 • CAUGHT IN LIGHTNING p262 • POWER SURGE p330

gas leak

Natural gas leaking from an appliance in your home is rare but dangerous. If a person is trapped in a room with leaking gas, it can result in asphyxiation and, if a leak builds up, the accumulated gas can cause a fire or explosion if set alight.

GET HELP Phone the gas emergency services if you think you smell a leak. The number should be in your phone directory or online.

assessment

● You should be able to smell a gas leak as fuel gas is given a very distinctive odour to enable quick detection. Although natural gas detectors are available for the home, they are only necessary if you have no sense of smell.

● A weak smell of gas could be caused by a pilot light going out in an oven, gas water heater or gas fire, or by a stove-top flame going out. This is the first thing to check.

● If the smell of gas persists after you have done these checks, you should take action immediately before the gas has a chance to build up.

● All work to gas pipes and fittings should be carried out by a qualified gasfitter.

action

1 TURN OFF THE GAS
Individual gas appliances have their own gas tap; the mains gas tap is a big lever on the gas pipe next to the gas meter, shown on the right here, in the ON position. Move the lever through 90 degrees to the OFF position and cut the gas supply.

2 AVOID SPARKS AND PUT OUT FLAMES Do not touch any electrical switches as turning them on or off may create a spark and trigger an explosion. Immediately snuff lit candles, turn off gas rings and douse natural flame fires. Lit cigarettes should be extinguished immediately with water.

3 DISPERSE GAS Open all doors and windows to allow any gas to disperse.

4 VACATE AREA Keep everyone away from the affected areas as the fumes could become overwhelming. Tell your nearest neighbours and ask them to pass on the warning.

5 PHONE THE GAS EMERGENCY SERVICES They will need to be told your location, name and telephone number, how many people are present, how long the smell has been noticeable and where it is coming from. Be ready to provide details of any special circumstances or access information.

 TAKE CARE
If you live in a block of flats and become aware of a smell of gas, turn off the supply to your flat immediately (see step 1, left). Follow the other steps, alerting people in neighbouring flats, and ring the gas emergency service, explaining your situation; follow their advice.

carbon monoxide build-up

Carbon monoxide (CO) is produced when gas is not properly burnt in a faulty or poorly maintained gas appliance. It has no smell, so you cannot detect it, though you may show signs of a number of physical symptoms if exposed to the gas. If allowed to build up, it can lead to serious poisoning and, ultimately, death.

be aware

• You cannot see, taste or smell carbon monoxide, but it can kill you without warning in a matter of hours.

• **The physical symptoms of CO poisoning include headache, nausea, dizziness, tiredness, stomach pain and confusion,** all of which may be confused with the symptoms of influenza or food poisoning.

• An appliance may produce carbon monoxide if it is poorly installed or maintained, or if there is a lack of fresh air for safe combustion of the gas, or a blocked flue or chimney.

• You are at particular risk if you sleep in a room with a gas appliance such as a gas fire or water heater, which is left on at night and does not have a balanced flue. A balanced flue – a two-part duct leading to the outside – allows the products of combustion of the gas to be taken outside and fresh air for combustion to be drawn in.

action

1 DISPERSE GAS Open all doors and windows to allow any gas to disperse.

2 VACATE AREA Tell the rest of the family and move them out of harm's way. Notify your neighbours.

3 SHUT OFF GAS SUPPLY If possible, turn off the faulty appliance or turn the gas off at the mains gas tap. Phone the gas authorities immediately.

■ SUSPECT SYMPTOMS If you are suffering from physical symptoms only when at home, visit your doctor or local hospital and tell them you suspect carbon monoxide poisoning.

Carbon monoxide detectors

Carbon monoxide detectors warn of a leak. They can be mains- or battery-operated, carbon monoxide only or combined CO/smoke detectors. The one shown below is a battery-operated carbon-monoxide-only detector.

• **APPROVED** Make sure your detector has an audible alarm and is approved to a recognised standard such as BS EN 50291 or UL 2034.

• **INSTALLATION** Battery-operated detectors need little or no installation. Some mains-operated detectors plug into a socket outlet, whereas others are wired into a circuit and need to be installed by an electrician. Refer to the manufacturer's instructions for the optimum location for any detector that you buy.

 WARNING

Make sure that you know the difference between the sound of your CO detector and your smoke alarm.

 TAKE CARE

For optimum safety, get your gas appliances checked annually by a qualified gasfitter.

heating system failure

When heating systems fail, the extent of the emergency will depend on the severity of the weather and whether there are very young or old members of your household. It is worth having some sort of alternative source of heating as a back-up.

assessment

If you have gas- or oil-fired heating, and your electricity supply is working (see pages 138–139), check the following:

- Is power reaching the heating unit (boiler or furnace)?
- Is the programmer working?
- Has the gas pilot light gone out?
- Is the water-circulating pump working?

Call a qualified professional if you are not confident of your ability to make the checks or if a component needs repairing or seems to be malfunctioning.

Heat pumps

Also known as reverse-cycle air-conditioners, heat pumps use refrigerant (compressed gas) to transfer heat from the outside air to the blower unit inside the house.

- **WON'T SWITCH ON** Check if the remote control needs batteries. Read the manual as different models vary in how they are switched on.
- **BLOWS COLD AIR** Check that you haven't switched settings (heat pumps can function as air-conditioners). Refer to user manual.

For all other problems, contact the unit's manufacturer and/or a heat-pump technician.

action

NO POWER TO SYSTEM

■ **CHANGE FUSE** The heating unit and controls require electricity. Check the supply via fuses or circuit-breakers in the powerboard (electrical panel). Turn off the power to the powerboard and reset the circuit-breaker or replace the fuse as necessary. If it fails again, call an electrician.

FAULTY PROGRAMMER

■ **CHECK PROGRAMMER** Make sure the programmer is set so that the heating is switched on. If it is not working, call an electrician.

GAS PILOT LIGHT OUT

■ **RELIGHT PILOT LIGHT** You should be able to see the pilot light through a small window on the front of the heating unit. If it has gone out, relight it by following the manufacturer's instructions. If you cannot access it or light it, call a gasfitter.

WATER PUMP NOT WORKING

■ **FREE SPINDLE** A sticking or jammed pump prevents hot water circulating properly around the system. Some pumps can be fixed manually by freeing the spindle. Follow instructions in your user manual. If the pump is of a style that does not allow you to access the spindle or you have any difficulty freeing it, call a plumber.

AIR-FLOW PROBLEMS

■ **CHECK FILTERS AND FANS** Turn off electricity to the heater. Clean air filters. If accessible, check that the fan turns freely. Replace filters and restore power. If the heater still does not work, call in a gasfitter.

 WARNING

In many countries, it is illegal to carry out gas, electrical and plumbing work yourself. Only carry out work you are legally allowed to do. If in doubt, seek the services of a qualified professional.

air-conditioning failure

The extent of the emergency will depend on whether you live in an area of extreme temperatures and on whether you have any alternative methods of cooling. In hot and humid parts of the world, it is worth having a second unit on hand to use if the main one fails.

action

NOT RUNNING AT ALL

1 CHECK ROOM THERMOSTAT Set the thermostat temperature to about 2.75°C (5°F) below room temperature. Check that the room thermostat is set to 'Cool' not 'Off' or 'Heat'. If the thermostat is not set to 'cool' it is turning off your air-conditioner.

2 CHECK POWER SUPPLY The air-conditioning unit requires electricity to run. Check service switches, including outside by the compressor, inside at the air handler, and fuses or circuit-breakers in the powerboard (electrical panel).

 TAKE CARE
To ensure the optimal efficiency of your air-conditioner, take energy-saving steps, such as installing insulation, sealing unwanted drafts or using blinds and trees to block direct sun.

 WARNING
In many countries, it is illegal to carry out gas, electrical and plumbing work yourself. Only carry out work you are legally allowed to do. If in doubt, seek the services of a qualified professional.

COOL AIR NOT DELIVERED

1 CHECK COMPRESSOR If the outdoor compressor-fan unit (the condenser unit) is not running, check that the outdoor service switch and the indoor power switch, fuse, or circuit-breaker are all switched on.

2 CHECK THE AIR HANDLER If the indoor blower unit is not running, check that the electrical power to the air-conditioner air-handler is switched on.

3 CHECK AIR FILTER The air filter may be blocked with dirt and debris. Another indication of a blocked filter is that the unit may be excessively noisy when running. Locate the filter and clean it or replace it. The filters on an air-conditioning system should be changed regularly.

4 CHECK AIR-SUPPLY REGISTERS The register should be in the 'open' position. Make sure you haven't blocked the supply registers with carpet or furniture.

5 CHECK BLOWER FAN If the blower fan itself won't start, discuss with the technician the need to clean the blower fan or ducts.

▶▶See also: **NO HOT WATER** pp136–137 • **BURST AND LEAKING PIPES** pp146–147

no **hot water**

Life without hot water can be uncomfortable and the problem should be identified and solved as quickly as possible. Here is an action list of things you can do yourself. For more serious problems you will need to get professional help.

> **WATCHPOINT** Keep the phone numbers of your electrician, plumber, gasfitter and energy provider handy so you can call them in an emergency.

action

ELECTRIC STORAGE WATER HEATER FAILS

1 CHECK HEATER IS ON Ensure that the heater is switched on (look for an electrical cable coming from the water cylinder to a wall-mounted on/off switch). If you have a timer, check that it is working and is set to come on.

2 CHECK POWER SUPPLY Check that the heater is receiving power. First check the main powerboard or electrical panel (see page 139) where there will be a circuit-breaker or a fuse for the water heater; reset the circuit-breaker or change the fuse.

3 GET HELP If the power supply to the heater seems to be working, it means that the heating element has burnt out or the heater's thermostat has failed. Call an electrician to sort out which and replace.

GAS-FIRED STORAGE WATER HEATER FAILS

1 CHECK PILOT LIGHT You should be able to see the pilot light through a small window on the front of the heating unit. If it has gone out, relight it by following the manufacturer's instructions. If you cannot access it or light it, call a gasfitter.

2 CHECK IGNITION If your water heater uses electronic ignition, check the power supply to the unit is switched on and that water flows from hot water outlets. If the heater still fails, call a gasfitter.

⚠️ **WARNING**
In many countries, it is illegal to carry out gas, electrical and plumbing work yourself. Only carry out work you are legally allowed to do. If in doubt, seek the services of a qualified professional.

INSTANTANEOUS GAS WATER HEATER FAILS

Also known as a combi boiler, continuous flow, multipoint or tankless water heater.

1 CHECK WATER PRESSURE If the hot water from one of these water heaters fails, it could be because of low mains pressure. When this happens, water may not be coming out of a kitchen cold water tap with its usual force. Contact a plumber.

2 CHECK GAS AND ELECTRICITY SUPPLIES Check that other gas appliances are working and, if required, power is switched on to the water heater.

3 CHECK PILOT LIGHT **If your water heater has a permanent pilot light and the pilot light has gone out, relight it, if possible,** following the manufacturer's instructions.

4 CHECK IGNITION If your water heater uses electronic ignition, check the power supply to the unit is switched on and that water flows from hot water outlets. Follow any other instructions in the owner's manual.

5 GET HELP If the water and gas pressures are satisfactory and the pilot light is working, call in a gasfitter to diagnose and repair the fault. Some heaters have a display that shows error codes to aid fault diagnosis.

INSTANTANEOUS ELECTRIC WATER HEATER FAILS

■ CHECK POWER SUPPLY Some homes have hot water supplied by individual electric heaters at sinks, basins or showers. If one is not working, check its power supply. First check the main powerboard (electrical panel), where there will be a circuit-breaker or a fuse for the heater. Reset the circuit-breaker or replace the fuse (see page 139). If this does not solve the problem, call an electrician.

CYLINDER THERMOSTAT FAILS

■ **CHECK CYLINDER THERMOSTAT** The cylinder thermostat is strapped to the side of the hot water cylinder or is an immersion thermostat in a pocket inside the cylinder. It controls the flow of water from the cylinder. Turn the dial on the thermostat. You should hear a 'click' as it passes the temperature of the water inside. If you think that the thermostat is faulty, ask an electrician to replace it.

SOLAR WATER HEATER FAILS

1 CHECK SOLAR HEATER BOOSTER SWITCH Ensure that it is switched on. Check that the timer is working and is set to come on.

2 CHECK POWER SUPPLY See 'Electric storage water heater fails', opposite.

3 GET HELP The unit's solar array, sensors, control unit or pump may not be working. Seek help from a specialist in solar heating systems.

HEAT-PUMP WATER HEATER FAILS

1 CHECK POWER SUPPLY The heat pump requires electricity to run. Check it is switched on. Then check the circuit-breaker or fuse on the powerboard (electrical panel). Replace or reset as appropriate.

2 CHECK TIMER Make sure sufficient time is allowed for reheating the storage tank.

3 CHECK THERMOSTAT Make sure thermostat is set to the required water temperature. Note that if the air temperature is outside a range of 3–55°C (37–131°F), the heat pump may not operate until heating is switched to a booster heating unit.

4 GET HELP If the above steps do not solve the problem seek the help of a heat-pump technician.

BOILER FAILS

1 CHECK FOR PIPES If your water cylinder is heated by a boiler you will see large pipes connected to the **side** of the cylinder as well as a cold pipe at the bottom and a hot pipe at the top.

2 CHECK HOT WATER IS ON If it is, then check that the programmer is working (see page 134). This governs when the hot water comes on.

3 IS THE BOILER WORKING? As well as heating water for washing and showering, the boiler heats water for the radiators (if you have them). If the radiators get hot when the room thermostat is turned up, then the boiler is working and you should go to step 4. If the radiators stay cold, check the pump (see page 134). If this is working then the problem could be the boiler itself, in which case you will need to call a qualified heating technician.

4 CHECK THE CYLINDER THERMOSTAT See 'Cylinder thermostat fails', above.

5 CHECK THE MOTORISED VALVE This controls the flow of water from the boiler to the heating or hot water cylinder. If there is heating but no hot water, the valve that sends water to the cylinder could be stuck. Try moving the manual lever (follow instructions in the user manual). If the lever meets resistance, the valve motor may have burnt out. Call a plumber or heating technician to replace it.

be aware

In most countries the law requires that every hot water system is fitted with a temperature pressure relief (TPR) valve if the system is not open vented. The safety valve releases water (so relieving the pressure) if the temperature or pressure in the hot water system gets too high. You will see it as a thin tube extending out from the water cylinder to a visible discharge point. The mains water supply pressure should be less than 80 per cent of the TPR valve's pressure range. **If yours is leaking water it could mean that the valve is old or faulty and needs replacing, or the pressure in the tank is higher than the relief point. Call a plumber to check it without delay.**

no **electricity**

Although most tasks should be undertaken by a qualified electrician, there are a few basic measures you can take to get the power in your home back on.

> **GET HELP** In many countries it is illegal to undertake any electrical repairs yourself. You must call a qualified electrician.

assessment

Follow this checklist to find out what to do. Call a qualified electrician for repairs, or if you feel unable to make any of the checks.

NO ELECTRICITY IN HOME

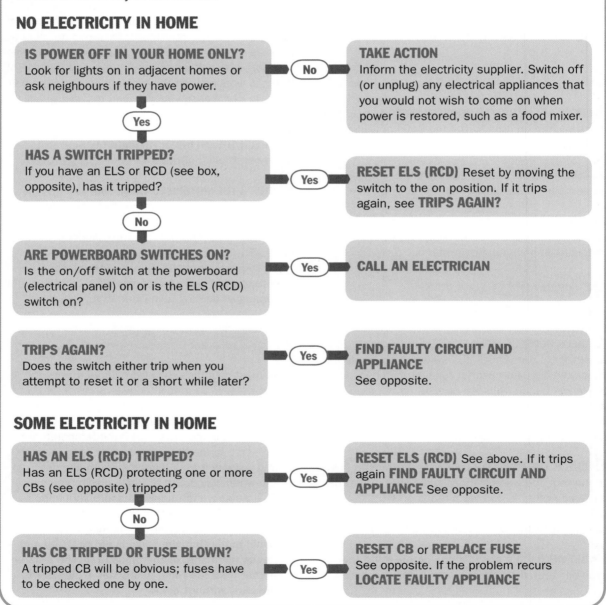

IS POWER OFF IN YOUR HOME ONLY?
Look for lights on in adjacent homes or ask neighbours if they have power.

(No)

TAKE ACTION
Inform the electricity supplier. Switch off (or unplug) any electrical appliances that you would not wish to come on when power is restored, such as a food mixer.

(Yes)

HAS A SWITCH TRIPPED?
If you have an ELS or RCD (see box, opposite), has it tripped?

(Yes)

RESET ELS (RCD) Reset by moving the switch to the on position. If it trips again, see **TRIPS AGAIN?**

(No)

ARE POWERBOARD SWITCHES ON?
Is the on/off switch at the powerboard (electrical panel) on or is the ELS (RCD) switch on?

(Yes)

CALL AN ELECTRICIAN

TRIPS AGAIN?
Does the switch either trip when you attempt to reset it or a short while later?

(Yes)

FIND FAULTY CIRCUIT AND APPLIANCE
See opposite.

SOME ELECTRICITY IN HOME

HAS AN ELS (RCD) TRIPPED?
Has an ELS (RCD) protecting one or more CBs (see opposite) tripped?

(Yes)

RESET ELS (RCD) See above. If it trips again **FIND FAULTY CIRCUIT AND APPLIANCE** See opposite.

(No)

HAS CB TRIPPED OR FUSE BLOWN?
A tripped CB will be obvious; fuses have to be checked one by one.

(Yes)

RESET CB or **REPLACE FUSE**
See opposite. If the problem recurs **LOCATE FAULTY APPLIANCE**

How electricity is supplied

Electricity reaches your home via a cable or wire that feeds into your powerboard (electrical panel), which has a system of circuit-breakers or, in older systems, fuses.

- **CB** Circuits run through your home from the powerboard (electrical panel), each protected by a circuit-breaker (CB) or a fuse. If a circuit gets overloaded, which can lead to overheating and be a fire hazard, a CB trips or a fuse blows, instantly cutting off the power to that circuit.
- **ELS OR RCD** On some powerboards (electrical panels) an Earth Leakage Switch (ELS) or Residual Current Device (RCD) is fitted to protect

against electric shock. Some homes have an ELS or RCD in place of a powerboard's on/off switch and some have them fitted to one or more circuits.

action

SWITCH KEEPS TRIPPING

1 FIND FAULTY CIRCUIT To work out which circuit is causing the problem, switch off all the CBs on the circuits protected by the ELS (RCD), reset the ELS (RCD) and then switch the CBs back on one by one until the ELS (RCD) trips again.

2 FIND THE FAULTY APPLIANCE If it is a socket outlet circuit that is causing the problem, switch off at the socket outlet then unplug every item on that circuit. Reset the ELS (RCD), then plug in and switch on the power to each appliance in turn until the ELS (RCD) trips again. The problem is most commonly caused by a faulty appliance and common culprits are kettles, irons, washing machines, tumble dryers or dishwashers. Replace the appliance that caused the trip or have it checked by an electrician.

CIRCUIT-BREAKER (CB) TRIPS

■ **LOCATE FAULTY APPLIANCE** When a CB trips, switch off at the socket outlet then unplug every electrical item on the CB's circuit. One by one, plug them in and switch on at the socket outlet then turn them on until the CB trips again. Replace the appliance that caused the trip or have it repaired by an electrician. The process is very similar for fuse-based systems.

FUSE HAS BLOWN

■ **REPLACE CARTRIDGE FUSE** In most places, rewirable fuses were succeeded by cartridge fuses. Turn the electricity off at the main on/off switch on the powerboard (electrical panel). Call an electrician to remove the blown fuse and replace the cartridge with one of the same rating.

⚠️ **TAKE CARE**
- The contents of a freezer will stay frozen (and so safe to eat) for several hours. To extend the period, do not open it, and cover it with blankets.
- A power failure may cause a burglar alarm to go off. If you cannot reset it yourself, ring the alarm company and ask them to come and do it.

⚠️ **WARNING**
If the power has failed and you are using candles for lighting, never leave them unattended. Be sure to keep children and pets away from naked flames.

▶▶See also: **HEATING SYSTEM FAILURE** p134 **139**

tree falls on house

Storms can bring trees crashing down onto houses, with dire consequences. Although rare in most areas, extreme weather events do happen so make sure you are prepared for the worst. You can also prevent damage with some timely pruning.

TIME TO ACT The best time of year to have a deciduous tree pruned to make it safe is late autumn when the leaves have fallen; prune broadleaved evergreens in spring.

action

1 GET OUT Use whatever route is safest to leave the property. This may or may not be the same as your fire-escape plan (see page 125).

2 CALL THE EMERGENCY SERVICES The fire service or state emergency services will come and make the house safe.

3 CONTACT INSURERS Get in touch with your insurance company as soon as possible – they will need to agree to cover expensive removal and emergency repair procedures.

4 SECURE YOUR HOME You will need a firm of roofing contractors or builders to make good the roof and any other structural damage. The first priority will be to make it waterproof so that there is no additional damage to your property and possessions.

what next?

- A firm of tree surgeons will be needed to cut up and remove the tree.
- If you are unable to live in the house immediately, ensure it is not a looting target. Secure doors and windows and put valuables in temporary storage.

Make nearby trees safe

- **PRUNING** Make sure you keep mature trees well pruned. If a neighbour's tree is getting out of hand, ask him to cut it back. You can cut branches off a neighbour's tree that overhang your property – but the wood and any fruit still belong to him, so you should offer them back.
- **FELLING** Cut down any trees that are dying, dead or dangerous, but be aware that some trees, especially endangered or old specimens, may be protected by a tree preservation order. In this case you must apply to the local authority for permission. There are differences in the law protecting trees in different countries, so check with your local authority.
- **ROOT TRIMMING** It is best to take professional advice before trimming a tree's roots.
- **ROOT DAMAGE** If a neighbour has complained to you that your tree roots are damaging his property and you have failed to take action, you could be held responsible for any damage.

 WARNING

A tree that has fallen on a house may not be stable. Stay well away from it and keep children and pets away until it has been made safe.

be aware

- Storm damage to houses by trees (and the cost of removing the tree if it has fallen on the house) is covered by most building insurance polices.
- If your tree falls on your neighbour's property, they will need to make a claim on their building insurance policy.

- Although unlikely to cause a sudden emergency, tree roots can extend under a property, causing damage to the foundations. The first signs of this might be cracks in the plaster inside the house or cracks in the brickwork on the outside.

chimney collapses

A chimney collapsing is – fortunately – a rare occurrence, but it can cause serious damage to your own and other properties and potentially to people passing nearby. There is nothing you can do if a natural disaster causes the collapse, but you can take steps to ensure that your chimney is not a danger.

be aware

- Chimneys can collapse in a serious storm and many that do have been weakened beforehand by other causes.
- A chimney fire (see page 130) can weaken chimney stacks because it causes the chimney to expand, which can crack the masonry.
- Cracking can also occur because of failed mortar pointing or failed chimney flashing allowing water to get into the brickwork. If the water freezes, it expands, leading to cracking.
- A satellite dish (or large TV aerial) can cause structural damage to a chimney, especially if it is mounted on a long pole and exposed to strong winds.

 TAKE CARE

One – avoidable – cause of chimney collapse is the removal of chimney breasts. Chimney breasts provide essential support to chimneys – and, in some houses, the whole chimney stack is an essential structural element of the house. Consult an architect or structural engineer before undertaking work on a chimney breast.

action

1 GET HELP Call the emergency services. The fire service can help to make the property safe and an ambulance will be needed if anyone has been injured by the collapse.

2 GIVE FIRST AID Do the best you can to help anyone who has been injured. If you are not sure what to do, ask the emergency services for advice when you ring them.

3 CALL A BUILDER What is left of the chimney will need to be secured and the roof weatherproofed to prevent further damage to your property and to any possessions.

4 CONTACT INSURANCE COMPANY Damage caused by a collapsed chimney should be covered by your building insurance policy – the only exception might be if you have caused the collapse yourself by removing the chimney breasts.

 WARNING

Do not go up onto the roof space to assess or inspect any damage from a collapsed chimney stack. The structure is likely to be unstable and you could cause more damage or injure yourself.

Safe chimneys

- **REGULAR INSPECTION** Inspect your chimney regularly (from the ground with binoculars) looking for cracks, leaning brickwork, loose or missing mortar and damage to flashing (the shaped bits of lead around the chimney stack). If you see any problems, get a builder to make repairs at once.
- **CHIMNEY REMOVAL** Seek professional advice and consult the building control department of your local authority if you are thinking of removing a chimney stack.
- **UNSTABLE AERIALS** Be aware of the dangers posed by large TV aerials and satellite dishes on long poles.
- **STRUCTURAL DAMAGE** Have the chimney checked for structural damage after you have had a chimney fire.

broken **windows** and **doors**

Discovering a break-in at your home is bad enough without the knowledge that your home's security is compromised by damage to windows and doors. There are immediate and effective short-term measures that you can take to secure kicked-in doors and shattered windows, although they will have to be professionally repaired or replaced later.

assessment

- If you think that your home has been burgled, take care if you suspect that the burglar might still be inside (see pages 164–166).
- If the breakage is the result of a burglary, call the police.
- If a door has been forced to gain entry, it will need to be secured until repaired or replaced. Call a carpenter, especially if you are not confident about making temporary repairs.
- Broken windows can be covered up before the glass is replaced. If you cannot mend a window yourself, call a glazier.

 TAKE CARE

Both broken glass and splintered wood can cause injuries, so always wear thick gloves when handling them – plus eye protectors when removing glass from a window pane.

action

DAMAGED DOOR

1 MEND THE DAMAGE If the door has been forced open, it is likely that the door frame will have been damaged so that the lock is useless. Contact a carpenter or builder to replace the frame, and the door, if necessary, so the door can be locked.

2 MAKE TEMPORARY REPAIRS If the door and frame are of solid wood, fit a bolt or two on the inside. This works if the door is inward or outward opening. If you have an inward-opening front door with a letter box at about waist height and with a wooden floor on the inside, you can temporarily secure it with a stout wooden prop (see box, below).

Prop a door shut

1 MAKE YOUR PROP You will need around 1.2m of 100mm by 50mm sawn timber or similar for the prop and 300mm for the floor support. This second piece of wood is screwed or nailed to the floor (watch for pipes or cables below).

2 SECURE THE DOOR With one end of the prop held in place by the floor support, jam the other end into the letter box or under the door handle. The prop can be kicked out if you need to open the door in a hurry.

BROKEN WINDOW

1 MAKE SAFE Smash out the broken glass from the window with a hammer. **Get a glazier to do this or wear gloves and eye protectors** and spread dust sheets on both sides of the window.

2 MAKE SECURE To keep the weather out, tape a sheet of heavy-gauge plastic sheeting over a window. If your window has a wooden frame, hold the plastic more securely with wooden battens (see above). A wooden-framed window can be boarded up with plywood or exterior strand board cut to size and screwed or nailed in place.

3 REPAIR THE WINDOW Call a glazier or, if you have a traditional wooden-framed window, you may want to replace a single pane of glass yourself. If you have double glazing or if the frame is damaged, get professional help.

what next?

- If the damage was caused by a burglary, you will need a case or crime number from the police for any claim you make from your insurance company. When the police have gone, assess the damage and what you need to do to make your home more secure.
- It is possible that burglars will have found some spare keys to let themselves out of the door so you will need to change the locks.
- Take the opportunity to review your level of security. Perhaps you need more (or better) door locks? Plus some hinge bolts (to prevent the door being levered out)? Think, too, about the type of replacement glass you use for a broken window. For vulnerable windows, toughened or laminated glass offers greater security.

locked out

A door slamming shut behind you, locking you out of your home, can be viewed as an emergency if there are children or vulnerable people in the house – or if you are cooking.

action

1 RETRIEVE A SPARE If you've left a spare key with someone, use it to get in. If you have a key that will not work, use the spare to assess whether it is the key or the lock that is damaged.

2 LOOK FOR A WAY IN Look for a door or window that can be opened so that you can get in without damaging it or injuring yourself.

3 RING AN EMERGENCY LOCKSMITH If all else fails you will need to call a 24-hour emergency locksmith who will be able to come quickly to your home and either pick the lock or drill it out so you can get in. This can be expensive as you may need to have new locks fitted. In a life-threatening emergency, call the emergency services. Depending on circumstances, there may be a charge for their attendance.

for next time...

- You can save yourself trouble and expense by leaving spare keys with someone you trust. An immediate neighbour or nearby family member are obvious choices.
- You can buy a secure key safe to hold spare keys. This is fixed to the wall outside and can only be opened by using a code on the key pad.

 TAKE CARE
- If a key starts becoming hard to use, replace it or the lock before it fails and locks you out.
- You may have to change your locks if you have lost your keys with anything that identifies where you live.

 WARNING
Never leave keys under a flowerpot or stone. Thieves will look there if they want to get in.

water coming through ceiling

When water comes through a ceiling you must act fast to avoid costly structural repairs, as well as serious damage to decorations, furnishings and floor coverings. There can be many causes: the roof may be damaged, a water tank in the roof space may have split, a bath may be overflowing or a washing machine in an apartment above may be leaking.

assessment

First do the 'Water through ceiling' action steps (see opposite), then identify where the water is coming from. If you cannot perform the procedures yourself, get professional help.

CEILING IS ON TOP FLOOR

IS THE ROOF LEAKING?
Is water dripping from the rafters and there are no pipes above the ceiling?

 Yes

ARRANGE FOR ROOF REPAIRS
It is unlikely that you will be able to fix a leaking roof, so call a roofing contractor.

 No

IS THERE A HEADER TANK?
Some water systems have a header tank, which is usually located in the roof space.

 Yes

TANK MAY BE LEAKING
Look to see if there is water around the tank. Turn off the water supply, and drain tank (see opposite).

 No

CHECK PIPES
Can you see or hear water leaking from a pipe or joint above the ceiling?

 Yes

IDENTIFY AND STOP THE LEAK
See 'Water through ceiling', opposite. Repair a leak (see pages 146–147).

CEILING IS ON LOWER FLOOR

CHECK BATHROOM OR KITCHEN
Is a bath, shower or sink overflowing on the floor above?

Yes

EMPTY BATH, BASIN OR SINK
Turn off taps, pull out plug or remove blockage. Contain and mop up any water.

 No

IS WATER ON THE FLOOR ABOVE?
Check around radiators, WCs, appliances and pipes (including waste pipes).

 Yes

IDENTIFY AND STOP THE LEAK
See 'Water through ceiling', opposite. Attempt to contain and mop up the water. Repair a leaking pipe or joint or reconnect waste pipes (see pages 146–147).

 No

CHECK UNDER FLOOR OF ROOM ABOVE
If the floor is wooden, lift the floorboards and search for pipe or joint leaks.

 Yes

IDENTIFY AND STOP THE LEAK
See 'Water through ceiling', opposite. Repair a leaking pipe or joint or reconnect waste pipes (see pages 146–147).

action

WATER THROUGH CEILING

1 TURN OFF THE ELECTRICITY Water can pose a risk of electrocution as well as damaging wiring circuits above the ceiling. **Turn off the electricity using the on/off switch on the powerboard (electrical panel)** (see page 139). Take a torch with you if it is dark.

2 CATCH THE WATER Place empty buckets to catch the water so that you can save your flooring.

3 TURN OFF THE WATER If the water is caused by a plumbing problem (see 'Assessment', opposite), turn it off (see pages 146–147).

CEILING IS BULGING

1 PREPARE TO CATCH THE WATER If the ceiling is bulging, you need to take action before it collapses. Start by putting a waterproof covering down, such as a heavy plastic sheet, and then place a large bucket underneath the bulge to catch the water. Have spare buckets or similar-sized containers standing by.

2 MAKE A DRAINAGE HOLE Use a pointed stick (or similar) to make a hole in the middle of a large bulge to let the water through.

3 PROP UP DAMAGED SECTIONS If it looks as though part of the ceiling is about to come down, make a temporary prop with a length of timber, wedged between two short planks of wood – one on the floor and one on the ceiling – to hold it up.

 WARNING
In many countries, it is illegal to carry out gas, electrical and plumbing work yourself. Only carry out work you are legally allowed to do. If in doubt, seek the services of a qualified professional.

LEAKY PLUMBING

1 TURN OFF MAINS WATER Turn off the water at the mains stop valve (see pages 146–147).

2 TURN OFF WATER FROM TANK If the leak is in a pipe or appliance fed by a header tank, turn off the flow from the tank at the stop valves (see pages 146–147). Drain any water remaining in tank-fed pipes or appliances to minimise the amount of water that might leak. Do this by turning on the hot and cold taps.

HEADER TANK LEAKING

1 TURN OFF MAINS WATER Turn off the water at the mains stop valve (see pages 146–147).

2 DRAIN TANK Turn on taps supplied by the tank (see above) to empty it quickly and so minimise the amount of water that can leak from it. Call a plumber to repair or replace the tank.

APPLIANCE LEAK

■ SWITCH OFF APPLIANCE If a washing machine or dishwasher is leaking, switch it off at the power point then turn off its water supply at the hot and/or cold taps. Call a plumber.

what next?

Call in a builder to inspect the ceiling to see if it needs repairing or replacing.

for next time...

If you live in an apartment with neighbours above, ask if you can keep a set of their keys. If water comes through your ceiling when they are out, you will be able to get in and take appropriate action. Keep their mobile phone number so you can phone them to let them know of any problem.

▶▶See also: **BURST AND LEAKING PIPES** pp146–147

burst and leaking **pipes**

Pipes may burst or their joints be forced apart as ice that has frozen inside begins to thaw. You can prevent pipes from freezing in the first place by insulating them effectively, but it is possible to stop a pipe from bursting if you thaw it in the correct way. A leaking pipe or joint may also be the result of other problems, such as damage or corrosion.

assessment

TYPES OF PIPE
- A copper pipe is the most common and is easily split by ice. It can be repaired with a clamp, a 'slip' coupling or a new section of pipe.
- If your house is an older property, replace old pipes with copper or plastic.
- A plastic pipe is the least likely to split and easiest to repair (with a new section).

BURST AND FROZEN PIPES
- Burst pipes are caused by water freezing in pipes. In the roof space and beneath the ground floor are likely places for burst pipes.
- In cold weather no water coming from a tap indicates a frozen pipe. This must be dealt with swiftly as the pipe could burst.

LEAKING PIPE OR JOINT
- The first sign of a leaking pipe or pipe joint is likely to be a damp patch on a wall or ceiling. Such a leak may be just a drip, but must be mended before too much damage is done.
- A separated waste pipe joint can leak out a lot of water and must be reconnected quickly.

Prevent pipes freezing
- **INSULATE** Cold water pipes in the roof space, under ground floors or outside should be properly insulated. Don't place ceiling insulation material under a cold water header tank, but make sure the tank itself is well insulated.
- **HEATING** If you live in a region of extreme cold, leave the heating on low if you are away in winter; for long absences, turn off the water and drain the system.

action

WATER IS LEAKING

1 TURN OFF THE ELECTRICITY **First, turn off the electricity at the on/off switch on the powerboard (electrical panel)** (see page 139). Take a torch (flashlight) if it is dark. Water leaking from pipes or pipe joints can get into electrical fittings, making them unsafe.

2 LOCATE THE LEAK Find the source of the leak as quickly as possible. Do not turn the water off until you have located the problem.

3 TURN OFF THE WATER Turn off the water at the mains stop valve and, if the pipe is fed from a header tank, at the stop valve on the tank as well (see box, opposite). If it is a hot water or central heating pipe that has burst, switch off the boiler and/or electric (immersion) heater.

BURST PIPE

■ **USE A CLAMP** The simplest way to temporarily stop water leaking from a burst or split metal pipe is to use an emergency pipe repair clamp (see right), screwed in place over the leak.

■ **SLIP ON A COUPLING** With a burst or split copper pipe, a 'slip' coupling (which has no internal pipe stop and so can be used on pipes in situ) can be used. The affected section is cut out and the slip coupling slid on. Call a plumber to do this.

FROZEN PIPE

1 IDENTIFY THE PIPE If all taps are affected, it may be the main pipe supplying the house or leading from a header tank; just one tap and it is the pipe leading to that tap. For hot taps, it is likely to be the cold feed pipe to the hot water cylinder.

2 MELT THE ICE Ask a helper to open each affected tap, while you work backwards along the pipe leading to it. Remove any pipe insulation first. If the pipe is made of copper use a hair dryer to heat it until water flows freely from the tap. Treat plastic water pipes in the same way as plastic waste pipes (see below).

3 USE HOT TOWELS If plastic waste pipes are frozen, soak towels in hot water and wrap them round the pipe until the waste water flows away.

LEAKING JOINT

■ **TIGHTEN COMPRESSION JOINT** If a compression joint is leaking, the leak can be stopped by tightening one or both nuts. Use two spanners, one on the nut and one on the fitting.

■ **REPAIR SOLDERED JOINT** A leaking soldered capillary joint is difficult to repair. Ask a plumber to drain the pipe and resolder it for you.

■ **REFIT WASTE-PIPE JOINT** If a 'compression' waste-pipe joint (with a knurled ring) has come apart, ask a plumber to unscrew the ring, push the pipe firmly back into the joint, and retighten the ring.

■ **TIGHTEN RADIATOR NUT** Leaks from radiators can usually be cured by tightening the 'union' nut – the one closest to the radiator at the bottom.

 WARNING
In many countries, it is illegal to carry out gas, electrical and plumbing work yourself. Only carry out work you are legally allowed to do. If in doubt, seek the services of a qualified professional.

LEAKING PIPE

■ **WRAP IT UP** A temporary fix for a leaking pipe is to wrap self-amalgamating (Alfa) tape tightly over the leaking section (no need to turn the water off first). The layers of tape will merge and create a fully waterproof seal, even on pipes with water at mains pressure.

Where to turn off the water

● **MAINS STOP VALVE** This valve controls the flow of water into your home from the water main. It can be found in different places, including outside the house with the water meter. In blocks of units (apartments) each one may have a stop valve under the kitchen sink or where the service enters the unit. Turn it clockwise to shut off the water.

● **TANK STOP VALVE** If you have a header tank, a stop valve (see right) controls the flow of water. Turn it off in an emergency.

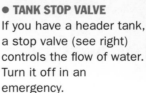 **what next?**

● If the repairs are temporary, call in a plumber to make permanent repairs.
● Assess the results of the leak or burst pipe and contact your insurance company if ceilings, floor coverings or wallpaper have been damaged.
● Ask an electrician to check the electric wiring before turning the electricity back on.
● Hire a dehumidifier to dry out the property.

▶▶See also: **WATER COMING THROUGH CEILING** pp144–145

flooding

If water entering your house cannot drain out quickly it may ruin your property and possessions and it will probably leave behind an unpleasant smell. There are a number of things you can do to make some types of minor flooding less likely, but tackling a proper flood is a difficult and often dirty job.

action

FLOODING FROM LEAKY PIPE

1 **TURN OFF THE WATER** If the cause of the flood is a burst or leaking pipe, turn off the water at the appropriate place (see pages 146–147).

2 **CATCH THE WATER** If possible put a bucket under the leak to catch the water. Have several containers standing by until all the water has drained from the pipe, which might take some time, even after you have turned off the water.

3 **PROTECT POSSESSIONS** Quickly get anything at risk from damage by the water out of the way. Call a plumber to have the pipe repaired.

4 **PUMP OUT THE WATER** Unless your flood is of major proportions (usually when it occurs from an outside source – see below), hire a submersible 'puddle' pump, which will remove all except the last few millimetres of water (the remainder can be sucked up with a wet/dry vacuum cleaner).

FLOODING FROM OUTSIDE

1 **USE SANDBAGS** If you are threatened by excessive rainfall, overflowing rivers or burst water mains, sandbags (see page 189) will stop water getting in under doors – but not for long.

2 **SAVE VALUABLES** With localised flooding or a burst water main in the street, you should have sufficient warning to move at least some of your cherished items out of the way.

3 **CALL EMERGENCY SERVICES** If rooms are awash with water, call your local emergency services.

be aware

● Serious flooding is usually the result of an 'outside agency' – typically excessive rainfall or a nearby burst water main.
● If you are concerned about the possibility of flooding, check whether an area is prone to it before buying or renting a house.
● Flooding not caused by something like a burst water main, can be the result of water seeping in through the walls or through the floor. Check the drainage under the house. If you have a basement or cellar that is flooding, it may need to be 'tanked' – a special waterproof treatment for the walls and floor. This is expensive, but if you use your cellar for storage you may decide it is worthwhile.
● As soon as it is safe to do so, start the clean up so damage to the floors is minimised. A sturdy broom is useful for pushing water out of the house.

running **Overflow**

Overflow pipes are positioned to attract your attention when they start running with water. They are there to warn you that you have a problem with one of your tanks (cisterns) – a WC cistern, hot water tank or cold water tank in the roof space.

TIME TO ACT Continuous discharge of water from the TPR valve (see 'Be aware', page 137) indicates a potentially serious problem. Call a plumber without delay.

assessment

● Running overflows may be caused by a problem with the float-operated valve (ball valve), which lets water into the tank (cistern).

● Older WC cistern overflows are normally positioned on the outside wall right next to the cistern – though many modern WCs conveniently overflow into the WC pan itself.

● The overflow pipes for any tanks (cisterns) in a roof space generally come out just under the eaves and often spill onto a paved area so that you can hear the noise of the water.

● Although it is possible to repair faulty ball valves, fitting a new one is a better choice – they are inexpensive to buy and relatively easy to fit.

action

1 TURN OFF THE WATER SUPPLYING A WC Many WCs have a tap-like valve or a small in-line valve (which is closed with a quarter turn using a screwdriver) in the supply pipe nearby. If a WC does not have a valve near it, it is either fed from a cold water tank or by water from the mains.

2 TURN OFF WATER TO TANK-FED WC If a WC is fed by a cold water tank, close the stop valve on the pipe leading out of the tank (see page 147).

3 TURN OFF WATER TO MAINS-FED WC If the WC is fed from the mains, turn off the mains stop valve (see page 147).

4 TURN OFF THE WATER TO A COLD WATER TANK The supply to a cold water tank is turned off at the mains stop valve (see page 147).

5 CHECK THE FLOAT HEIGHT It could be that the float height is incorrect so that the ball valve does not stop water entering the cistern correctly (see step 6).

 WARNING

In many countries, it is illegal to carry out gas, electrical and plumbing work yourself. Only carry out work you are legally allowed to do. If in doubt, seek the services of a qualified professional.

6 SET THE WATER LEVEL For a cold water tank (cistern) the water level when the valve has closed should be around 25mm below the overflow pipe. **With WCs the correct water height is often marked on the inside of the cistern.** If the level is not correct, adjust the float height using the screw provided. On older ball valves you will have to bend the float arm.

7 CHECK THE FLOAT If you have an old type of ball valve and the metal float is punctured, you can make a temporary repair to keep the system running while you buy a new float. Empty as much water out of the old float as possible then wrap a plastic bag around it and secure the bag with an elastic band.

8 REPLACE THE BALL VALVE If you cannot stop the ball valve running, it is faulty and will need to be replaced. If you do not feel capable of doing this yourself, ask a plumber to fit a new ball valve for you.

toilet blocked or will not flush

A WC that will not flush is a problem that needs to be sorted out as soon as possible – especially if there are young children or older people in the home. As an emergency measure you may be able to flush away the contents of the WC by pouring a bucket of water into the pan. But you need to find out what caused the problem and make repairs.

assessment

Follow the chart below to find out what may be preventing the toilet bowl from emptying. Then either unblock it or fix the flush yourself or call out an emergency plumber.

DOES IT FLUSH?
Does the toilet flush when you operate the lever or button?

No →

REPAIR THE FLUSH
There is a problem with the flushing mechanism.

↓ **Yes**

IS THE WASTE BLOCKED?
Are any other nearby wastes blocked, such as a bathroom basin?

Yes →

UNBLOCK SEWER DRAIN (SOIL PIPE)
The problem is in the sewer drain or the underground drains (see pages 154–155). You will need to call a plumber.

↓ **No**

THE WC'S SOIL PIPE IS BLOCKED
For blockages in the trap, you will need a WC plunger. For blockages further along, a drain auger or plumber's eel may work. If you cannot unblock the WC yourself, call a plumber.

A dual-flush toilet

Dual-flush button
Inlet valve
Overflow
Float
Half-flush float
Full-flush float
Outlet valve

Modern dual-flush toilets have various designs. In the one shown you depress one part of the flush button for a low-volume flush and both parts for a full-volume flush. The push button is linked to a valve-controlled plunger to operate the flush. Some models are designed so that the whole valve unit can be removed for maintenance. But many models aren't and you will have to call out a qualified plumber.

NOT FLUSHING Check the height of the flush button; next check the inlet valve and valve unit.

WATER RUNNING In a dual-flush system, the overflow is designed to let water run into the back of the pan. Water continually running into the pan may mean that the inlet valve is faulty or that the washer at the outlet valve needs to be replaced.

GET HELP You can take simple steps to make your toilet flush properly or clear a blockage, but be aware that in many regions it is illegal to carry out plumbing work yourself. Call a plumber.

WATCHPOINT For all WC repairs, wear protective clothing (heavy-duty waterproof gloves with long cuffs) and cover the floor with old towels. Disinfect equipment after use.

TIME TO ACT If you notice the WC starting to empty more slowly than usual, use a plunger to clear the blockage that is starting to form.

action

The following advice is for a single-flush syphon system – a common type of old-style WC. Modern toilets tend to have a more complex dual-flush mechanism (see box, opposite).

BROKEN FLUSH LINK

1 EMPTY THE CISTERN
Turn off the water to the cistern (see page 149). If it is not easy to do this, tie up the inlet valve arm to a piece of wood resting on top of the cistern. Flush the cistern by pulling up the rod sticking out of the top of the siphon mechanism.

2 REPLACE LINK Unscrew the plastic arm from the lever spindle and pull out the link. Buy a new link from a hardware store or plumbing suppliers, connect to plastic arm and hook the metal link on to the end of the siphon rod.

3 SECURE ARM With the lever in its 'rest' (horizontal) position, fit the plastic arm (with the link) to its spindle. Turn on the water or untie the float arm and allow the cistern to fill.

SPLIT FLAP VALVE

1 REMOVE THE SIPHON Many modern WCs have the cistern fixed to the back of the pan, and need some complex disassembling – a job best left to a plumber. On older WCs that have a separate cistern, turn off the water supply (see left), flush the cistern to empty it and mop out the remaining water. Undo the smaller nut underneath the cistern to disconnect the flush pipe; then undo the larger one to release the siphon mechanism.

2 REPLACE VALVE Remove the lifting rod, take off the failed valve from its base and fit the new one from a hardware store or plumbing suppliers. Cut it to shape if necessary. Reassemble and test.

BLOCKAGE

1 USE A PLUNGER Plungers for clearing WCs are larger than the ones for basins, sinks or baths, but are used in exactly the same way by pushing and pulling them up and down, using water pressure to clear the blockage. **A household mop, covered with a plastic bag, makes a good alternative.**

2 USE A FLEXIBLE PLUMBER'S EEL (DRAIN AUGER) You may be able to wiggle WC blockages out with a straightened-out metal coat hanger. But the correct tool is a plumber's eel (drain auger) with a turning handle. This needs to be used with a pushing and pulling action as well as a turning one to dislodge the blockage.

 WARNING
Use drain cleaners with care: the chemicals are corrosive. Do not use them on fully blocked WCs as the chemical will not drain and will give off dangerous fumes.

▶▶See also: **BLOCKED DRAINS AND DOWNPIPES** pp154–155

blocked **basin, sink** or **bath**

When water will not drain away from a basin, sink or bath, the most likely cause is a blockage in the trap or in the waste pipes under or behind the sink (or basin, bath, shower tray or bidet). If you have the right tools, you may be able to clear the blockage yourself.

action

1 REMOVE VISIBLE OBSTRUCTIONS Use fingers and tweezers (or a straightened-out metal coat hanger) to pull out any bits you can see.

2 USE A PLUNGER Use a wet cloth to block the overflow (if there is one), fit the rubber cup of a sink plunger over the plughole and pump the handle sharply up and down. Repeat this several times until the waste is clear.

3 REMOVE TRAP Place a bucket underneath the trap and unscrew the knurled rings to remove the trap. Clean the trap out in another sink or in a bucket – remember that you cannot use a sink or basin while the trap is in pieces.

4 CLEAR PIPE If the blockage is not in the trap, but is further along the waste pipe, use a sink augur (plumber's snake) to wiggle it out.

⚠️ **WARNING**

In many countries, it is illegal to carry out gas, electrical and plumbing work yourself. Only carry out work you are legally allowed to do. If in doubt, seek the services of a qualified professional.

Partly blocked waste pipe

● **PROTECT OUTLET** Chemical drain cleaners can be used if waste pipes are slow to clear. To protect the waste pipe outlet from attack by the aggressive chemicals, smear petroleum jelly (Vaseline) over it first.
● **POUR IN CHEMICAL CLEANER** Wearing gloves, pour the chemical cleaner down the plughole, following the instructions. Do not use chemicals to clear a totally blocked waste as these might not run away and so leave a dangerous liquid in your basin, sink or bath.

for next time...

● **Avoid putting either grease or fat down the plughole in kitchen sinks** – they solidify and block the waste.
● Similarly, avoid flushing food scraps down the sink and use a plughole strainer. If food does go down the plughole, run the water to rinse it away well.
● In baths, basins and shower trays, human hair is the main problem – pick out loose strands whenever you see them.
● To keep waste pipes clear, pour a cupful of washing soda (bicarbonate of soda) crystals down the plughole once a month (once a week for sinks).
● If the flow from a waste pipe has slowed down, attend to it as soon as you can before it gets fully blocked.

water gushing from gutter

When it rains heavily, water can spill in a splashing torrent out of the gutter, rather than into the downpipes. If left, faulty guttering can cause damp problems, as well as being annoying for you and your neighbours. Grab an umbrella and go outside to find out where the water is coming from, then take appropriate action or get professional help.

assessment

- Gushing gutter leaks are most often the result of blockages within the gutter. These are usually caused by leaves and birds' nests and also by moss washed off the roof.
- Similar blockages can happen in the downpipes leading to the drains or sump pit (soakaway).

- A spilling gutter may not be blocked – it could be that it is sagging (so water runs the wrong way), usually caused by failure of one or more of the gutter brackets.
- The gutter may also be split or leaking at a joint and will need a new joint or some sealant.

action

BLOCKED GUTTER

1 PREPARE YOUR TOOLS Go up the ladder armed with a bucket (plus a hook to secure it to the ladder) and a gutter scoop or garden trowel. Wear gloves.

2 CLEAR DEBRIS Stuff a rag into the top of the downpipe and then work along the gutter from there, scooping the debris out and putting it into the bucket.

3 FLUSH OUT Ask a helper to pass up the garden hose to you and you can then direct them to turn the tap on and off as required, flushing out the gutter until it is clear. Work from the high end down towards the downpipe.

 TAKE CARE
Wait until the rain has stopped before using a ladder to work on gutters and only do so if you feel confident working at a height. The ladder must be properly secured and at the correct angle – 1m out for every 4m up the wall (see page 335).

SAGGING GUTTER

■ **REATTACH BRACKET** Gutters sag when the screw holding a bracket in place has come out. Screw the bracket back into a solid fixing.

LEAKING GUTTER OR JOINT

1 FIT NEW SEAL With plastic gutters, you should be able to buy a new seal (gasket) for the brackets where lengths of gutter meet. This is simply pressed into place with the gutter removed.

2 USE GUTTER SEALANT On metal gutters (and plastic gutters where no replacement seal is available), you can stop leaks by applying roof and gutter silicone using a caulking gun, or with self-adhesive gutter repair tape.

for next time...

- Place gutter guards in your guttering. There are two main types: mesh that fixes over the guttering or bottlebrush types that sit in the guttering. Both let rainwater in but keep most of the leaves and debris out.

blocked drains and downpipes

The homeowner and not the water or sewerage company is responsible for all external pipes and drains up until they join a public sewer. If your system is blocked you will need to employ a plumber yourself. It is helpful to know how to deal with a blocked drain as you can avoid emergency call-out charges for simple problems.

assessment

A blockage can occur in waste pipes or the gully trap they discharge into; in the sewerline (soil pipe), which goes straight into the underground drain; or in the underground drain itself. Look for the following signs:

PROBLEM	WHAT TO DO
OVERFLOWING GULLY TRAP An overflowing gully is a sure sign of a blockage.	Clear gully trap You should be able to clear the blockage yourself (see below).
BLOCKED BASINS AND SINKS If a bath, basin, sink, bidet or shower will not clear (and it is not the trap – see page 152), there is a blockage in an external waste pipe, the main sewerline (soil pipe) or the underground drains.	Clear pipes or drain You might be able to clear a blockage in an external waste pipe. Only tackle this if you feel confident that you can (see opposite), and if local laws allow. Otherwise, call a qualified plumber.
WATER AROUND ACCESS HOLE Filthy water flowing out around an access hole definitely indicates a blockage in an underground drain.	Clear underground drain Call a plumber who specialises in drain clearing.

action

BLOCKED GULLY TRAP

1 REMOVE THE GRATING Remove surface debris from the gully grid cover and prise the cover out.

2 USE YOUR HANDS Wearing household rubber gloves, plunge your arm into the gully and scoop out debris. Use a trowel to break up a solid blockage.

3 USE RODS If you have drain rods, use the plunger plus a single drain rod to create sufficient water pressure to force any remaining blockage along the underground drain.

4 CLEAN GULLY TRAP Scrub a gully trap thoroughly with soapy water when you have cleared a blockage. Disinfect gloves and any tools used.

BLOCKED DRAIN

1 CHECK LOCAL LAWS Before you embark on any kind of plumbing work, check that you are allowed to do so. If not, call a qualified plumber.

2 PREPARE YOURSELF What comes out of a blocked sewer drain (soil pipe) is not pleasant, so wear full protective clothing (including goggles) and have large buckets ready to collect it. If you are working inside the house, make sure the area is well ventilated as there may be unpleasant and poisonous fumes.

GET HELP If a blockage or leak is persistent, a drain-clearing firm can send tiny cameras along your drains to check for cracks and to find blockages such as tree roots.

TIME TO ACT Drains rarely get blocked suddenly. If they are beginning to slow down, take action to clean them out before they become completely blocked.

3 **CLEAR SEWER DRAIN (SOIL PIPE)** A modern plastic pipe will have an access point on it (at ground level) with a cover you can unscrew – stand well back! The access point allows you to clear the pipe using drain rods or a large eel or auger (see page 151).

BLOCKED DOWNPIPE

1 **START AT THE TOP** Check for what is causing the blockage. A bird's nest or ball can simply be removed. But the most likely obstruction is a collection of wind-blown leaves lodged in the mouth of the downpipe. A pipe with a swan-necked section at the top is more likely to become blocked than a straight downpipe.

2 **LOOK FOR LEAKS** If there is no obvious blockage in the mouth of the downpipe, look for where the water is leaking. The blockage will be in the section of pipe immediately below a leaking joint (see box, right).

3 **OBSTRUCTIONS NEAR THE TOP** You can usually clear these by probing with a length of wire. Cover the drain at the bottom of the pipe to prevent any debris from falling into it. Hook out debris if you can; if you cannot, probe until it becomes loose.

4 **FLUSH OUT THE PIPE** Unscrew the fixing brackets, remove the downpipe from the stormwater connection and flush away remaining loose debris by pouring buckets of water down the pipe or playing a strong jet of water down it from a hose. If the pipe is straight, not swan-necked, tie rags firmly to the end of a stick and push the obstruction loose with it. Fix the pipe back to the wall.

Obstructions out of reach

Hire a flexible drain rod or plumber's eel to clear an obstruction lower down a pipe or in a swan-necked pipe. You will need to dismantle the downpipe to reach the point of obstruction.

1 REMOVE FIXING BRACKETS Start with the lowest section of downpipe connected to the stormwater system. Remove the screws that hold the fixing brackets to the wall. Work from the bottom and remove the screws and clips up to the point it leaks. If the pipe is held by two-part brackets, undo the bolts holding the rings to the back plates; leave the back plates in place.

2 FREE EACH SECTION OF PIPE As you free the clips or lugs that hold it, free each section of pipe from the section below and lift it away from the wall.

3 CLEAN OUT THE SECTIONS Use a long stick to push out any obstructions inside the sections. Alternatively, flush out the blockage with a jet of water from a hose.

4 REPLACE PIPE Replace the pipe section by section, working from the top down, and screw or bolt back in place the clips (or nail the lugs) that hold the section to the wall.

 WARNING

In many countries, it is illegal to carry out gas, electrical and plumbing work yourself. Only carry out work you are legally allowed to do. If in doubt, seek the services of a qualified professional.

▶▶See also: **BLOCKED BASIN, SINK OR BATH** p152

vermin infestations

Pests, such as mice and insects, can cause damage to your home and, because many carry germs, may transmit diseases to the occupants. Fortunately, you can turn a siege into a rout if you stand your ground and put up a strong defence.

WATCHPOINT When handling traps, poison or dead vermin, wear rubber gloves to avoid getting poison or germs on your hands. Dispose of the gloves immediately after use.

assessment

● By the time you notice the damage that vermin have caused, their numbers could be in the hundreds if not thousands. Act the minute you discover any signs in your home.

● Serious infestations may require the analysis and advice of a pest-control specialist. Find reputable companies recommended by the local authority or on the internet.

SPOTTING SIGNS OF INFESTATION

PEST	WHERE FOUND	SIGNS	
RATS AND MICE	Outhouses, sheds, roof space, crawl space, cavity wall area and other interior spaces	Rod-shaped black droppings 4–8mm long (mice) or 8–12mm (rats), gnawed holes in packaging and chewed wires and skirting. Both rats and mice give off a distinctive musky smell.	
COCKROACHES	Moist areas such as outside taps and leaking pipes; kitchen areas	Cockroaches are nocturnal so if you see them during the day this could mean you have a serious infestation. In large numbers cockroaches produce an unpleasant almond-like smell.	
CARPET BEETLES	Carpets, fur, leather and wool	Small, round, grey-brown beetles mottled with cream enter houses to lay eggs. The larvae are tiny, hairy grubs, known as 'woolly bears'. Holes appear in carpets and other textiles.	
FLEAS	On pets and their bedding, in carpets and soft furnishings	Your pet is constantly scratching – place it on a white sheet and groom it. If it has fleas, their telltale black comma-shaped droppings will appear underneath. Itchy red bites on humans indicate flea infestation.	
WASPS	Roof spaces, sheds, cavity wall area, hanging from the eaves of buildings	Wasps flying in and out of a hole every few seconds is the sign of a nest within. Nest building begins in late spring. Nests may be large paper globes or umbrella-shaped, hanging inside the house or from eaves.	
TERMITES (WHITE ANTS)	Any timber such as frame of house, floorboards, panelling, wood piles, waste wood	Swarms of winged termites in spring, often after rain. Pencil-sized mud tubes at foundation walls and floor joists. Wood damage – a hollow sound when tapped. Dark blistered areas on wooden floorboards.	

action

RATS AND MICE

1 **CLEAN AREA** Scrupulously clean everywhere, place food in sealed containers and seal waste bins. Make sure there are no food scraps on compost heaps.

2 **SET TRAPS** Use spring mouse traps and rat traps with poisoned bait. Place traps and bait within tamperproof bait stations and cover securely. Set a series of traps and bait with garlic sausage, bacon or offal. Using too few traps or bait stations may prolong the infestation.

3 **PLACE TRAPS** Mice run near walls, so place mouse traps along the perimeter of a room. **Rats will avoid anything new – bait a large number of unset traps for a week before setting them.**

 WARNING
Rats spread disease through their urine, faeces and the fleas they carry. A potentially fatal condition is Weil's disease, also known as leptospirosis. Rats, mice and cockroaches can spread salmonella, causing food poisoning, by contaminating food.

COCKROACHES

1 **BE HYGIENIC** Keep waste bins clean and sealed, do not throw food scraps on compost heaps and sweep up leaves and other organic debris. Ventilate moist areas and check for leaking taps or pipes.

2 **SEAL AND TREAT** Seal all cracks and holes in walls, door frames and where pipes pass through the fabric of the house. Treat with proprietary spray; if this does not clear the infestation, seek professional help.

CARPET BEETLES

1 **REMOVE HEAVILY INFESTED ITEMS** If there is much damage, discard the article along with the carpet moth larvae that have caused the problem.

2 **CLEAN AND TREAT THE AREA** Thoroughly vacuum and clean the affected carpet and furnishings. Dispose of the vacuumed dust and debris. Use a proprietary chemical spray to treat the affected area.

FLEAS

1 **TREAT PET** Consult your vet for the safest and most effective treatment for your pet. Never use a flea treatment intended for dogs on a cat. Once clear, apply a suitable treatment to your pet on a regular basis, on your vet's guidance.

2 **TREAT SURROUNDINGS** Wash bedding using a disinfectant in the water and vacuum thoroughly, discarding the vacuum debris. If your pet is allowed on beds or furniture, wash all bedding and treat mattresses and upholstered furniture with a safe and effective spray, and vacuum as before.

■ **BITES ON HUMANS** If the occupants of the house have bites, it is likely that there is a serious infestation that requires professional treatment.

WASPS

1 **TAKE CARE** Angry wasps release a pheromone that makes other wasps more aggressive. Only treat a small nest – no bigger than a tennis ball – yourself and wear a protective veil and gloves. Note that wasp stings can trigger an allergic reaction (see page 20). Ask a professional to destroy a larger nest. Nests are vacated in autumn. Some species reuse the nest, so it is best removed.

2 **TREAT THE NEST** Spray the whole nest with a proprietary spray if you have access or direct the spray through the nest entrance.

TERMITES (WHITE ANTS)

1 **SEEK HELP** Eradication of a termite infestation is best carried out by a licensed pest controller. He will destroy the nest if possible (usually found near trees or woodpiles within 100m of the house) and apply chemicals to infested timber as a liquid or dust. To deter reinfestation, he may install physical or chemical barriers under and in the house.

2 **BAITING** If you live where there are termites you should inspect your home once a month. Ask a pest controller to install a baiting system that will act as a continuous monitoring system.

▶▶See also: **ALLERGIC REACTION** pp54–55 • **BITING INSECTS** p317

trapped bat or bird

Your first instinct will be to get the bat or bird out of the house at all costs. But you can minimise injury to the creature – as well as damage to your home caused by its terrified flutterings – if you keep calm and act slowly and purposefully. If you have a cat, dog or other pet, make sure it is safely out of the way.

action

TRAPPED BAT

1 ENCOURAGE ESCAPE A bat will only fly off at night. Turn off lights and open all windows and external doors. A bat navigates by echolocation (it uses sound waves to locate and avoid objects) so it is unlikely to fly into a closed window and injure itself.

2 REMOVE BAT If it does not fly out, wear gloves, then cover the bat with a shoebox and slide the lid underneath to seal it. Or place a cloth in the box, with a small jar lid filled with water, and gently pick up the bat and put it in the box. Put the lid on. The bat will be able to crawl into the cloth and hide.

3 RELEASE BAT After dusk, place the box outside at least 1.5m above the ground – do not place on the ground as bats need to swoop to become airborne again. Remove the lid and leave the bat to fly off.

PANICKING BIRD

1 PROTECT BIRD Stay at a distance from the bird so you do not frighten it further and make it fly about. Draw the curtains or cover all windows to reduce the risk that the bird will fly into the glass and injure itself.

2 GUIDE BIRD Close internal doors, open wide any external doors and uncover and open the largest window. The bird should then fly towards the light.

3 CATCH BIRD If there is no suitable exit, or the bird does not fly out, darken the room and throw a sheet over the bird. Gently scoop it up and let it go outside.

⚠ TAKE CARE

Do not try to entice a bird with food or water. It will be too frightened to eat or drink. If it is injured, seek advice from a local vet or a wildlife rescue service.

for next time...

BAT IN THE HOUSE
● Young bats learning to fly are most likely to stray inside. Keep large windows and doors closed or partly covered on summer nights.
● Make sure the hatch to your roof space is secure and there are no spaces around pipes, light fittings or between ceiling boards. A young bat can fall through the tiniest of gaps into the room below.

BIRD IN THE HOUSE
● Birds will occasionally fly into a house through open doors. Prevent this with screens, nets or blinds.
● Most birds are brought in by the family cat. Fitting the cat with a bell or beeper on a quick-release collar, so that the bird is aware of the cat's presence, can reduce the incidence of it bringing in hunting trophies.
● Prevent birds falling down your chimney by installing wire or mesh chimney-pot guards.

pet goes missing

A missing pet usually turns up after a few days – a little bedraggled and hungry, but no worse for wear. If a pet is out for any longer, it may become seriously ill or suffer a road accident. To find your pet promptly, mount a search and enlist help.

WATCHPOINT If your pet is valuable, it may have been stolen. You are reporting a theft, not just a missing pet and quick action may help the investigation.

be aware

- Your dog should wear a collar with a tag giving your contact details. To help identify them, cats should be similarly tagged.
- As collars can be removed or lost, it is highly recommended that a pet is fitted with a microchip. The microchip is a small radio chip, about the size of a grain of rice, which is harmlessly injected beneath the skin. The pet can then be traced through a national animal database once you register it.

action

PET HAS DISAPPEARED

1 COMB YOUR HOUSE AND GARDEN Cats and small dogs can get into some unlikely places. Check your property thoroughly, including behind appliances, inside wardrobes, the roof space, cellar or shed – even tiny crawl spaces and drains. Do not assume that your pet will respond to your frantic calls.

2 CHECK THE NEIGHBOURHOOD Talk to as many people as possible, including delivery persons and local children. Leave a written description or photograph with your neighbours – include your phone number – and ask them to check outbuildings. Use a powerful torch (flashlight) in your search.

■ **MAKE FAMILIAR NOISES** As you walk around, call your pet's name, rattle a box of treats, squeeze a favourite squeaky toy or use an ultrasonic whistle to get your pet's attention – they work for both cats and dogs. Stop regularly and listen for a response.

■ **ATTRACT WITH SCENT** Animals find their way by smell as well as sound, so place some strongly scented items outside your home – its bedding or a favourite toy, or an unwashed article of your clothing.

■ **MISSING ON WALK** If your dog went missing while off his lead when you were walking him, return to the place where you last saw him. After a reasonable period of time phone home to see if he has returned instinctively. If not, wait for as long as possible before mounting a local search.

PET MISSING FOR LONGER

■ **INFORM THE AUTHORITIES** If a dog is lost, tell the police and animal control of your loss and obtain a reference number from them. You will need this if you want to claim on your insurance. Contact your vet to register a dog or cat missing.

■ **CONTACT ANIMAL ORGANISATIONS** Get in touch with the animal database register (if your pet is microchipped), and any other relevant national registers of lost pets, such as the (R)SPCA and cat and dog rescue groups. Many of these organisations can be found online and they will tell you where you can register your missing pet (see page 339).

■ **PUT UP A POSTER** Write a full description of your pet, including its colour, size and gender – include as many details as possible – and find a colour photo showing any distinguishing marks. Make up a poster stating when your pet went missing and where it was last seen. Give your contact details and the amount of the reward, if you are offering one. Put up posters around the local area, including community noticeboards, local shop windows and sports facilities (with the permission of the owners).

■ **USE LOCAL MEDIA** To reach as many people as possible in the area, advertise in the local press and on radio stations. To be most effective, do this in the first week after your pet has gone missing.

pet is taken ill

Because of an animal's natural instinct for self-preservation, it is sometimes hard to tell that your pet is unwell until the ailment is fairly well advanced. There are a number of key signs that may signal that a pet is seriously ill. These include behavioural changes, loss of appetite and excessive thirst as well as acute symptoms such as breathing problems.

assessment

Certain signs and symptoms demonstrated by your pet can indicate an acute crisis, which must be treated immediately by your vet. Be especially on the lookout for the following:

DOG OR CAT

SYMPTOM	INDICATION
Breathing difficulties	Can indicate a physical obstruction, heart problem, poisoning or lung disease. See opposite for emergency action. Consult your vet urgently.
Bloating, vomiting and diarrhoea	Your pet may have eaten something that has disagreed with it, perhaps when out. This can indicate something more ominous, such as parvovirus in young dogs. Call your vet and follow his advice.
Loss of appetite	This is very unusual if a pet is healthy and can be a sign of illness or stress. Consult your vet.
Drinking more than usual	May be a sign of serious complaints such as diabetes or kidney problems. Monitor your pet and call your vet to tell him what you have observed. Follow his instructions.
Scratching, shaking head	May be caused by parasites or a foreign body stuck in the animal's ear. If your pet will let you, gently look into the ear, using a torch (flashlight). Remove any foreign body with tweezers or a cotton bud, being careful not to push it further in. Ask a vet to examine your pet whether you have removed a foreign body or not.
Dry skin bald patches	Can be a sign of parasite infection or mange, which if untreated can become a serious condition. See your vet and ask about parasite prevention.

CAT

SYMPTOM	INDICATION
Straining, repeat visits to the litter tray, difficulty urinating and blood in the urine	May be a sign of a blocked bladder, which can be life-threatening. Consult your vet immediately.
Membrane over eye	All cats have what is known as the 'third eyelid' – a membrane that covers the eye. This acts to lubricate and is visible in a normal, healthy cat when it wakes or is drowsy. If it is visible at other times, it may indicate an underlying health problem, such as a viral infection, and you should consult your vet. Take the cat to the vet immediately if its eye looks sore or there is any discharge.

TIME TO ACT An ill or injured cat is likely to hide away until the condition is far advanced. If you do observe any warning signs, act promptly to prevent further deterioration.

WATCHPOINT Do not give your pet anything to eat or drink, unless your vet tells you to do so, as it may need a general anaesthetic later.

GET HELP Always seek veterinary help if possible. An animal in pain may lash out, causing further complications, so be very careful and do not put yourself at risk.

action

 TAKE CARE

- **You have a far better chance of your pet surviving if you can get to a vet quickly.** Always try to seek advice from a veterinary practice, who may direct you to a local out-of-hours veterinary service.
- If you cannot reach a vet – you may be on a long country walk in the middle of nowhere, for example – the following techniques can be used, but should only be attempted in an absolute emergency. If not carried out properly they could be harmful. Do not attempt these techniques unless your pet's life is in immediate danger. Always put your safety first.

UNCONSCIOUS PET

1 CHECK FOR HEARTBEAT Gently grasp the chest, just behind the elbows, with one hand, while supporting the animal with the other hand. If you are sure you can feel no heartbeat, start chest compressions.

2 START COMPRESSIONS Lay your pet on its right side. Place your hands over the ribs just behind the front leg. Compress 2–4cm every second for 5 seconds. Puppies, small dogs, and cats may only need 1–2cm gentle compressions with the fingertips.

3 GIVE RESCUE BREATHS If an animal is not breathing, extend the neck and check and clear the back of the throat. Pinch the mouth shut and make a funnel with your hand around the nose that you can breathe into. Breathe into this funnel, avoiding direct contact with the nose, so that the chest expands. Do this five times, once every five seconds.

4 REPEAT ACTION For a small or medium-sized animal (under 25kg), repeat one breath with three compressions until you can feel a pulse and the pet is breathing. For a larger animal, repeat three breaths with five compressions.

APPARENT CHOKING

1 IS PET CHOKING? In most animals, what appears to be choking is vomiting. Cats rarely choke, and in dogs apparent choking can be a form of reverse sneezing, which, though alarming, is harmless.

2 CHECK FOR AN OBSTRUCTION If possible, get someone to firmly hold the pet's mouth open. Carefully remove any visible blockage – do not push further in. Do not do a blind finger sweep – look into the animal's mouth to avoid injuring your pet. If there is evidence of a needle or fishing hook, do not pull on this, as it can have a thread or line attached.

3 DISLODGE THE OBJECT Lift the animal's back legs; give its body a firm shake to expel the obstruction.

■ **THE HEIMLICH MANOEUVRE** This technique should only be used when all other alternatives have been tried and failed. On a large animal (over 25kg), wrap your arms tightly around its belly just under the rib cage. Give one quick, forceful squeeze, to expel the object. Take the pet to the vet immediately, as the procedure might have caused internal damage.

SUSPECTED POISONING

1 DO NOT INDUCE VOMITING Act quickly if you suspect your pet has ingested poison. Do not attempt to get your pet to vomit as this may cause further damage.

2 REMOVE POISON ON COAT Wash the poison from your pet's coat to prevent more being ingested. Your pet will frantically try to lick it off.

3 CALL THE VET Describe the symptoms. If you know, give details of the poison; keep a sample of it and, if possible, the original container, and take this to the vet. Follow the vet's advice.

▶▶See also: **ANIMAL OR HUMAN BITE** p106

pet is injured

When dealing with pet injuries, a little knowledge of first aid goes a long way. As long as you learn the basics such as how to stop bleeding and what to do if there is a suspected broken limb, you will be equipped to deal with most situations. Be aware that an injured animal is likely to be very distressed.

action

WOUNDS

1 STOP ANY BLEEDING If your pet is bleeding heavily, cover the wound with a clean cloth and apply pressure until the bleeding stops.

2 CLEAN AND DRESS THE WOUND Clean a small wound with a weak salt solution. Dry, and apply a dressing to keep it sterile. **Cat bites, in particular, can form abscesses if not promptly treated.**

3 WATCH FOR INFECTION Always get any wound checked over by a vet. It may need further, professional cleaning and your vet will decide if any other treatment, such as stitches or antibiotics, is required.

BROKEN LIMB

1 KNOW THE SIGNS Your pet may limp or its limb may swell up. It will not necessarily keep still.

2 AVOID BEING BITTEN Your pet may normally be docile and affectionate, but it may bite when in pain. To gently restrain it, use a muzzle or towel if it is safe to do so.

3 CONTACT VET Call your veterinary practice and explain the situation. Follow the advice given.

SHOCK

1 CHECK FOR PULSE AND HEART RATE Shock can result from blood or fluid loss, pain or infection. The animal will have a rapid heart and pulse rate. Check the pulse at the inner thigh or below the ankle.

2 PLACE IN RECOVERY POSITION Lay the animal on its side with its head extended and cover with a blanket to keep warm. Raise the chest and hindquarters above the level of the head by placing a soft support under the animal. Do not give your pet any water. Talk to your pet in a soothing tone.

3 CONTACT VET Call your veterinary practice, explain your pet's symptoms and follow the advice given.

Pet hit by car

Whether it is your pet that is hit, or someone else's, an accident is distressing. Keep calm, clear the road and give the animal first aid.

- **CLEAR THE ROAD** Move the animal away from further harm, making sure you are not bitten.
- **ENSURE AIRWAY IS CLEAR** Check the animal's breathing and pulse.
- **KEEP WARM** Shock can cause a drop in temperature. Cover the animal with a coat or blanket to keep it warm.
- **CONTROL BLEEDING** Hold a clean cloth, such as a handkerchief, firmly over any wound until bleeding slows and stops.
- **MOVE ANIMAL AS LITTLE AS POSSIBLE** After moving the animal away from the road, minimise further movement. Make a rigid stretcher from a car's parcel shelf or similar.
- **GET HELP** Phone a vet or the (R)SPCA (see page 339) for advice. Give your location and what injuries you believe the animal to have. If the pet is not yours, check any tags for details, and contact the owner, or ask the vet to check for a microchip.

 ▶▶See also: **ANIMAL OR HUMAN BITE** p106

CRIMINAL
ACTS

break-in at home

Every year, thousands of homes are burgled. Many crimes are opportunistic, with thieves getting in through open doors and windows. A break-in brings a sense of violation and loss – and if you disturb an intruder you may be in danger.

WATCHPOINT Join your local neighbourhood watch group, if there is one, or think about setting up a new group. These groups are known to be effective at deterring crime.

action

BURGLAR MAY BE PRESENT

1 TRUST YOUR INSTINCTS If you sense something is wrong as you approach your home, stop and think. What have you noticed that is not quite right? Is the door not shut properly? Did you hear a sound?

2 LOOK FOR SIGNS OF A BREAK-IN Has the door been forced or is a window broken? If you find a weapon, or potential weapon, just inside your door, leave at once.

3 RETREAT TO A SAFE PLACE If anything makes you suspect that someone has broken in to your home and that the intruder might still be there, go to a neighbour's house and call the police.

 WARNING

If you walk in on a burglar, try not to appear aggressive and do not challenge the intruder. Either leave quickly or allow the burglar the opportunity to escape. Once you are safe, call the police. Then write down as full a description as you can.

BURGLAR HAS GONE

1 CONFIRM THAT YOU HAVE BEEN BURGLED Could there be another explanation for what you have found? Have you definitely been broken into? The burglar may have been disturbed, in which case the theft may not be obvious at first. Do not forget to check the contents of your garage or garden shed, if you have one.

2 CALL THE POLICE Phone the local police station (you can get the number from the phone directory or online), rather than the emergency services. You may have to wait some time for the police to arrive.

3 DO NOT TOUCH ANYTHING Resist the temptation to tidy up or move anything until after the police have been, as you may damage vital evidence. Take photos of everything exactly as you found it.

4 SECURE YOUR HOME Once the police have attended, take steps to prevent another burglary, such as installing additional or more secure locks. Burglars often come back for valuable items they spotted first time round.

A burglar's-eye view

Your house is likely to become a target if a burglar can spot a weakness in its defences. Learn to look at your property from his point of view.

● **DO YOU HAVE BASIC SECURITY?** Homes without simple security, such as window locks and deadlocks, are much more likely to be burgled. Ensure that all doors and ground-floor windows have locks and bolts, and fit an intruder alarm.
● **IS THERE A DOG?** Dogs are a deterrent. Even if you don't have one, a sign can put off a burglar.

● **HOW GOOD IS THE LIGHTING?** Fit security lighting, with motion or infra-red sensors, around your house. Trim trees or hedges near doors or windows that could provide cover for an intruder.
● **IS ANYTHING VALUABLE ON SHOW?** Keep any valuable items out of view of windows. As soon as it is dark outside, draw the curtains.
● **IS THE HOUSE UNOCCUPIED?** If you go away for a few days, ask a friend or neighbour to pick up your post and open and close curtains in different rooms. Cancel any weekly deliveries.

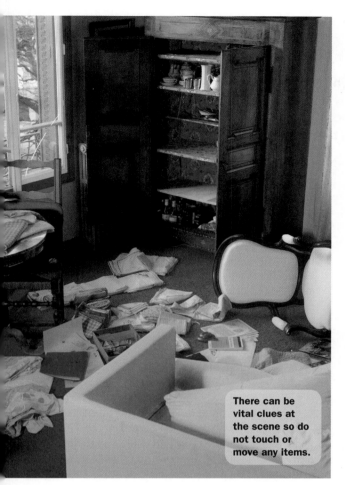

There can be vital clues at the scene so do not touch or move any items.

REPORTING THE CRIME

1 GET YOUR THOUGHTS IN ORDER Think back to the moment that you discovered the break-in. Jot down what time you arrived home and what you first noticed. Start making an inventory of items that have been taken. Do not touch anything.

2 TALK TO POLICE When the police arrive they will make a crime report and may take a statement from you. This may include questions about how the thief got into your home and what has been stolen. If they anticipate that a crime scene investigator will become involved, they will give you advice on what you can touch or move before his arrival.

3 COOPERATE WITH THE INVESTIGATOR A police investigator may photograph the signs of break-in, such as tool marks, take fingerprints – including yours for elimination – and search for other evidence, such as footprints or clothing fibres.

4 KEEP TABS ON THE INVESTIGATION Once the police have gathered evidence, they will begin their inquiries, starting with your neighbours. You may be given a crime reference number, which you can use to track the progress of the investigation. If a suspect is charged with your burglary, you may be asked to be a witness.

for next time...

● Keep cash, jewellery and important papers in a safe bolted to the wall or floor, or hide them somewhere unpredictable, such as in the kitchen. Burglars often overlook the kitchen.
● Mark valuable items such as televisions and computers with an ID number, such as your driver's licence number, using a UV pen.
● Make a list of all your valuable possessions and documents. Take photos of unusual items, such as jewellery. Note serial and model numbers and give this list, along with receipts and photographs of the items, to a friend or relative for safe keeping.
● If you don't want to install security systems, opt for a fake alarm box and fake CCTV cameras. These cost very little but can discourage an opportunist burglar.

what next?

● Contact your insurance company at once to report the loss, giving the crime reference number if you have one. Your insurers may offer an all-hours emergency service to make your home secure.
● Compile a list of all the items stolen or damaged. If possible, locate receipts, photographs or other proofs of purchase. Take your time. You may only notice something is missing when you go to use it.
● If the burglary has left you feeling traumatised, you may wish to seek counselling. Some countries run schemes offering free counselling for the victims of serious crime. Your local police officers will know where and if you can access such support.

 TAKE CARE
Close and lock side gates and accessible windows. Store ladders in a garage, if possible, and put away garden tools that can be used to force entry.

▶▶See also: INTRUDER IN THE HOUSE p166

intruder in the house

Discovering a stranger in your home can be frightening and disorienting. You will want to do whatever you can to protect yourself, your family and your home. But be careful: the law sets strict limits about the use of force – even against an individual whom you believe may wish you harm. It is generally best to avoid confrontation if at all possible.

action

1 BE VERY QUIET If you hear a strange noise, keep quiet and listen. Is there really someone in your home? If so, is it one person or more? What are they doing: are they ransacking the place or do they appear to be approaching the room you are in? Phone the police if practicable and you can do so without attracting attention.

2 MAKE YOURSELF SAFE If you are alone, barricade your door or lock yourself in the bathroom. If you can safely access a back door or another way out, leave at once and go to your nearest neighbour for help.

3 GATHER TOGETHER If there are others in the house, take your phone and quickly gather everyone into one room. There is safety in numbers, and it is less likely that you will come to harm if the intruder has to face you all together.

4 CALL FOR HELP If you have not done so already, phone the police and tell them that there is an intruder in your home. Tell them where you are located in the house and where you think the intruder might be. Stay on the line until you are sure the intruder has left, or the police have arrived. Do not be tempted to investigate to find the intruder.

What is reasonable force?

It is never advisable to confront an intruder, especially if they are armed or under the influence of drugs or alcohol, yet you do have a right to defend yourself and others using reasonable force. Be aware that the legal definition of what constitutes 'reasonable force' varies in different countries. A number of factors come into consideration.

- **JUSTIFICATION** Was the use of force justified? Did you act only to defend yourself and others?
- **EXCESSIVE FORCE** You may be prosecuted if you use excessive force. Force may only be used in defence of yourself or others, or to prevent an offender stealing your property. Be wary of using more force than necessary. For instance, shooting or stabbing an unarmed intruder is likely to be considered unreasonable, depending on the circumstances. Never use force in anger to punish an intruder or use it in revenge.
- **LAWS** It is worth familiarising yourself with the laws of the country in which you live, so that you know where you stand regarding 'reasonable force'.

for next time...

- Always secure your home before going to bed. Make sure all main entry doors are locked and bolted and all easily accessible windows are closed and locked.
- Keep a phone by the bed at night so you can make calls without leaving the room.
- If you have an alarm, set it to protect particular zones, such as the ground floor, or entry points, such as doors and windows.

- It may be worth having a panic button fitted that connects to a central monitoring station of a security company. If triggered, the security company will respond and may call the police.
- If you live in a particularly crime-heavy area, consult with local police as to how best to protect your home. Some houses are built with a 'safe room'. This is a specially prepared room into which you can retreat if threatened.

stranger at the door

Each year, many people – particularly the elderly – are robbed by tricksters who talk their way in. Bogus callers may pretend to be employees of a utility company, or they may impersonate builders or handymen who claim that your home needs urgent attention. In some cases, robbery is not the sole motive and the householder can be seriously harmed.

precautions

- Fit a spy-hole in your door and a porch light. This will enable you to have a good look at whoever knocks at your door **before you open it.**
- Fit a sturdy door chain, or bar, to your front door. This will help you to retain control of who you let in to your house.

action

STRANGER KNOCKS AT DOOR

1 RETAIN THE INITIATIVE Keep the door chain on as you open the door. Do not be badgered by cold callers. Consider the request. If the person is offering something you do not want, refuse politely and close the door. If he has called at an inconvenient time, ask him to come back later.

2 REQUEST PROOF OF IDENTITY If a caller claims to be from an authority or a utility company, ask for identification, especially if the caller is unexpected. **But remember ID cards can be forged.** Ask him to wait or call back later so that you can telephone the company he works for (using the number in the

directory not one given by the stranger). If someone tells you your roof needs fixing or your chimney requires repointing, do not go outside or agree to anything. Instead, take the caller's details and tell him you will look at the problem later.

3 REFUSE ENTRY If you cannot confirm a caller's identity or feel at all uneasy about letting someone in, simply apologise politely and close the door. Alternatively, ask the person to call back later and arrange to have someone with you.

STRANGER COMES IN

1 LEAVE THE FRONT DOOR OPEN If you invite a caller in, show him where to go and walk behind him. Keep the door open so that you will have an escape route should you need it.

2 STAY ALERT If the caller is only going to be in your home for a moment, stay with him. Watch out for attempts to distract you, such as a request for a drink or to fetch something from another room. If he is going to be longer, make sure the room he is in does not contain any valuables. If you let more than one person into your house, try to have someone else with you while they are there.

3 AVOID CASH PAYMENTS If you have to pay a caller, use a card or cheque. Only pay by cash if you trust the caller or are satisfied with the service. Try to have more or less the right money and never take it from your safe or other hiding place in view of the caller. Get a receipt and contact details. If you have any doubts, check the contact details are genuine. If they are not, stop your cheque or card payment.

⚠ WARNING

Some criminals work in pairs – one knocks on the front door and the accomplice uses the opportunity to enter through the back door.

potential violence

Too much alcohol, intense sporting rivalry and groups of people in search of excitement can often be a potent mixture that leads to violence. If you are in the vicinity, you may unwittingly find yourself caught up in an unwelcome and frightening scenario. But you can use prior knowledge to defuse such situations and escape to safety if necessary.

assessment

BE AWARE OF YOUR SURROUNDINGS
You can easily find yourself in circumstances that bubble over into violence. Be wary of:
● Sporting events, especially where local rivalries increase the risk of violent behaviour
● Political rallies or protest demonstrations that incite powerful emotions – you might be perceived as 'the enemy'
● Places where people gather to drink. Alcohol – and drugs – are a major cause of violence
● Anywhere that is crowded – bumping into someone and infringing personal space can lead to trouble
● A situation where you are outnumbered by a group or gang who appear threatening.

SPOTTING AN AGGRESSOR
Take note of a person's body language. You can often spot a troublemaker before he has a chance to confront you. Invasion of your personal space is a dangerous sign and you should create distance by stepping away and projecting your palms in front of you. Also watch for:
● Excessive eye contact
● Gritted teeth, with head and jaw pushed forward; clenched fists
● Raised voice and challenging or abusive language
● Obvious signs of alcohol or drug abuse from the person's appearance or behaviour (see page 56) or the obvious presence of drugs or alcohol.

G20 Protest, in London 2009. Steer clear of demonstrations, even if they appear peaceful.

WATCHPOINT Don't be goaded into a fight. When someone uses threatening behaviour they often want a response that they can use to 'justify' further aggression.

GET HELP If you are injured as a result of violent crime, you may be due compensation. it depends on the laws of the country in which the attack happened. Report the incident as soon as possible.

action

TENSIONS ESCALATE

1 ASSESS AND DE-ESCALATE In any potential conflict you need to make an almost instant risk assessment and act accordingly. If the person you are faced with is armed, very drunk or appears to be on drugs, escape must be your priority. Otherwise, do what you can to calm things down.

2 REMAIN CALM As the adrenaline begins to flow, it is easy to become – and appear – more aggressive, even without realising it. So take a few deep breaths, drop your shoulders and try to stay calm.

3 REGAIN YOUR PERSONAL SPACE When people act in a threatening way, they usually come close to you and invade your personal space. This only heightens the tension, so **try to step back or to the side to increase the space around you.**

4 COMMUNICATE Your tone of voice is your most powerful tool with which to control the temperature of the exchange when tensions escalate. Try to use the best volume and tone to communicate, calm or de-escalate any situation.

YOU ARE THREATENED

1 WEIGH UP YOUR OPTIONS Be aware of your environment and as soon as you feel you are in danger, quickly scan your surroundings for escape routes, such as doors, pathways or roads. Are there places of safety nearby, such as public offices, shops or a vehicle, or sources of help, such as the police, security staff or bystanders? Trust your instincts: if you feel unsafe, act immediately.

2 LOOK FOR PHYSICAL BARRIERS Anything you can put between you and the person threatening you will make you safer. Inside, this might be a table or chair, or even a lockable door. Outside, it could be a wall or fence, a vehicle or a busy road.

3 SUMMON HELP How you get help will depend on how threatened you feel. Simply walking towards other people might be enough to stop the situation getting out of control. If not, scream and shout as loudly as you can. Only use your mobile phone if you are temporarily secure.

4 COMMIT TO ESCAPING If you must escape, choose your route and run as fast as you can. Do not look behind you, just run until you are somewhere safe. If you can distract the other person, or put a barrier between you before you run, so much the better.

Self-defence

It is always best to avoid any aggression, but if you are physically attacked you may have little choice but to defend yourself.

● **APPEAR UNWILLING TO FIGHT** Always try to avoid escalating the conflict. Apologise and appease as appropriate. If there are onlookers, the less 'face' the aggressor loses, the safer you will be. Do not respond to insults or even physical contact. Keep telling the person that you do not want any trouble.

● **KEEP YOUR HANDS UP AND OPEN** If the conflict starts to become physical, hold your hands up, palms out. This looks like a gesture of appeasement or surrender, which is helpful, but it is actually a very good position from which to protect yourself or strike back.

● **DEFEND YOURSELF** Use force only if it becomes absolutely necessary. Do not use more force than is reasonable. For advice on self-defence see pages 172–175.

▶▶See also: **PHYSICAL ATTACK** pp172–175 ● **CAUGHT IN A RIOT** pp210–211

encountering a **mugger**

Street robbery, or mugging, is a traumatic experience that can rob you of your self-confidence as well as your possessions. Remember that muggers choose targets whom they believe will be both easy to rob and worth the risk. Find out how to make yourself less appealing on both counts and the best way to respond if you are attacked.

action

YOU ARE MUGGED

1 GAUGE THE LEVEL OF THREAT If you are confronted by a mugger who is armed, appears high on drugs or has one or more accomplices, focus on compliance first and then escape.

2 STAY CALM Although you may feel frightened, the calmer you appear to be, the more you will reassure the mugger that you are going to comply. He is then less likely to act aggressively or irrationally.

3 TELL THE MUGGER YOU WILL COMPLY Once the mugger has made his demands for your money, phone or valuables, verbally confirm that you will comply. This should reassure him that he need not be aggressive. Try to be non-confrontational.

4 HAND OVER YOUR POSSESSIONS As you hand over what he wants, try to create some distance so that you can escape: place your wallet on the ground and step back; toss your bag slowly to the mugger so he has to catch it, or hold it at arm's length so that you can step away as he takes it.

5 FLEE Unless you are fit and fast, do not simply try to outrun your attacker. Instead, run towards an obvious place of safety that will discourage his pursuit. This might be a shop, bar or office, or simply a more crowded street.

6 SCREAM OR SHOUT If you are pursued, scream and shout as loudly as you can and do not stop. Even if no one comes at once, it will unnerve the mugger and he will probably give up the chase.

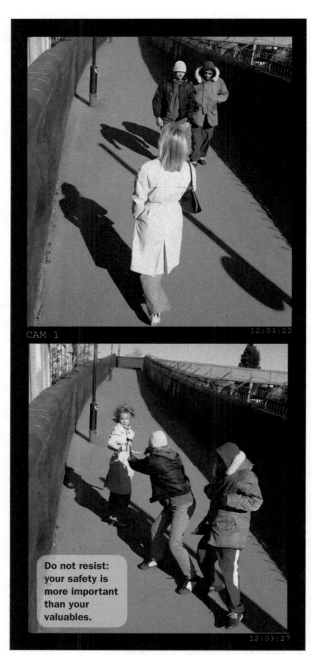

CAM 1   12:03:22

Do not resist: your safety is more important than your valuables.

12:03:27

WATCHPOINT Avoid subways, alleys and other isolated routes, even in broad daylight. When travelling, ask locally for advice about dangerous areas and do not set foot in them.

TIME TO ACT Tell the police exactly what the mugger took, in case an arrest is made. Advise your bank of stolen credit cards and your insurance company of stolen valuables.

 WARNING

● Never argue or fight with a mugger. If the motive is robbery, giving up your belongings quickly should ensure that you escape unharmed.

● Quickly scan your surroundings to identify your best escape route or nearest source of help. But remember, **complying with the mugger's demands is the safest option in the first instance.**

IF YOU ARE ATTACKED

1 FIGHT BACK If the attack continues even after you have given up your belongings, defend yourself (see pages 172–175). The mugger may produce a knife or gun (see pages 178–181).

2 GET HELP If you have been injured, seek medical assistance at once. Make a complete record of your injuries as this will help to secure criminal justice. Seek support from friends, family or a trained counsellor if the event leaves you with any lasting feelings of fear, isolation or depression.

Being a good witness

All muggings and robberies should be reported to the police as soon as possible: research shows that the quicker you report an incident, the more likely the offender will be caught.

● **EVIDENCE** Make a note of the time and place of the attack, and write a full description of your attacker and anything he said. The stress of an attack can affect your memory, so the sooner you commit your description to paper, the more accurate it is likely to be. If possible, take photographs of any injuries you have sustained – it is a useful way of providing proof.

for next time...

● Try not to flaunt expensive items in high-risk or solitary areas. Carry cameras and laptops in backpacks or sports bags.

● Do not carry cheques and guarantee cards together or with a record of your PIN. Carry your keys separately from any record of your address.

● Disperse your belongings between your pockets and any bags you may be carrying.

● When travelling in risky areas, consider wearing a cheap watch and taking an old phone with you. Hide cards and cash in a money belt.

● Make a list of everything you have in your wallet, including the numbers you need to call if you lose your cash or credit cards. Keep this safe at home.

PHONE AWARE

● Young people, in particular, are at risk of being mugged for a phone, so children should be taught not to display or 'show off' mobile phones (or other kinds of covetable gadgets) in public. The best advice is to keep a phone hidden when not in use and to only make calls in a public place. When you use your phone, remain alert to your surroundings.

● Make a note of the 15-digit IMEI number, the network contact number, so that you can bar the phone if it is stolen. On most phones you can find the IMEI number by typing in * # 06 #. Call your network provider to bar the phone.

▶▶See also: **PHYSICAL ATTACK** pp172–175

physical attack

Most conflicts can be resolved without resorting to violence, but sometimes it is impossible to pacify an aggressor. If you are attacked, and unable to escape, fighting back may be your only option and, whatever your training or physical strength, there are actions you can take to protect yourself and reduce injury.

precautions

- Stay alert and vigilant. When you are in a public place, never switch off. Do not do anything, such as wearing headphones, that cuts you off from your surroundings.
- Be polite but cautious. If you do not wish to engage with a stranger, avoid making eye contact. Keep him in your peripheral vision.
- Manage conflict. If someone steps on your foot or spills your drink, take a deep breath and try to defuse the situation. But be alert for the possibility that violence may be the other person's intention.
- Remain sober. Alcohol dulls perception and slows reaction times.
- Watch out for drugs. In bars criminals sometimes slip drugs into drinks, making you a soft target and more easily robbed. Always buy your own drinks and keep an eye on them.

PRACTISING SELF-DEFENCE TECHNIQUES

Improve your chances of surviving an attack with minimal injury by being prepared.

- Practise with a partner. A good way to practise palm heel strikes (see opposite) is to get a friend to hold up an old telephone book for you to hit.
- Practise alone. Even when you are alone you can use a mirror to practise strikes (but do not hit the glass). Work on your aim and try not to give away your intentions.
- Go to the gym. Most gyms have a large punchbag or bodybag. This is the ideal target for focusing your aggression and practising elbow strikes, knee strikes and kicks (see pages 174–175).
- Join a self-defence class. Martial arts, such as Karate or Muay Thai boxing, also help to develop physical skills that can help you to defend yourself.

 WARNING

If you enter into a physical conflict, there is a very real risk that you will be injured.

Lawful self-defence

When you are physically attacked by someone, and have to defend yourself, remember that there may be legal ramifications if that person gets injured. They may sue you for assault and you will need to be able to prove you were using reasonable force to defend yourself. Be aware that the legal definition of what constitutes 'reasonable force' varies in different countries. The four factors below give some idea of the issues considered in such cases, but it is worth finding out exactly what the law states concerning 'lawful self-defence' in the country where you are living.

- **NO ESCAPE** Did you try to escape from the situation but were unable to do so? Fighting back when cornered or captured is judged differently from fighting back when you had the chance to flee.
- **REASONABLE FORCE** Were you feeling genuinely threatened and did you respond with 'reasonable' force as a way of defending yourself? Was your reaction proportionate to the threat posed?
- **PERCEIVED THREAT** How great was the perceived threat? The greater the actual or perceived threat, the greater the amount of force would be judged to be reasonable, as long as it is used purely in self-defence.
- **RETREATING** Did you retreat when it was possible and safe to do so or did you continue to fight when it was no longer necessary? Continuing an attack when the other person is unconscious or is fleeing would be considered unreasonable.

action

APPROACHED WITH MENACE

1 **MAKE USE OF PERSONAL SPACE** If you believe an attacker is approaching you, try to stay calm and retain a safe distance. Your personal space is your safety zone: fists, feet and knives are only effective at close range. Keeping an area around you means your attacker cannot reach you. (It also means you cannot reach him to fight back either.) Use your outstretched arms to keep some distance between you and the attacker.

2 **HOLD YOUR HANDS UP** Keep your hands up, open and in full view. This looks non-threatening, but if violence becomes inevitable you will be ready to either strike first or push and run.

3 **REASSURE** Let your assailant know that you mean no harm and you do not want a fight. Try to keep your tone of voice calm and reassuring.

4 **ASSESS YOUR OPTIONS In most cases of violent assault the conflict lasts less than 30 seconds** and the person who is struck first usually suffers most.

5 **BE DETERMINED** If you decide you have no option but to strike first, attack with all the aggression you can muster. Aim for your attacker's throat, nose, chin, eyes or groin (see pages 174–175).

ATTACKED FROM THE FRONT

1 **BE PREPARED TO ACT** Most violent conflicts escalate from a face-to-face argument. To defend yourself against a frontal assault, master your natural instinct to freeze and do nothing. Use surprise, speed and aggression to strike.

2 **USE THE HEEL OF YOUR PALM** If you feel justified to strike, do so without hesitation and as hard as possible to give you the best chance of ending the attack and escaping. Fold in your fingers and thumb and flex your wrist back.

3 **FOLLOW THROUGH** Aim the heel of your palm at your attacker's chin or the base of his nose. Strike using all your bodyweight in an upwards motion to drive your palm full force into your attacker's face. Another effective target is the attacker's groin.

 TAKE CARE

In a conflict situation the body produces stress hormones, including adrenalin, and the heart rate jumps from 70 to 200 beats per minute. Take deep breaths to help you to control your response.

▶▶See also: **POTENTIAL VIOLENCE** pp168–169 • **ENCOUNTERING A MUGGER** pp170–171 • **RAPE** pp176–177

ATTACKED OR GRABBED

1 ACT QUICKLY If you are grabbed either in a surprise attack or when attempting to flee, you need to act quickly. The longer you take to respond, the more time your attacker has to hold you more securely or begin to choke you.

2 USE YOUR BODYWEIGHT Try to unbalance your attacker by rapidly stepping forwards and backwards and by dropping down and then springing up again. Even if these moves do not help you to break free, they will provide you with opportunities to hit out at your attacker.

3 STRIKE BACK The most effective way to break the grip of someone stronger than you is to strike them. If the attacker is holding you strike him in the face or groin with whatever is free. A good saying is 'Use what is free to free what is being held'. The aim is to incapacitate the attacker and break the hold long enough for you to make an escape.

4 HEAD BUTT If you are grabbed from behind, immediately throw your head backwards into your attacker's face. The back of your head is a lot harder than his nose, teeth or jaw.

5 USE YOUR ELBOW Even a small, light person can generate a huge amount of power with an elbow strike. For maximum impact, throw your elbow back swiftly, with full force, without letting your attacker read your intentions. Keep your hand open and stretched on impact to deliver the most effective strike. Aim directly for the face or the groin, depending on what you can reach.

6 STAMP Use a forceful stamp to the attacker's instep, ankle, knee or shin. Bend your knee and use all your bodyweight and the outside of your heel for maximum force.

PINNED TO A WALL

1 STRUGGLE THEN STRIKE Many attackers use their strength to pin their victim against a wall or restrain them in a grip. The longer you are held, the more vulnerable you become. As soon as you are grabbed, squirm and struggle as violently as you can to make it hard for your attacker to take control. Turn around to face the attacker if you can. You will then be in a better position to strike.

2 STRIKE QUICKLY Take advantage of any space you have created to knee your attacker in the groin or kick his shins. Punch his throat or gouge his eyes as aggressively as you can (see opposite). If he is behind you, deliver a forceful elbow strike. 'Use what is free to free what is being held.' Try to stay on your feet.

3 AIM FOR THE HEAD The best targets for an elbow strike are the jaw, neck and temple – but this strike can be so powerful that it will be effective landed anywhere on the head or in the solar plexus. It is also effective in the groin. If you can incapacitate your attacker even momentarily, you can make your escape.

⚠️ WARNING

● Elbow strikes are potentially very dangerous. The elbow bone is hard and sharp, and when the strike is delivered with force to the jaw or temple it can render a person unconscious, fracture his skull or cause brain or nerve injury. Only use an elbow strike when your personal safety is gravely threatened.
● If you strike hard parts of the head, such as the jaw or temple, with your fist, you will very likely damage your knuckles or break bones in your hand or wrist. If you strike your attacker's teeth you could also get badly cut. Always seek medical attention after any sort of attack.

TIME TO ACT If faced with an unprovoked attack, you may be justified in using an improvised weapon to defend yourself, as long as it is proportionate to the threat directed against you.

PINNED TO THE FLOOR

■ **GET UP OR LASH OUT** If you get knocked to the floor get up again as fast as you can. If you can't get up, kick your feet aggressively at your attacker in a cycling motion to stop him getting on top of you. Scream and shout, and fight any way you can.

■ **KICK AT HIS KNEES** The knee joint is easily damaged and a sharp kick to the attacker's knees may give you time to get up and away.

■ **PUNCH THE THROAT** A single strike to the throat can end a conflict instantly, provided it is carried out swiftly. Try to strike with as much speed and force as you can, without giving away your intention. Use a clenched fist or straight finger strike, with the tips of your fingers aligned and your thumb tucked in.

■ **TARGET THE EYES** When you are being held down, it can be difficult to get sufficient space to put much power behind a strike. In this situation, press your thumbs hard into your attacker's eyes or use your fingernails to claw and attack his face as aggressively as you can.

■ **USE YOUR LEGS** Remember that your legs are powerful weapons. Use them to knee your assailant between his legs and to kick out and unseat him.

Effective techniques

It is vital to keep your actions simple. If you have to fight, use direct strikes with your elbows, hands and feet as soon as you can.

● **EYE ATTACK** An eye attack of any sort – throwing sand, or even throwing a drink – will make it easier for you to escape, as a blinded attacker cannot follow you. Eye attacks also benefit from the element of surprise, as they are not conventional forms of attack.

● **GROIN ATTACK** A kick to the groin, if on target, can instantly disable a male attacker. But it does require some power and accuracy. If you miss your target or fail to strike hard enough you will simply enrage your attacker. Use a 'snap kick', delivered from a raised, bent knee, if your attacker is not yet holding you, or your knee if you are already being held.

● **KNEE POWER** Increase the effect of a knee strike by holding on to your attacker and either pulling him onto the strike, or using your bodyweight behind the strike. If you miss his groin you can also aim for his stomach or his solar plexus.

● **CHOOSE THE MOMENT** To strike effectively you have to be at close range and your blow must come as a complete surprise. You may have to step in towards your attacker, suddenly, after seeming to back away.

● **STAY IN CONTROL** There will be lots of adrenaline pumping through your body. Focus on slowing down your breathing to remain calm.

rape and attempted rape

Rape is a violent crime that occurs throughout the world. If you find yourself in an uncomfortable or threatening situation that you fear may escalate into a sexual assault, you need to know how to protect yourself from harm. If you are raped, it is important to act quickly so that you receive appropriate medication to lower the risk of catching HIV.

action

YOU FEEL THREATENED

1 MAKE YOUR WISHES CLEAR If you are in a situation that is moving in a direction you do not wish to go, make it clear that you do not want to have sex and leave, if necessary. If the person you are with is intoxicated, you may need to repeat your wishes or state them more forcefully.

2 CALL FOR HELP If your wishes are ignored, shout or scream for help at once. If you have a personal alarm, use it. The quicker you do this, the more likely it is that you will unnerve your attacker and convince him to leave. Crucially, once you begin screaming or shouting, do not stop until you are sure you are safe.

3 CONSIDER YOUR ESCAPE OPTIONS If you are in a deserted location where calling for help is not an option, you must escape. But before making your move, decide what you are going to do. Given a short head start how far could you get? Is there a nearby room that you could lock yourself in or a vehicle you could get into? Could you rouse a neighbour or reach a public place? Kick off high-heeled shoes so that you can run away faster. These can be a useful weapon in self defence, too.

4 KEEP TALKING Try to control your fear and talk. **Rape is about power and control, so try to stay calm and confident and do not plead or beg.** The longer you can keep talking, the better your chance of being able to escape.

5 FIGHT BACK Deciding whether to fight back has to be a personal decision. There is some evidence that those who resist have better outcomes. If you do decide to fight, make it count. Strike quickly and hard (see pages 172–175) and then get away as fast as you can.

YOU ARE RAPED

1 SEEK REFUGE Go somewhere you will be safe, such as the home of a good friend or family member.

2 TALK TO SOMEONE Think about whether or not you want to report the rape to the police: the sooner you report it, the more evidence there will be to support your case. Confide in a friend, whatever you decide, or phone a rape helpline (see Get Help, opposite).

3 GET MEDICAL HELP To lower your chances of catching HIV, you will need to take a course of post-exposure prophylaxis (PEP) as soon as possible, or at least within 72 hours. You may also need emergency contraception or tests for other sexually transmitted diseases. A rape helpline should be able to direct you to the nearest centre offering PEP.

4 PRESERVE EVIDENCE If you decide to report the rape, do not shower or bathe, clean your teeth or discard clothing until you have spoken to the police or been to a sexual assault referral centre (step 5).

5 VISIT A SEXUAL ASSAULT REFERRAL CENTRE (SARC) Some countries have special centres, separate from the police, where you can have a forensic and medical examination, and have any evidence stored. A rape helpline should be able to direct you to your nearest centre.

⚠ TAKE CARE

If you travel alone, consider carrying a personal alarm that emits an ear-piercing shriek at 140dB. Such an alarm can unnerve an attacker, giving you time to escape, or help attract the attention of anyone nearby.

WATCHPOINT Most rapes are committed by friends, relatives or acquaintances of the victim, which can make the decision to report the rape more difficult.

GET HELP For immediate help and advice, contact your nearest rape support centre. For more information on the organisations in different countries, see page 340.

TIME TO ACT To lower the risk of catching HIV, you must take post-exposure prophylaxis within 72 hours. Your doctor or rape helpline can tell you where to obtain the medication.

be aware

- If you are alone, stick to well-lit public areas. Avoid going to an isolated area or getting into a car with someone you do not know.
- Use a licensed taxi or a mini-cab from a firm you know.
- Try to sit with other people or near the driver when you travel on public transport.
- Walk facing the traffic. If a car stops and you carry on walking, it has to reverse or turn around to follow you. If a motorist asks for directions, stand well away from the vehicle as you give them so that you are out of reach.
- If you are leaving your car in daylight when you know you will return after dark, park under a light or in a public place. Think ahead. When you return to your car at night, have your keys in your hand and lock the door once inside.

- Do not accept drinks from strangers and ask your friends to watch over your drink if you leave it at a party or bar so that it cannot be tampered with. Keep your hand resting over the top of your glass or bottle.
- Drinking alcohol can make you more vulnerable. Book a taxi to take you home well in advance and stay with your friends at all times.

Seek counselling

Rape is frequently followed by feelings of fear, isolation, guilt and depression. The sooner you have professional counselling, the better your recovery is likely to be.

- **CONTACT A SUPPORT SERVICE** There are various support networks, such as the Centre Against Sexual Assault in Australia, Rape Outcry or Lifeline in South Africa and Rape Education Prevention in New Zealand. For more information, see page 340.
- **JOIN A SUPPORT GROUP** Gain strength and come to terms with what has happened by talking with other victims of rape, either online or in person. Your rape support service will be able to give you contact details.

what next?

- If you decide to report an incident, contact your local police station. In some countries there will be an officer who has been specially trained to deal with sexual offences and she will chaperone you through the whole reporting process.
- You will be examined and asked to provide some 'early evidence' samples, such as urine samples and mouth swabs, for forensic evidence. Clothes or bedding may be collected.
- You will be asked for a full account of what occurred and this will form the basis of your statement. At this time you may like to make your own detailed notes about what took place, as the case may not come to court for a long time.

▶▶See also: PHYSICAL ATTACK pp172–175

knife attack

In recent years there has been a rise in provoked and unprovoked knife attacks. Often a stabbing occurs after the escalation of an argument so it is always worth backing down in any dispute so as not to provoke an attack. If you are attacked, learn how best to defend yourself.

action

THREATENED WITH A KNIFE

1 TAKE THE ATTACKER SERIOUSLY If someone pulls a knife on you, assume that he intends to use it and immediately go on the defensive. No amount of self-defence training can guarantee your safety.

2 KEEP TALKING Stay calm and try to persuade the attacker that you do not want a fight. If he wants your possessions, give them to him. Talking also gives you time to weigh up your options, including calling for help or trying to escape.

3 KEEP YOUR DISTANCE While you are talking, do anything you can to increase the distance between the knife and your body. Try to stay balanced so that you can move quickly.

be aware

- In any dispute – even when you know you are in the right – try to keep calm and avoid being drawn into a physical encounter. **Many stabbings occur when an argument escalates into a fight.**
- If you are unavoidably drawn into a conflict, such as with an aggressive drunk or road rage driver, always assume that the person could be armed with a knife and act defensively.
- Being aware of what is going on around you is your best defence. Many knife attacks occur suddenly, with the victim unaware that he has been stabbed until he sees the blood.
- Avoid dangerous flashpoints at home and overseas. These include places where rival fans are likely to come together at international or local football matches and parts of cities that have a reputation for violence.

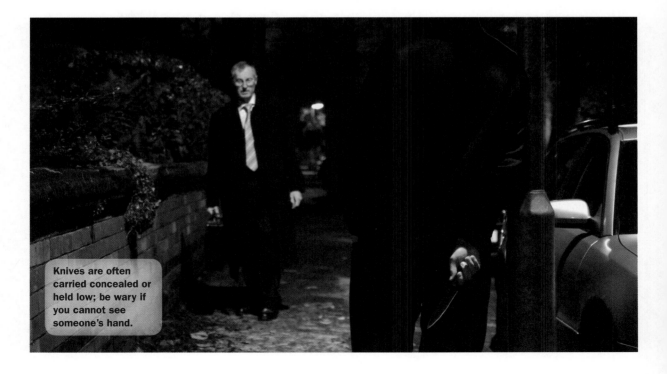

Knives are often carried concealed or held low; be wary if you cannot see someone's hand.

ATTACKED WITH A KNIFE

1 ESCAPE IF YOU CAN If someone comes at you with a knife, you need to escape, but if you turn your back on the attacker there is a risk you will be stabbed in the back. Try to distract your attacker first, by throwing your bag or wallet at him or pulling something, such as a table or chair, between you. Then run as fast as you can without looking back.

2 DEFEND YOURSELF If you cannot run, try to block the knife with anything you can grab, such as a chair, a book or a coat. If there is nothing to hand, turn your body sideways to present a smaller target.

3 FIGHT BACK In a serious attack, fighting back may be your only option and you must commit to fighting for your life. Use anything you can as a weapon; otherwise, attack using your hands, feet, elbows and knees (see pages 172–175). Try to keep the palms of your hands between the weapon and your body, to protect vital organs. Scream and shout at your attacker as you fight and try to grab the hand/arm holding the knife. To make him drop the knife you should simultaneously aim palm or heel strikes at his head or groin.

4 DISENGAGE Once your attacker flinches or doubles up, disengage immediately and escape to a safer place, putting as many obstacles between you and him as possible.

SOMEONE IS STABBED

1 ASSESS THE SITUATION Whether you have been stabbed or you have witnessed a stabbing, once there is no threat of further violence, try to assess the injuries. All puncture wounds require urgent treatment. If you can, ask someone to call the emergency services while you staunch any bleeding.

2 APPLY FIRST AID If possible, elevate the injury to reduce blood flow and then apply pressure directly to the wound to stop the bleeding (see page 99), using a towel or a clean piece of clothing if you can. Never remove a knife that is still embedded as its position may be helping to limit the bleeding.

3 PROTECT AGAINST SHOCK If you are helping an injured person, make him lie down and loosen any tight clothing. Reassure him that help is on its way and try to keep him calm.

⚠ WARNING

● Always do your best to help someone who is being attacked or who has been stabbed, but do not put yourself at risk. Call the police as soon as you can and find other bystanders who can help.
● If you see someone brandishing a knife or witness a knife crime, call the emergency services at once.

Areas of greatest risk

Any penetrating injury, whatever the depth, that perforates a major organ or arteries in the neck or thigh can be fatal.

● **CHEST** A stab wound just 4cm deep can penetrate the heart. Stab wounds just 3cm deep can puncture a lung.
● **ABDOMEN** Wounds to the liver, spleen, bowel or kidneys can lead to major haemorrhaging.
● **HEAD AND NECK** A head wound can cause a brain haemorrhage; a wound to the neck may cause paralysis or sever an artery, resulting in rapid blood loss, unconsciousness and death.

▶▶See also: **UNCONSCIOUS ADULT/CHILD/BABY** pp14–19 • **SEVERE BLEEDING** p22 • **STAB WOUND** p99

gun attack

In the USA around 30 people are killed in gun incidents every day and 240 shot and injured. Gun crime is a growing problem all over the world, even in countries where guns are prohibited, as criminals can obtain them illegally. If you find yourself caught up in a gun attack, it is possible to minimise your risk of injury and to help casualties effectively.

action

YOU HEAR GUNFIRE

1 STOP AND LISTEN If you hear a sound that you think might be gunfire, stop and listen. Do not move towards the sound, as you could be heading for danger. As you listen, scan your surroundings for possible escape routes and places to shelter.

2 TAKE COVER If you recognise the sound as gunfire, take cover at once. Try to identify the direction of the sound and get to the far side of a barrier that will protect you, such as a wall, a tree or a vehicle.

3 GET DOWN If there is no cover in your immediate vicinity, get down on the ground and keep as low as possible. Lie motionless, as if dead, while you decide on your next move.

4 ESCAPE FROM THE AREA Can you pinpoint the gunman's location? Is he firing in your direction? If he is, the best tactic is to play dead until the shooting stops and you believe he has gone. Otherwise, make a run for cover or escape the area.

YOU ARE FIRED AT

1 SEEK SHELTER Put barriers between yourself and the gunman. Even though some of these may not be bullet proof, if they obscure you from view the gunman may choose an easier target.

2 RUN FOR COVER If you decide to run, try to run at a 90-degree angle to the gunman's line of fire. Do not stop, even if bullets hit the ground near you, and do not waste time zig-zagging. A fast-moving target across the line of fire is the hardest to hit.

3 KEEP RUNNING If you are hit by a bullet, keep running. Unless it is a serious wound and you drop automatically, you should not stop, as this will make you an easier target.

The shopkeeper let the armed robbers take the money and was unharmed.

Which weapon?

- Automatic weapons pose the greatest danger as they can spray a wide area with bullets. You will hear the rapid gunfire immediately.
- Rifles are deadly at several hundred metres.
- If you are more than 50m from a handgun or shotgun, you are likely to be beyond effective range.

SOMEONE IS SHOT

1 GIVE EMERGENCY FIRST AID Always ensure your safety before attending to others. Treat gunshot wounds in the same way as any other wound. Staunch the bleeding with a pad of clean material, torn from clothing if necessary, applied firmly to the wound (see page 98).

2 CONTACT THE EMERGENCY SERVICES Call, signal or send someone for help as soon as you can. But recognise that you may have to wait a considerable time, as medical personnel will not be allowed to enter the area until it is considered safe.

3 REASSURE THE VICTIM Try to keep the victim as calm as possible and watch for symptoms of shock (see pages 38–39). Reassure him that help is on the way.

4 MAKE A MOVE If you fear for the life of a gunshot victim and help is not at hand, you must balance the risks of staying where you are with making a move to get help. Remember to put your own safety first.

5 IMPROVISE TRANSPORT If the person is badly injured or unconscious, the safest way to move him is on a stretcher made from a door, desktop or ladder. If you are on your own and he is too heavy to carry, wrap him in a coat, blanket or rug and drag him behind you as gently as you can. Be aware that you may become a target.

be aware

- If you know someone who is seriously disaffected with society in general or has been the victim of a conflict, take any threat he makes very seriously – especially if you know he has access to firearms. Raise your concerns with his family and your local police.
- Some public shootings have followed video warnings broadcast on the internet. If you discover a blog or website containing such threats, pass the details to the police at once.
- If you are travelling to a country with a reputation for gun crime, be especially vigilant. Avoid areas that are known to be hot spots.

 TAKE CARE

- Whenever you are passing banks, jewellers or security vans, be vigilant for anything suspicious. Pay particular attention to anyone who appears to be loitering nearby or sitting in a car waiting. If you are seriously concerned, leave the area and call the police or alert a member of staff.
- If you own or have access to firearms, you should keep them in a locked cabinet and keep ammunition locked away separately. It is also wise to store weapons partially dismantled, with key components kept elsewhere.

Armed robbery

If you are caught up in an armed robbery, you will be at great risk. This type of organised violent crime is likely to involve several highly motivated, ruthless criminals who use the threat of firearms to guarantee that their demands are met.

1 KEEP CALM Faced with an armed gang at close quarters, there is little chance of escape. Keep a low profile and do not challenge them.

2 DO AS YOU ARE TOLD Follow the robbers' instructions obediently and do not make any sudden movements. If you need to move or reach for something, ask permission first, in case your movements are misconstrued.

3 DO NOT BE A HERO While no one is being harmed, do not resist in any way or hinder the robbers. Let them steal what they want and make their getaway.

4 BE A GOOD WITNESS While sitting or lying still, try to memorise the robbers' appearance and actions, without staring at them too obviously. After they have left, try to get a description of their vehicle and note their direction of travel.

5 CALL THE POLICE Once the robbers have left, call the police immediately, even if an alarm has been activated. If you are in a shop or bank, close the doors and wait for the police to arrive. All witnesses to the robbery should remain at the scene, ready to provide statements.

stolen car

Discovering that your car has been stolen can become a serious emergency if you find yourself isolated, especially at night or in an unfamiliar place, without any transport. But there are a few simple precautions that can help to reduce the chances of you becoming a victim of car crime and increase the chances of your vehicle being found.

action

YOUR CAR IS MISSING

1 CONFIRM THE THEFT First consider whether your partner or another keyholder may have taken the car. Make sure you are where you left your car.

2 CONTACT THE POLICE Call your local police station and be ready to give them the make, model and registration number of the car and details of anything valuable or potentially dangerous that it contained. Do not phone the emergency services.

3 CONTACT YOUR INSURERS Report the theft to your insurance company so that you can make a claim.

A CAR IS BEING STOLEN

1 RAISE THE ALARM If you see someone attempting to steal a car, call the police without delay.

2 STAY SAFE Do not confront the thief or get too close to the front or rear of the car if it is about to be driven away. No vehicle is worth a serious injury.

3 MAKE NOTES Jot down as much detail as you can, including a description of the thief, how he stole the car, the direction he took and the time it occurred.

Tracking devices

A tracking device fitted covertly to your car will allow it to be traced using GPS in the event of theft. For a monthly fee or annual contract, your car's location is monitored constantly. Some systems allow you to see where your car is on your own PC; others allow the police to track and locate your vehicle.

YOU FIND YOUR STOLEN CAR

1 DO NOT TOUCH IT If you find your car through your own endeavours – cars are often abandoned in car parks or streets nearby – contact the police before you touch it. They may want to examine it for clues.

2 RECORD ITS CONDITION Photograph the car exactly as you found it. This will support any insurance claim you make for damage.

3 MAKE A SAFETY CHECK Before you drive your car away, consider having it checked over by a mechanic to ensure that it has not been damaged by the thief.

precautions

- Always lock your car and ensure it is alarmed. Consider fitting a steering wheel immobiliser or a wheel clamp if it is often left parked for a long period of time.
- Keep your car keys safe at all times. Do not leave your keys in a hallway where they can be stolen by someone entering your house.
- Keep the purchase receipts for your car and any extras fitted. Take photographs of your car.
- Never leave valuables on display. Remove or hide CD or DVD player fascias and satellite navigation devices when you leave the car.
- Keep your car in a garage, if possible. Otherwise park in well-lit, public places.
- Have your car's vehicle identification number (VIN) engraved on the windows and other parts. You can buy DIY kits and engrave the number yourself. Register the VIN on a database that buyers can check to find out if a car is stolen. Ask at your local police station for details of how to register with such a database.

identity theft

Your name, date of birth and address are often all that an identity thief requires to impersonate you. If your identity is stolen, it can be fraudulently used to obtain credit, open bank accounts or acquire official documents.

TIME TO ACT If you have been a victim of identity theft, request a copy of your credit report from a credit reference agency. Ask them to correct any inaccuracies.

How can you tell?

- **CREDIT REFUSAL** You are refused a loan or new credit card despite a good credit history.
- **UNEXPECTED BILLS** You receive demands for payment for goods or services that you did not order or request.
- **STATEMENT ERRORS** Unauthorised items appear on your bank or credit card accounts.
- **MISSED POST** Important post from your bank or financial company fails to arrive.
- **BENEFIT DENIAL** You apply for a state benefit and are told that you are already claiming.

action

YOU DISCOVER A THEFT

■ **INFORM YOUR CARD PROVIDERS** If you suspect the fraudulent use of your bank account or credit cards, contact the service provider at once. They will have a specialised department that investigates criminal activity. You will usually get your money back, but the responsibility is on you to check your statement. The card company may be less willing to help if you have given your card details to someone, especially if the transaction was on the internet and used the extra level of security attached to most cards.

■ **REPORT MISSING OR STOLEN DOCUMENTS** If you discover that important documents, such as your passport, driving licence, or workplace identity card, have gone missing, inform the police. If workplace identity documents have gone missing, you will also need to tell your employers.

■ **CONTACT THE MAIL SERVICE** If you believe that your mail has been or is being stolen, contact your mail delivery service. They can also tell you if a mail redirection service has been set up falsely in your name and stop it at once.

YOUR IDENTITY IS STOLEN

■ **CLOSE ALL FRAUDULENT ACCOUNTS** Contact all the companies that have been used by your impersonator and close all fraudulent accounts.

■ **MAKE NEW MAIL ARRANGEMENTS** If you cannot guarantee the security of your mail, arrange to have your mail delivered to a trusted friend or relative.

■ **TAKE OUT FRAUD PROTECTION** Register for credit fraud protection at www.experian.com to alert potential lenders that you have been a victim of identity fraud and to add security measures to your accounts. The website also has lots of useful advice about preventing credit fraud.

for next time...

- Dispose of documents that contain personal information with care. Shred sensitive material, such as bank statements.
- Never give personal information to cold callers. If someone asks you for sensitive information, request proof of their identity. **You would never be asked for a PIN number over the phone,** even by your bank.
- Only give personal information to trusted sites when you use the internet, and only via a secure page (see page 185).
- Protect your mail. Fit a lockable mailbox. Ask your bank to arrange for you to collect debit and credit cards from the branch. If you move, have your mail redirected.

▶▶See also: **CASH/CREDIT CARD CRIME** pp184–185

cash/credit card crime

Cash and credit card crime is on the increase. An apparently ordinary cashpoint can conceal a trap set up by criminals to snare your card and your PIN number. And the online world can be full of potential traps and loopholes in which you can unwittingly lose cash. So when you visit a cashpoint, buy goods online or check your emails, take some prudent precautions.

action

LOST OR STOLEN CARD

1 CANCEL YOUR CARD Call the card company immediately – the number is on your bill but it is worth storing in your phone. Note the time of the call and who you speak to. You will need your account number, details of when you noticed the loss and, ideally, the last legitimate transaction you made. Follow up the call with a letter.

2 CONTACT THE POLICE If you believe that your card was stolen, provide a full account to the police of where and how you believe it was taken.

TROUBLE AT A CASHPOINT

■ **CHECK THE MACHINE** If anything about the cash machine looks at all suspicious, do not use it. Check that there is no exterior fitting on the slot where you enter your card and run your finger along it to check for the edges of a plastic sleeve (see right). Report any suspicions to the bank or machine owner.

■ **ENTER YOUR PIN ONLY ONCE** If you forget your number, cancel the transaction and contact your bank to avoid losing your card. If a machine does not return your card, contact your bank immediately. If possible, stay at the machine to make the call to prevent criminals gaining access to it.

■ **CHECK FOR LOITERERS** Be suspicious of helpful strangers, who could be trying to observe your PIN number or who may try to distract you by saying you have dropped something while you are at the cashpoint. It has been known for criminals to sit in a parked car and use binoculars to watch the machine. So be aware of lines of sight and keep the keypad shielded with your hand, purse or wallet as you enter your PIN.

CLONED CARD

1 STUDY YOUR STATEMENTS Although chip and PIN cards are almost impossible to clone, there are ways that they can be used fraudulently if criminals gain access to some of your details. Check your bank and credit card statements carefully to ensure that all the transactions are genuine.

2 REPORT UNAUTHORISED TRANSACTIONS If you find any transactions on your bill that appear suspicious, contact your card company immediately. They will investigate for you (see page 183).

Look for a miniature camera fitted anywhere around the machine. This is used to record your PIN as you tap it in.

The 'Lebanese Loop' is a simple plastic sleeve that fits inside the card slot. It prevents your card being read so you have to re-enter your PIN, which gives the criminal more chance of recording it. The card gets stuck and the criminal retrieves it once you have left.

WATCHPOINT Always keep your PIN secure. Banks will not reimburse 'phantom' cash withdrawals from a chip and PIN card not reported lost: they say these cards cannot be cloned.

GET HELP If your credit card is refused, contact your card company immediately. They may have observed an unusual pattern of spending and suspect fraudulent use.

TIME TO ACT Before you buy from an unfamiliar or dubious website, check the contact details and try to phone them. If you are unsuccessful, do not make a purchase.

SENT AN EMAIL SCAM

■ **IGNORE 'PHISHING' EMAILS Beware email requests for personal information** (known as 'phishing'). The request may come disguised as a communication from your bank or an online company such as PayPal, and claim to be updating your security information. Such requests are always fraudulent.

■ **DELETE UNSOLICITED PROPOSITIONS** Many email scams involve offers of well-paid work, unclaimed competition winnings or romantic liaisons. Many feature long, persuasive storylines intended to get you hooked. Inevitably what follows is some plausible request for 'expenses'. Delete on receipt.

■ **NEVER CLICK A LINK** Links in emails are often not what they seem and may take you to a fraudulent site. If you hover your cursor over a suspicious link or right click on it and choose 'Properties', you will see its true address. If in doubt, type out web addresses directly into your browser.

CAUGHT IN A WEB SCAM

■ **AVOID SPOOF SITES** Spoof sites are built to look like genuine ones and tempt the unwary to enter their credit card details. If your browser warns you that a site is suspicious, or if it does not open a secure page (see box, right) when it requests personal information – leave at once.

■ **SHOP WITH CAUTION** When you shop online, apply the same caution that you would in a market. Does the site look genuine? Does it have real-world contact details? Are the prices what you might expect or are they suspiciously cheap?

■ **BEWARE ONE-PRODUCT SITES** A typical scam is to set up a site that advertises a popular Christmas item, such as a games console, at a very competitive price. In a week or two the site will be shut, your money will be lost and the thieves long gone.

Online safety

Internet fraud is growing faster than any other sector. Be cautious when providing your details.

● **PERSONAL INFORMATION** Only ever enter personal information, such as credit card details, on a web page that is secure. You can tell when a page is secure by the appearance of a locked padlock icon in your browser window. If you click on the padlock you will be able to see more information about the site and its security rating. On a secure page the prefix to the web address will also change from 'http' to 'https'.

● **UNWARY PAYMENTS** If you ever fall for a scam and send a payment to a fake website, contact your bank or credit card provider at once and cancel the card. Depending on the precise circumstances, you may still be liable for some or all of the money lost.

for next time...

● Keep your browser software up to date. The latest versions will be the most secure and so protect you more effectively.
● Consider installing security software that checks that websites are genuine and that any security certificates they may have are up to date.
● Keep a separate credit card for your online transactions and use a separate email address for online subscriptions that you can cancel if you need to.
● Use the internet to research online scams. Sites such as www.onlinescamsexposed.com and www.fraudwatchers.org keep you up to date with the latest online frauds.

threatening **calls**

Receiving an abusive or intimidating call can be particularly frightening if you live alone. But there are effective ways to deal with and stop these calls, and you can prevent further intrusion with the help of the latest technology.

GET HELP Do not hesitate to report abusive calls to the police. In many countries, making malicious or abusive telephone calls is an offence.

action

1 **DENY THE CALLER SATISFACTION** If you pick up a call that is abusive or threatening, put the handset down immediately. **Do not respond in any way – this may just encourage the abuser.** Repeat this response each time you receive this type of call. Disconnect your landline and turn your mobile off at night so you are not disturbed.

2 **KEEP A RECORD** Note the date and time of the calls and write down what the caller says. Alternatively, record the call; some answering machines have the capacity to record calls or you can buy a recorder that makes it easy to record the phone calls for the police to hear. This fits between your phone and the phone socket. A cheaper version has a lead that you plug into your own recorder.

3 **REPORT ABUSIVE CALLS** Tell your phone provider. They may be able to monitor your line or block a particular number. Call your local police station if you feel threatened by calls.

4 **BLOCK CALLS** With many modern phones you can not only see the caller's number, so you can choose to not answer calls from certain numbers, but can also automate the process and simply bar them. You can also choose to bar all calls from numbers that are withheld.

5 **CHANGE YOUR NUMBER** If the problem persists, ask your phone provider to change your number and ask to be ex-directory. Although this service usually incurs a fee, if your provider has been monitoring your case, or the police have been involved, they may offer this without charge.

 WARNING
If the caller makes any kind of threat against you or your family, contact the police at once.

Mobile phones

Abusive calls – and texts – to mobile phones can be extremely invasive as many people carry their mobile with them at all times. Young people, in particular, are often victims of this form of abuse.

● **SCREEN CALLS** All mobile phones feature caller ID, and if you add all your contacts to your address book you will see the name of the caller, if it is someone you know. If you do not recognise the number, or it indicates 'number withheld', you can choose to ignore it or let the call go to voicemail.
● **BAR CALLS** Many mobile phone handsets also feature call barring and text barring. Add the nuisance number to a 'blocked list' so that when the phone receives a call from that number it disconnects immediately.

for next time...

● You have the option of keeping your number private – simply request to be ex-directory.
● Use a phone with a 'caller ID' feature, so that you can see who is phoning before you answer a call.
● Install an answerphone and use this to screen calls, allowing a caller to indentify himself before you pick up the handset.
● Use the prerecorded message on your answerphone rather than your own voice, or ask a male member of the household to be the voice on the answerphone. Avoid saying 'I am not here at the moment' as this makes it clear that you live alone.

PUBLIC
EMERGENCIES

flood

Flooding is one of the most widely occurring natural disasters. Short periods of intense rainfall may produce flash floods, prolonged heavy rain can cause rivers to break their banks and tidal surges give rise to widespread coastal flooding. The severity of a flood can be unpredictable, so it is advisable to prepare for the worst.

be aware

THE POWER OF WATER
- 15cm of fast-moving water can knock a person off their feet and will reach the bottom of a car. It may cause a driver to lose control or stall the car.
- 30cm of water is enough to float many family cars.
- 60cm of fast-moving water will float and sweep away larger four-wheel-drive vehicles and vans.
- If there is any doubt about your safety, do not attempt to drive through a flooded river crossing.

HELP AND INFORMATION
- If heavy rain and flooding are forecast, check online or call your local emergency services to find out if your area is at risk.
- Listen to local radio and television for flood warnings or updates. Act as soon as a warning is given for your area.
- If you are in immediate danger, pack your emergency supplies and move to high ground without delay.

Flood warnings

Government flood warnings, which are given by the emergency services or national weather service, advise you on what action to take.

- **FLOOD WATCH** Warns of the risk to low-lying ground that is prone to flooding, and cautions people in these areas to remain alert.
- **FLOOD WARNING** Warns of flooding to vulnerable properties and recommends that defensive action, such as sandbagging (see box, opposite) be taken at once.
- **SEVERE FLOOD WARNING** Warns of serious widespread flooding with additional risk to life. Prompt action and evacuation is required by all those in affected areas.
- **ALL CLEAR** Warnings no longer apply.

North Karnataka, 4 October, 2009. Torrential rains and floods in southern India swept away thousands of homes.

TIME TO ACT Make an emergency plan that includes provision for your family and pets, so that you are ready if a warning is issued. Fill sandbags (see below) in advance.

WATCHPOINT Fill jugs and saucepans with drinking water before floodwater enters your home or keep bottled water with you. Water supplies may become contaminated.

action

HOME IN DANGER

1 **FIT PROTECTIVE BARRIERS** Board up windows and doors and cover air bricks and low-level ventilators. Use proprietary products designed for this purpose, marine plywood, or chipboard and PVC sheeting. Put plugs in sinks and baths and weight down.

2 **CUT OFF UTILITIES** Turn off gas, electricity and water supplies before floodwater enters your home.

3 **MOVE UPSTAIRS** If you live in a two-storey house, move as many possessions upstairs as you can. Begin with important documents, personal treasures and expensive electronics. Then consider furniture, carpets and curtains.

4 **RAISE ITEMS ON BLOCKS** Items that cannot be carried upstairs should be raised off the ground. Move or protect the contents of your garage or shed.

YOU ARE IN DANGER

■ **IF YOU HAVE TO DRIVE THROUGH FLOODWATER** **Keep your speed down, stay in a low gear and keep the engine revs high to avoid stalling.** If you can feel water coming in beneath your feet, stop and get out at once. You will be safer on foot than in an uncontrollable vehicle floated by the floodwater.

■ **IF YOU ARE SWEPT AWAY** Try to float on your back with your feet out in front of you. Watch out for obstacles or debris in the water that might injure you. Look around for something you can grab or climb onto and pull yourself to a place where the force of the water is not as strong.

■ **IF YOU ARE STRANDED** Whether at home, in your car or on isolated high ground, if you are in immediate danger from rising floodwater, phone the emergency services.

Building a sandbag wall

Sandbags are a very effective way of keeping water out of your property, especially when used with PVC sheeting. How high you build the wall depends on the severity of the expected flood. As a guide, you will need 80 sandbags to build a 60cm wall.

1 **LAY DOWN SHEETING** Clear debris and lay PVC sheeting on the ground, preferably on a firm, level site. One edge will be held in place by the sandbag wall and the surplus sheeting should face towards the flood.

2 **TO BUILD A SINGLE THICKNESS WALL** Lay sandbags lengthwise and build up the wall in layers. Use half-filled sandbags to stagger the joints. Draw up the PVC sheeting so that it is taut, and secure it under the top row of sandbags.

3 **TO BUILD A DOUBLE THICKNESS WALL** Lay two rows of sandbags lengthwise, side by side. Place the next layer of sandbags across the first layer, with bag mouths facing inwards (see right). Pull up the sheeting.

▶▶See also: CONTAMINATED WATER p206

blizzard conditions

Heavy snowfall, combined with high winds and poor visibility, causes major disruption, both for travellers and those at home, especially in more isolated areas, as power lines come down and water supplies freeze. Even a prolonged cold snap has its dangers, especially for the elderly. Prepare yourself so that you can keep warm and safe, whatever the conditions.

precautions

- Make sure that you have torches (flashlights) and spare batteries, candles, gas or oil lamps and matches handy in case of a power cut.
- Insulate all your pipes to reduce the risk of them freezing.
- Where the risk of power failure is high, consider installing gas appliances or purchase a portable gas or coal-fired stove and heater.
- Keep a well-stocked first-aid kit (see page 334) and keep at least a week's supply of any prescription medicines.
- Use the internet or a mobile phone to get accurate weather forecasts for your location.
- Conserve supplies (see below).

Care of the elderly

- **SPECIAL CARE** If you have elderly friends or relatives, consider inviting them to stay until the weather improves. Alternatively, visit them regularly to make sure that they are well and have everything they need.
- **IF YOU ARE ELDERLY** Stay indoors and keep warm (see opposite). Eat at least one hot meal a day and sip hot drinks regularly all day long. Take a flask containing a hot drink to bed with you in case you wake up feeling cold. Remain as active as you can, doing light chores in between periods of rest. Arrange to phone a friend or relative first thing in the morning and last thing at night.

action

HEAVY SNOWFALL PREDICTED

1 SAVE WATER If there is a chance that your pipes may freeze, fill the bath tub and every spare container you have with water. To make a leaky bath plug more watertight, first dry the plug and the plug hole and then coat them thickly with petroleum jelly. **If you allow water to drip from the cold tap, the constant slight movement in the pipes may help to prevent them from freezing.**

2 BUY FOOD PROVISIONS If you live in, or are visiting, an area prone to heavy snow and low temperatures, always keep a week's supply of food, using frozen or canned goods to supplement fresh fruit and vegetables. Be aware that people may start panic-buying as soon as heavy snow is forecast.

3 CHARGE YOUR BATTERIES Make sure that your mobile phone and laptop, as well as any spare batteries you may have for them, are fully charged while you still have electricity.

SNOWED IN

1 BE EFFICIENT To clear snow, work forwards and then sideways – this is less tiring than moving snow you have walked on and compacted. Take care not to overdo snow-clearing if you are not used to vigorous exercise. Work slowly, rest and drink water as often as you need to. Share the task with neighbours if possible.

2 TAKE PREVENTIVE MEASURES Spread rock salt or table salt over essential paths and driveways. These lower the melting point of snow and ice and help to prevent water refreezing. Alternatively, scatter sand, grit or a gritty substance such as fresh cat litter.

TIME TO ACT If a cold spell is forecast, make sure that you are up to date with all your utility bills. This is not the time to have your gas or electricity supply cut off.

WATCHPOINT Moderate snowfall can escalate to blizzard conditions in a short space of time. Avoid travel on high or exposed routes where you are particularly vulnerable.

GET HELP If you need urgent assistance, call the emergency services. Similarly, call them if an elderly relative is not answering the door or responding to phone calls.

LOSS OF HEATING/POWER

1 **DRESS IN LAYERS** You will be much warmer if you wear several thin layers of clothing rather than just one or two thick items. For maximum warmth, make sure the outer layer is windproof.

2 **WEAR A HAT** Although your head may not feel cold, a hat will help you to conserve body heat.

3 **CONSUME HOT FOOD AND DRINKS** While there is still power and sufficient food, have plenty of hot food and warm drinks. If you are relying on an emergency supply of gas, oil or solid fuel, use it sparingly to cook, rather than heating the house.

4 **HEAT ONE ROOM** If you have lost power to your home, or have a limited source of heat, insulate and warm a single room as effectively as you can. Use this room day and night.

5 **EXCLUDE DRAUGHTS** Heat escapes through any opening. Draught-proof windows with plastic wrap. Stretched taut over the window frame and taped down, plastic wrap still lets the light in but traps a layer of air between it and the glass. Draw heavy curtains. Put draught-excluders, or wedge old clothes or tea towels, around doors. Block up disused chimneys with cushions, blankets or boards held tightly in place by furniture.

6 **BURN GAS** If your cooker is on mains gas, use it to warm your kitchen. It is safer to use the oven rather than the stove, but the burner may not ignite without electricity (try using matches). If you use the oven, do not leave the door open while it is on or you may melt the control knobs. A gas barbecue can provide a useful emergency source of hot food and warmth, but make sure that you use it in a well-ventilated area (see 'Warning', right).

When all else fails

If you are in a completely isolated area, with no heat source, you may have to generate your own. Do so with extreme care.

● **CONTAIN AN OPEN FIRE** Use house bricks to contain your fire and its ashes. Stacked bricks will allow pans and kettles to be heated and will retain heat after the flames have died down.
● **MAKE A CANDLE HEATER** Stand a candle in a candle holder and put it on a heat-resistant surface. Place an upturned terracotta pot over the top, supporting the edges on bricks. Not only will you gain some light, but the pot will retain most of the candle's heat.

 WARNING

● If you use an open fire, gas heater or the stove for warmth, it is vital that the room has adequate ventilation. When fuels, such as gas, oil, wood and coal, do not burn fully, carbon monoxide is produced, which can be fatal.
● Never leave an open fire or candles burning unattended. Extinguish them before you go to bed.
● Be aware that an elderly person could suffer from hypothermia (see page 46) if left without warmth for some time. How long this might take depends on the temperature, how healthy the elderly person is, and the availability of warm clothing, hot food and drink. A frail person could succumb in just a few hours.

 TAKE CARE

Avoid all unnecessary travel. If you have to travel by car, wait until the roads have been gritted and take warm clothes, boots, water, food, a torch (flashlight) and shovel. Let someone know your route and arrival time. Drive slowly – it can take 10 times longer to stop in snow and ice – and use the highest gear possible. If you get stuck, stay with your car.

▶▶See also: INHALING FUMES pp44–45 • HYPOTHERMIA p46

avalanche

Each winter, huge amounts of snow and ice build up on steep mountainsides in an unstable union of friction and gravity. If you are caught in an avalanche, swift and appropriate action can be the difference between life and death.

GET HELP Put the number of the local emergency services or mountain rescue service into your mobile phone, if you have a signal, so you can call quickly if you need help.

be aware

- Avalanches are a product of the interaction between the terrain, the snow and the weather conditions. Always check the local International Scale of Avalanche Hazard Rating before you ski or snowboard off piste. The local ski resort will have information.
- In 90 per cent of avalanche accidents, the avalanche was triggered by the victim or someone in the victim's party.
- Be wary of areas of deep snow for 3 days after a snowfall. Avoid pockets of deep snow on steep-sided mountains. If you see any avalanche activity, avoid that area.

Safety equipment

If you are planning to ski or snowboard off piste, three pieces of equipment are essential.

- **AVALANCHE TRANSCEIVER** This radio device transmits a signal that can be tracked if you are buried in an avalanche.
- **AVALANCHE PROBE** This is used to find a person's exact location beneath the snow. It saves unnecessary digging and precious time.
- **AVALANCHE SHOVEL** Speed is essential to survival. Using a lightweight, collapsible shovel is far more efficient than using your hands.

action

CAUGHT IN AN AVALANCHE

1 **SCREAM AND SHOUT** Warn your companions to make sure that they have seen the avalanche – and you. If they know where you are, they will have a better chance of rescuing you. As soon as you sense an avalanche, look up to see if you are in its path and get out of its way as quickly as you can.

2 **DISCARD HEAVY ITEMS** Get rid of bags, clothing and anything that will drag you down deeper into the snow. Discard your ski poles and skis.

3 **'SWIM' THROUGH THE SNOW** If you get caught up in the avalanche, try to 'swim' to keep yourself at the top of the snow. Grab hold of anything, such as a tree, bush or rock: the more snow that passes you by, the less there will be to bury you.

4 **PUT UP A HAND** Try to keep one hand raised to help mark your position and the other in front of your face. As the avalanche slows, try to maintain a pocket of air in front of your nose and mouth.

As the snow settles around you, try to keep moving. Rock your head and wiggle your body. The more space you can create around yourself, the better.

5 **REMAIN STILL** Once you are buried you may not be able to move, so try to control your breathing and stay calm. Snow is a good insulator, so do not waste oxygen shouting. If you feel faint, allow yourself to black out. You will use less oxygen if unconscious.

An avalanche is most likely on sheltered slopes of 28–45 degrees.

SOMEONE IS BURIED

1 **GET HELP** Shout a warning to those around you, then watch closely. Try to pinpoint the last spot that you saw the person before he was buried.

2 **ASSESS THE RISK** Ascertain whether another avalanche is likely and plan your escape options. Then mark the point where the victim was last seen with a ski pole.

3 **ALERT MOUNTAIN RESCUE** Use a phone or radio to request assistance, but only send someone for help if you can spare him. He will be more valuable helping to dig: **if you can find the victim in 15 minutes, he has a 90 per cent chance of survival;** after 35 minutes, this drops to 30 per cent.

4 **SEARCH** If you have an avalanche transceiver, set it to 'receive' to locate the buried skier. Otherwise, look quickly for clues, such as ski poles or clothing. These may give you a trajectory you can follow to focus the search area. Look for signs in the snow that someone might be buried underneath.

5 **DIG** Use shovels or your hands to dig down to where you think the victim might be. Clearly mark the places that you have already searched.

6 **MAKE AN AIRWAY** As soon as you locate the person, reach in with your hands to create an airway to his face. Dig him out as quickly as you can.

7 **BEGIN CPR** If he is not breathing, begin resuscitation at once (see pages 16–17).

8 **AWAIT RESCUE** Keep the casualty warm, but do not move him if he is unconscious in case there are unseen injuries. If he is conscious and movement causes no pain, transfer him onto a dry surface and keep him comfortable until medical help arrives.

⚠ TAKE CARE

● Whether you are going for a walk or skiing off piste, always let someone know your planned route.
● If you are skiing or snowboarding off piste, go in a small group with a minimum of three people.
● Never enter or traverse a slope above other people as you could trigger an avalanche. Most avalanches are triggered by people moving.
● Take note of avalanche hazard warnings and flags: yellow indicates low risk; yellow and black check, considerable to high risk; and black, very high risk. Never cross an avalanche warning fence.

earthquake

About half of the world's largest cities are situated in regions where there is a possibility of a serious earthquake. Although tremors often strike without warning, there are precautions that you can take if you are in a high-risk area.

WATCHPOINT In coastal areas a tsunami (see pages 200–201) may follow an earthquake. Stay away from the coast and be prepared to move inland or onto high ground.

precautions

High-risk areas

● Minor earthquakes can occur almost anywhere, but earthquakes are most frequent, and most frequently severe, at places where the Earth's tectonic plates meet.

● Where these locations coincide with high human population density, the potential exists for a major disaster. Such areas include large parts of the northern and north-eastern Mediterranean and the so-called Ring of Fire, which circles the Pacific Ocean and includes the Philippines, Indonesia, Japan and the west coast of the Americas.

● Over the past 20 years, the most deadly earthquakes have occurred in Haiti, Indonesia, China, Pakistan, Iran, India, Turkey, Japan, Afghanistan, Mexico and Colombia.

● If you plan to travel in a high-risk zone, check with your tour operator that your accommodation meets local 'earthquake-proof' building standards.

● When you arrive at your accommodation, identify places of safety, indoors and out, and make sure your travelling companions are aware of them too.

● Agree with your companions what you will do if an earthquake strikes, including how you will make contact with each other if you are apart. Choose a relative or friend who lives a long distance away as a contact point – long distance calls are often easier to make as local networks will be overloaded.

● Take a survival kit (see pages 334–337) and keep it handy. Keep your mobile phone fully charged.

Christchurch, New Zealand, on 4 September 2010, after it was rocked by an earthquake with a magnitude of 7.1.

action

INSIDE A BUILDING

1 **STOP WHAT YOU ARE DOING** Even if you feel a very slight tremor, prioritise your safety until the all-clear is given. You may simply have felt a foreshock that precedes a much more powerful earthquake.

2 **DROP TO THE GROUND** If the shock is more severe, get down. This will lower your centre of gravity and reduce the chance of being hit by debris.

3 **TAKE COVER** Get under a sturdy table or other piece of furniture for protection and hold on to it. If there is nothing suitable nearby, **crouch down in a corner where two interior walls meet,** well away from windows or other glass. Cover your head and face with your arms. Do not shelter in a doorway – if it doesn't have a load-bearing structure, it may collapse.

4 **STAY WHERE YOU ARE** Do not move until the shaking stops, even if the lights go out or automatic sprinklers come on. Most people who are injured are those who move about during an earthquake.

OUTSIDE A BUILDING

■ **RUN TO AN OPEN SPACE** Quickly move away from buildings, trees, overhead wires or anything else that might fall on you. The larger the open space you can find, the safer you will be. People are rarely injured during an earthquake simply by the ground moving.

■ **DRIVE TOWARDS AN OPEN SPACE** If you are in a car, find an open space, such as a large car park, and stop the car. Do not stop on a bridge, beneath an overpass or beside tall buildings or trees. Stay in the car until the shaking stops.

TRAPPED UNDER DEBRIS

1 **COVER YOUR NOSE AND MOUTH** Avoid inhaling potentially harmful dust. Try to get your bearings and check yourself for injuries.

2 **GET HELP** Listen for sounds of rescue and try to tap on something to alert rescuers. If you can get to it, use your mobile phone to call someone or to generate intermittent music, beeps or other sounds. Only shout as a last resort, as it is tiring and can result in you inhaling more dust.

 WARNING

If you find yourself trapped, do not strike a match for light. Dust-filled air can be explosive and gas may have escaped from broken pipes.

what next?

• If you are inside, do not go out until you are certain that it is safe. Be alert for fallen electricity cables, broken glass, loose tiles or damaged masonry. Beware of the risk of fire.
• If you are outside, do not approach a building that looks unsafe. If in doubt, do not enter. Seek advice from the authorities or wait for the all-clear.
• If you are in a car, drive cautiously and slowly. Watch for large cracks or potholes. If possible, avoid driving over bridges and through underpasses.
• Do not smoke as there may be leaking gas pipes.
• Try to obtain up-to-date information from the emergency services, internet, radio, television or by telephoning someone outside the area.

Aftershocks

An earthquake is usually followed by a series of aftershocks. Their size and frequency is unpredictable, although generally, the bigger the main earthquake, the greater the size and number of aftershocks. Aftershocks are especially dangerous because they cause further collapse to already damaged buildings and infrastructure. Treat them seriously and act as you would for an earthquake.

volcanic eruption

Between 50 and 60 volcanoes erupt every year: 20 to 30 produce sometimes deadly lava flows and the same number are more violently explosive, creating clouds of suffocating ash. There is also the possibility of mudflows and flooding.

TIME TO ACT Volcanologists are increasingly skilled at predicting when a volcano is likely to erupt, but evacuation warnings may be given just hours beforehand.

action

ERUPTION PREDICTED

1 KEEP INFORMED Listen to the radio, watch television or use the internet to keep up to date with events. The website www.noaawatch.gov/themes/volcanoes.php gives hourly volcano reports.

2 HEED OFFICIAL WARNINGS Be ready for evacuation. Plan what to take, where you are going and the safest routes to get there. Follow any evacuation order issued by the authorities immediately. If you are not required to evacuate, make sure you have supplies of water, food and batteries.

3 PREPARE A SURVIVAL KIT You should include goggles and disposable breathing masks for each person as well as standard items (see page 336).

 WARNING

The danger area around a volcano is usually a radius of about 30km, but be aware that ash can spread to cover up to five times this distance, depending on the nature of the eruption and weather conditions. Stay upwind of an eruption if at all possible.

 TAKE CARE

● Keep pets indoors until the all-clear is given.
● Turn off electricity and gas at the mains.
● Agree how to reunite your family. Ask a relative or friend who lives a good distance away to act as a contact point and make sure that everyone has their phone number and address. Keep your mobile phone fully charged.
● Erupted volcanic material ranges from ash-sized particles to larger volcanic 'bombs' as big as a fridge. Be aware of what is likely in your area.

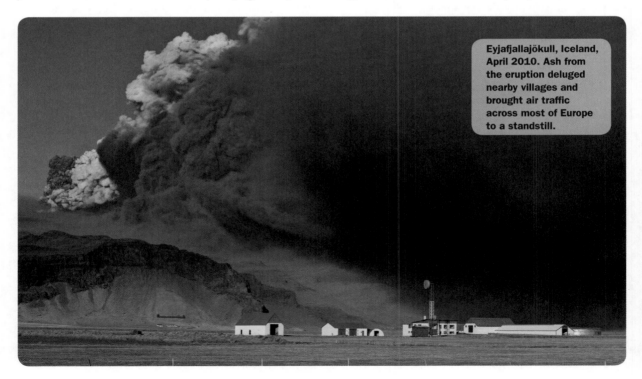

Eyjafjallajökull, Iceland, April 2010. Ash from the eruption deluged nearby villages and brought air traffic across most of Europe to a standstill.

FALLING ASH

1 PROTECT YOURSELF If you are outside when ash starts to fall, use clothing to cover yourself as much as possible and put up an umbrella, if you have one, to protect yourself from sharp particles of rock. Wear goggles and a mask, if possible. If you do not have a mask, tie a scarf or handkerchief soaked in water over your mouth and nose. Wear spectacles instead of contact lenses.

2 FIND SHELTER If you can, take shelter inside a building or a car. If you are indoors when the ash begins to fall, stay inside – unless there is a risk that the roof will collapse – and keep all windows tightly closed. Seal off other vents and chimneys with cardboard and duct tape.

3 PREVENT STRUCTURAL DAMAGE If you are sheltering in accommodation with a flat or low-pitched roof, periodically sweep or shovel the ash from the roof to prevent it collapsing under the weight. Once mixed with water, ash becomes even heavier and may solidify like cement.

4 AVOID TRAVEL Do not drive unless essential or you are told to evacuate. If driving, do so slowly to avoid kicking up ash that could affect the engine. Use your headlights and ensure washer fluid is fully topped up. Use lots of water to keep the windscreen clear.

 WARNING
Volcanic ash is gritty and acidic, and can cause lung damage, such as silicosis. The young and old, and those with respiratory illnesses, are most at risk.

Mudflows

Volcanic mudflows, known as lahars, are a potentially deadly combination of water and volcanic ash. They are often produced when lava or hot ash melts snow or ice during an eruption, or as a result of the breach of a crater lake. But mudflows can also be triggered by heavy rain long after the eruption. Mudflows can travel at 80km/h and are capable of sweeping away houses, roads and bridges, and burying everything in their path beneath tonnes of mud that rapidly sets like concrete.

LAVA FLOWS

1 EXERCISE CAUTION Although lava flows are the least hazardous aspect of a volcanic eruption, travelling at speeds of just a few metres to a few hundred metres per hour, **they are extremely hot – with temperatures reaching 700–1,400°C.** Do not approach them or you risk burns. Beware of walking on lava, even once it appears solid and cold.

2 FORMULATE AN ESCAPE ROUTE The direction of a lava flow can generally be predicted and monitored. If you find yourself in its path, you will have time to plan your escape. The best tactic may be to dodge it by moving uphill or to one side.

PYROCLASTIC FLOWS

■ **MOVE QUICKLY** Made up of hot clouds of gas, dry rock fragments and dust, pyroclastic flows (or nuée ardentes) can move far faster than you can run or drive in a car. Your best hope of escape is to evacuate, avoiding the stream channels and valleys that a pyroclastic flow usually follows. Make for high ground as fast as you can.

what next?

● If you are evacuated, do not return to your accommodation unless you are advised that it is safe to do so. If you are staying in a holiday home that has been damaged in any way, have it inspected to confirm that it is structurally safe.
● Ash can damage car engines. Do not start your car unnecessarily during or shortly after an ash fall. Before you use it again, flush out any ash from the engine compartment with a garden hose and have the car serviced as soon as possible.

▶▶See also: INHALED FUMES pp44–45 • BURNS AND SCALDS p23 • EMERGENCY PREPARATION pp334–337

hurricane, typhoon and cyclone

Hurricane, typhoon and cyclone are all names for large tropical storms characterised by swirling winds of 250km/h and more. Although the destruction they cause to property can seldom be avoided, there is usually sufficient warning to guarantee your personal safety. Follow advice from the authorities on whether to take shelter or evacuate.

be aware

If you are travelling to an area where strong cyclonic storm activity occurs, avoid travelling during the stormy season. The main tropical storm regions and their seasons are given below.

- Caribbean Sea and Gulf of Mexico, including Central America, Mexico and US Gulf States: June to October. Worst months: August to September.
- East North Atlantic (eastern seaboard of the USA): June to October. Worst months: August to September.
- West North Pacific, South China Sea, including Japan: June to November. Worst months: August to September.
- North Indian Ocean, Bay of Bengal, Arabian Sea: May to November. Worst months: July to September.
- South Indian Ocean: December to April.
- Australia – north, north-west and west coasts: January to March.
- South Pacific, including Fiji, Samoa and New Zealand: December to March.

PLAN AHEAD
- Make sure that your car has a full tank of fuel and you have packed everything you need, including a survival kit (see pages 334–337).

HURRICANE, TYPHOON AND CYCLONE CLASSIFICATION

Tropical storms are categorised from 1 to 5, based on their wind speed, pressure and destructive potential. Take local advice on when to stay in your accommodation and when to evacuate.

CATEGORY	WIND SPEED	DAMAGE
1	120–150km/h	Minimal: signs, vegetation, unanchored mobile homes. Storm surges up to 1.5m.
2	151–175km/h	Moderate: mobile homes, roofs, small craft, electricity. Storm surges 1.8–2.5m.
3	176–210km/h	Extensive: small buildings, low roads cut off, electricity. Storm surges 2.6–3.9m.
4	211–250km/h	Extreme: roofs destroyed, trees down, roads cut off, mobile homes destroyed, beach homes flooded, electricity cables down. Storm surge 4–5.5m.
5	251km/h +	Catastrophic: most buildings destroyed, trees down, major roads cut off, homes flooded, electricity cables down. Storm surge of more than 5.5m.

action

STORM PREDICTED

1 STAY INFORMED Check the radio, television or internet (www.hurricanezone.net) for information. Carry a portable radio and torch (flashlight) in case of electrical failure. If you are staying in a hotel, check the front desk for information.

2 FOLLOW SAFETY PROCEDURES Local radio and public services should give details of the location of the nearest storm shelter (see box, below), or procedures for evacuation. If you are in a hotel, you will be told areas that are safe within the building or whether you should evacuate.

3 PREPARE FOR EVACUATION Put together essential items to take to the shelter (see box, below) or pack in readiness for evacuation. If on holiday, you may be able to organise transport and flights home.

Storm shelters

As soon as you are advised to, or the 201 storm hits, go to a storm shelter. If you are not staying in a hotel, find the location of your nearest shelter by searching on the internet or by contacting the local Red Cross or public services, such as local libraries, councils and the police.

● **WHAT TO TAKE** Many national shelters recommend that you come equipped with certain items, including water (1–2 litres per person per day), canned foods, milk and beverages, medicine, toilet paper, sanitary towels, nappies, baby food and baby supplies, battery-operated radio, torch (flashlight), eating utensils, blankets or sleeping bags, passport and valuable papers, cards, games and books.

 WARNING

National advisory bodies maintain a 24-hour watch on weather situations that could develop into tropical storms. They issue warnings of high winds, storm surges and floods to any area under threat.

tornado

Tornadoes or 'twisters' are the most violent and unpredictable of all storms. With winds of up to 500km/h, they can cut a swathe of destruction 2km wide and over 100km long.

be aware

● Find out whether the region you plan to visit is prone to tornadoes. Although these storms can occur almost anywhere, they are most common in central states of the USA, known as 'Tornado Alley', where they are more frequent in spring and early summer between 3pm and 9pm.
● Tornadoes generally form from the trailing edge of a thunderstorm. So whenever the weather turns stormy, be alert and listen to local radio for weather bulletins and tornado warnings.

action

■ **MOVE TO SAFETY** Try to move to the centre of the building you are in and hide beneath something strong to protect yourself from falling debris. Move to a shelter if possible (see left).

■ **ESCAPE** Tornadoes typically move at 50km/h, with winds 10 times this speed, but can travel twice as fast. So **if a storm is about a kilometre away, you have a minute or so to find shelter** or move out of its path. If you are in a car on the open road, you should drive away from the storm.

■ **GET OUT** If you are in a stationary vehicle, caravan or mobile home, get out at once and seek shelter in a building or storm shelter. Failing that, you will be safer sheltering in a ditch or on open ground away from trees and fences: vehicles are often tossed around in the violent winds.

tsunami

A tsunami is a series of huge waves created by an underwater disturbance, such as an earthquake or landslide. To survive, you need to act quickly: tsunamis can reach more than 30m and travel at 500–1,000km/h, inundating whole islands.

WATCHPOINT There may be time for a warning if the earthquake is distant, but if the quake is closer to the shore you may only have minutes before the tsunami hits.

be aware

REGIONS AT RISK OF TSUNAMI
● In the USA, the coastlines of California, Oregon, Washington and Alaska are most at risk because of their position near tectonic plate boundaries in the Pacific Ocean. Coastal landslides can trigger tsunamis in Hawaii.
● Countries in and bordering the North and South Pacific oceans along the so-called Ring of Fire are particularly prone to tsunamis, including Japan.
● The Maldives, Indonesia, Thailand, Sri Lanka and India may be affected by the Indian plate moving.
● You could be at risk if you are on the coast and at low altitude. Land less than 8m above sea level and within 2km of the shore is vulnerable.

MAKE AN EVACUATION PLAN
● If you are in an area at risk, prepare an emergency three-day pack for each person (see pages 334–337) and a family evacuation plan.
● Consider where you will go and how to contact each other. Keep your mobile phone fully charged.
● Choose a relative or friend who lives outside the area as a back-up contact point. Make sure that everyone knows their phone number.

UNDERSTAND THE WARNINGS
● If an earthquake has occurred in the Pacific basin and may generate a tsunami, an advisory warning is issued. Tsunami warning centres in Hawaii will issue hourly bulletins for the USA and countries of the Pacific basin. For details of warnings see http://www.prh.noaa.gov/ptwc/.
● 'Watch' status is given if a tsunami may have been generated but is at least 2 hours away.
● A 'Warning' is given if a tsunami has been generated that could cause damage.

Spotting the signs

● **EARTHQUAKE TREMOURS** If you hear or feel rumblings offshore, it could be an underwater earthquake. If it is near enough to hear, a tsunami could be upon you in minutes.
● **CHANGING SEA LEVELS** A rapid change in the level of coastal waters – either rising or falling – means a tsunami is imminent.
● **TIDE IN REVERSE** If the tide goes out suddenly, it is being sucked into the wave and will return as a wall of water that sweeps away all before it, travelling as far as 2.5km inland.

⚠ WARNING
● Everything that is in the water will be swept back to sea with the tsunami or dumped on the way – most tsunami-related deaths are caused by drowning and injury from floating debris. If you can climb aboard something that floats, it will help you to conserve energy and protect you from collisions with other flotsam.
● If you know that the building you are in is secure, it may be safer to stay inside and move to as high a floor as possible, above water level. Do not stay on the ground floor.

The first of six tsunamis rolls towards a beach in Thailand on 26 December, 2004. Around 230,000 people died in countries from Indonesia to Africa.

action

WARNING OF TSUNAMI

1 LEAVE AT ONCE Put your evacuation plan into effect immediately a tsunami warning is issued, or if you believe a tsunami may be imminent (see box, opposite). Major cities often issue warnings just a couple of hours before the wave hits.

2 RUN TO SOMEWHERE HIGH If you notice **the sea rapidly receding, leaving a large area of the shore uncovered, you may have only minutes before a tsunami hits.** Run for higher ground or the upper floors of a sturdy building. Climb a tree only as a last resort: unless the tree is strong and tall, it may be knocked over or submerged by the tsunami.

3 KEEP MOVING INLAND Tsunamis come in waves, so the flooding may continue to get worse. Distance is important, so you should try to move at least 2.5km inland, or onto high ground. If a wave hits the coast, the waters will rush inland along channels and other low-lying land, so avoid valleys and rivers.

4 STAY PUT If you have reached somewhere safe, stay there for at least a day. Waves can keep coming for several hours and even when they have stopped, the affected area may be extremely dangerous. Flooding may take a while to recede, roads may be damaged and utilities may be suspended. Check with the emergency services before returning.

SEPARATED FROM FAMILY

1 PHONE YOUR AGREED CONTACT NUMBER If you set up a contact point as part of your emergency plan, phone to find out whether other family members or travelling companions have phoned in.

2 SEARCH LOCALLY If there has been no contact, find out whether a survivor reception centre or humanitarian assistance centre has been set up where you can register your details and those of anyone who is missing. Bring photos if you have them. Your national Red Cross organisation can also help to trace missing persons.

▶▶See also: **FLOOD** pp188–189 • **DROWNING** pp250–251 • **EMERGENCY PREPARATION** pp334–337

Bushfires

A threat to life in any large area of forest, scrub or grassland, bushfires (or wildfires) can move at speed, sometimes 60km/h or more, jump rivers and roads, and change direction as quickly as the wind. Often, evacuation is the only option.

GET HELP If you see a fire taking hold – or a situation you consider to be a fire risk in dry weather – call the emergency services without delay. For phone numbers see page 338.

be aware

- Whether you live or are holidaying in an area that is surrounded by woodland, scrub or grass, you need to be alert to the possibility of fire. The risk is especially high in summer during a prolonged period of dry weather.
- Listen to weather reports on local and national radio and television. High winds and low relative humidity increase the risk during times of drought, and bushfire danger ratings are often given with the general forecast.
- Check danger ratings for your particular area and the progress of current bushfires on the appropriate National Park or Forest Services website on the internet.
- If a bushfire threatens, keep up to date with reports and evacuation information. Follow the advice that is given by the local authorities.

action

IN A BUILDING

1 TAKE PREVENTIVE ACTION Do what you can to reduce the fire risk for the property you are staying in. Move combustible materials, such as garden furniture, barbecue grills and gas bottles away from the building and turn off gas supplies at the mains. Douse buildings with water (see box, opposite).

2 PREPARE TO LEAVE Plan several different escape routes in case one is blocked. Pack your belongings in the car, together with plenty of drinking water. Park the car facing outwards with the keys in the ignition and all the windows and air vents closed.

3 EVACUATE If the authorities advise evacuation, follow their advice. Before you leave, put on all interior and exterior lights to make your accommodation visible to firefighters.

Bushfires in Canberra, Australia's capital, in 2003 claimed 500 homes and four lives.

IN A CAR

1 **STAY IN THE VEHICLE** If you are cut off by a bushfire while in your car, **do not get out and try to flee on foot.** Close all the windows and air vents to prevent smoke from getting into the vehicle.

2 **STOP SAFELY** Do not drive in thick smoke, but if you can get the vehicle away from any large trees or thick bush, then do so. Then stop, turn on your lights to make the car visible, and turn the ignition off. Get onto the floor of the vehicle and cover yourself with coats or blankets.

3 **MAKE A SMOKE MASK** Moisten a scarf or a piece of cloth with a little water and hold it over your nose and mouth to help you to breathe.

4 **BE PATIENT** Stay in the vehicle until the main fire passes. It may get hot and smoky and the vehicle may start to rock, but do not panic. The tyres may burst but petrol tanks rarely explode.

IN THE OPEN

■ **CLOTHES CATCH FIRE** If your clothes catch alight, quickly drop to the ground. Flames, and their heat, rise up, so by lying on the ground you are more likely to prevent them from reaching your face and hair. Roll around vigorously to extinguish them.

■ **CUT OFF BY FIRE** Try to find a ditch or other depression in the ground that will afford you shelter. If there is time, quickly remove as much wood, brush or other flammable material from the immediate area as you can. Lie down and cover yourself with a coat or blanket and wait until the fire has passed.

⚠ TAKE CARE

● If you are camping in a National Park or forest area, check the local bushfire danger rating. Respect any temporary restrictions placed on access to high-risk areas and bans on campfires.
● Site a campfire at least 3m from trees, bushes or buildings and contain it in a fire pit or with a ring of stones. A fire pit should fully contain the hot embers: dig it to about a third of the width in depth. Keep a bucket of water nearby to extinguish the fire. Ensure that all the embers are cold to the touch before you go to bed or leave the area.

Protecting property

You can take action to reduce a building's flammability while it is still safe. But always put your own safety first.

1 **USE HOSES AND SPRINKLERS** Use the firefighting technique of soaking house walls, roofs, fences and other nearby structures with water. Put a lawn sprinkler on flat roofs. Douse surrounding trees and grass.

2 **LET TRAINED FIREFIGHTERS FIGHT THE FIRE** Do not stay to fight the blaze. Leave before you and your escape routes are overtaken by fire.

what next?

● Wait for the fire service to give the all-clear before returning to an area affected by bushfires. Fires can reignite from hidden hotspots many days after all visible flames have died down.
● Watch out for damaged power lines and keep a safe distance. Report any damaged pylons or poles to the local authorities.
● Be aware that charred trees or buildings may be unstable. Use caution and good judgment when re-entering any building affected by fire.
● Avoid falling into ash pits. These are holes full of ash that are created when trees burn right down to their roots. Mark any that you find to warn others.

⚠ WARNING

If you are found to be responsible for causing a bushfire, you may be prosecuted and/or fined.

▶▶See also: **BURNS AND SCALDS** pp112–113 • **CAUGHT IN A BLAZING HOUSE** pp122–125

heat wave

A prolonged period of hot weather can be more than simply uncomfortable. Dehydration and heatstroke can affect anyone and the death rate – among the elderly, in particular – can rise sharply, so make sure you know how to stay well.

> **TIME TO ACT** Do not wait until you are thirsty to drink: you will already be dehydrated. In hot weather, a sedentary adult needs to drink at least 2–3 litres of water a day.

precautions

- Stock up on bottled water, fruit juice and other cold drinks before the weather turns hot.
- Plan for power cuts, which are common in hot weather when the power grid is overloaded. Keep a torch (flashlight) and candles to hand and your freezer fully stocked: food stays colder for longer in a power cut when the freezer – or fridge – is full.
- Make lots of ice, and ice pops for children. These can also help to fill your freezer.
- Buy fans or air-conditioners, if possible, to help keep you cool.

Who is vulnerable?

The elderly and the very young are most susceptible to heat-related illness, including dehydration, heat exhaustion and heatstroke. Pay particular attention to:

- **SPECIAL HEALTH NEEDS** If someone's heart condition or breathing problem becomes worse in hot weather, seek medical advice.
- **KEEPING COOL** If you cannot cool a house adequately, find out if there is a local air-conditioned community centre or library that the person could visit.

action

KEEP YOUR HOUSE COOL

■ **USE SUN SHADES** Keep all windows that are in direct sunlight closed and covered. Use awnings, shutters, garden umbrellas or gazebos to block out the sun.

■ **VENTILATE** While the air temperature outside is lower than that inside your home, open windows that are in the shade. Open doors and windows early and late, but close them during the heat of the day.

■ **SWITCH OFF** Avoid unnecessary use of electrical appliances and lights, especially halogens. Low energy bulbs and fluorescent lights run coolest.

■ **MICROWAVE FOOD** If you want to eat hot food, use a microwave – it produces less collateral heat than the oven or stove.

■ **COOL THE AIR** Fans help you to stay cool by moving the air and improving your body's ability to sweat. Make your own air cooler by placing a fan behind a shallow bowl filled with ice and water.

STAY COOL

■ **DRESS APPROPRIATELY** Wear light, loose clothing made from natural fibres or from technical sports synthetics designed to wick away perspiration.

■ **CHOOSE COLD DRINKS** Chilled water or fruit juice will rehydrate and cool you. Tea or coffee may quench your thirst, but will raise your temperature. Avoid drinking alcohol as it increases dehydration.

■ **EAT COLD MEALS** Eat light, low protein, uncooked meals such as salads. These can meet your energy needs without firing up your metabolic rate; they also have a high water content.

■ **SHOWER OR BATH** Have a cool shower or bath. A wet towel draped over your head or shoulders can also be very cooling.

■ **REST BY DAY** Carry out any strenuous activities, such as housework, very early in the morning or at night. Try to exert yourself as little as possible during the hottest part of the day (11am to 3pm).

pandemic influenza

A pandemic is an epidemic that becomes very widespread, affecting several regions, continents or the world. Sometimes it is caused by the mutation of an animal virus into one that affects humans. The virus may also change as it spreads, becoming more dangerous and resistant to drugs. Because it is new, or has not been active for long, no one is immune.

assessment

The World Health Organization alerts the world to a new pandemic, classifying it into six phases.
Phases 1–3: The virus has been observed predominantly in animals – in phase 1, there is no human infection; by phase 3 there may be sporadic cases of human infection.
Phase 4: Human-to-human transmission occurs in significant numbers in a community.
Phase 5: There is widespread human infection in at least two countries in one WHO region – it usually signifies an imminent pandemic.
Phase 6: A new outbreak in a different region or continent to phase 5 signals a pandemic.

SYMPTOMS OF INFLUENZA
- Sudden high fever of 38°C or more
- Headache and aching muscles
- Dry cough/shortness of breath
- Runny nose/sore throat
- Diarrhoea or vomiting.

 WARNING
Anyone with the above symptoms who is aged over 65, is pregnant, has a pre-existing medical condition or is less than five years old should seek immediate medical advice by phone.

action

IF FLU IS ABOUT

1 PRACTISE GOOD HYGIENE To prevent the spread of germs, cough or sneeze into a tissue and put it in a bin. **Wash your hands frequently, and always after you have caught a sneeze or cough in your hand or a tissue;** clean surfaces regularly.

2 DO NOT RELY ON A MASK Most masks that are generally available do not filter out virus particles, which are particularly small. The moist conditions these masks create may even increase the chances of catching the virus. Only masks that conform to European standard FFP3 or US standard N95 are effective and these require training in how to wear them and how often to change them.

3 CONSIDER A VACCINE If you have a serious chronic underlying illness, such as heart or respiratory disease, a compromised immune system, are pregnant or usually receive a vaccination against seasonal flu, ask your doctor if you should have a vaccination to protect against pandemic flu.

IF YOU HAVE FLU

1 STAY AT HOME Drink plenty of fluids and take paracetamol-based cold remedies to bring down a fever and relieve symptoms.

2 CONTACT YOUR DOCTOR Phone your doctor, emergency department or government flu helpline if one has been set up. You may benefit from anti-viral medication and testing may help public health physicians to monitor the outbreak.

3 GET A FLU BUDDY Ask a friend or relative to collect prescriptions and medicines for you, and to prepare meals. If you keep your distance and practise good hygiene, your friend should not become infected.

4 SEEK MEDICAL ADVICE If you suddenly get much worse, or are not improving after 7 days (5 days for a child), phone your doctor or nearest emergency department for advice.

contaminated water

With well over half the human body comprised of water, this precious liquid is our most vital requirement. If your water supply becomes contaminated with harmful bacteria or dangerous chemicals, it is possible to stop it affecting you.

GET HELP If someone is ill after drinking contaminated water, seek medical advice or call your local Poison Control Centre (see page 341). Notify the water provider.

be aware

- Take heed of any local authority or water company warnings concerning water quality and stock up on bottled water in case your supply is compromised.
- Be particularly vigilant during and after flooding, as water supplies frequently become polluted at such times.
- If you receive a warning of a possible threat to your water supply, store as much water as you can in containers and in the bath tub.

⚠ WARNING

- **Wash dishes using boiled water and disinfectant, not the dishwasher.** The water temperature in a normal dishwasher cycle is unlikely to be high enough to kill all bacteria.
- When travelling in developing countries, drink bottled water that you can verify has a proper seal and use bottled or boiled water to clean your teeth. Avoid having ice cubes in drinks, or eating ice cream, salad and fruit, unless you wash and peel it yourself.

Water treatment

Contaminated water can be treated using either filters or chemicals. Both are available from outdoor shops and online.

- **CHEMICAL TREATMENTS** These use carefully controlled quantities of chemicals to remove bacterial, viral and parasitic contamination.
- **FILTER SYSTEMS** Filters that use active carbon, and membrane filters, remove bacteria, chemicals, pesticides and heavy metal pollution.

action

SUSPECTED CONTAMINATION

■ **CHEMICAL CONTAMINATION** Examine your water. Fill a large glass and allow the water to stand for 5 minutes. If it remains cloudy, has an oily surface or smells strange, you should treat it as contaminated. Drink bottled water until the situation is resolved or use specialist filters or chemical treatments (see box, below left).

■ **BACTERIAL CONTAMINATION** Bacterial, parasitic and viral contamination can be neutralised by boiling the water for at least 3 minutes. Remember to boil the water you use to wash your food in and the water you use to brush your teeth. Store boiled water in containers cleaned with a mild disinfectant or a weak solution of bleach.

SYMPTOMS OF ILLNESS

1 WATCH FOR SYMPTOMS Diarrhoea, vomiting and fever are common symptoms of bacterial infection such as *E. coli* or viral infections such as rotavirus. Symptoms of chemical poisoning can be similar but also include headache, dizziness, change in skin colour, throat pain, blistering of the mouth, respiratory problems and abdominal pain.

2 SEEK HELP Contact your water company for information and seek expert medical advice. Avoid further consumption of the contaminated water. Drink plenty of clean, fresh water, eat normally and rest. Avoid alcohol.

⚠ WARNING

Babies and young children with diarrhoea are at much greater risk of dehydration. Seek medical help at once if they develop additional symptoms.

radiation incident

Radiation incidents are those that involve a significant release of radioactive material that may pose a significant health risk to the general public. They are extremely rare, and stringent measures are in place to prevent them. If you live near to a major nuclear installation, make sure you are familiar with the official emergency plan.

be aware

- Most countries have devised an authorised emergency plan in case of a radiological accident. You may be notified of an incident by siren or the emergency services. In some cases an automatic system has been set up to send out text and phone messages. In most countries there are regulations governing the notification of the public. For example, a nuclear power plant must have plans in place for contacting people in the community during an emergency and must inform the community each year of its evacuation plans and routes.
- Make sure that you have at least one battery-powered radio so that you can listen to news bulletins even if there is a power cut.

action

■ **FOLLOW THE ADVICE GIVEN** Listen to the radio, television or check the internet and follow the instructions given by the authorities. Do not evacuate until you are advised to as you must ensure you know which way the radioactive plume is travelling and how to avoid it.

■ **STAYING SAFE INDOORS** There are some important safety measures that you must follow if you are told to stay indoors: close all doors and windows and turn off any fans and air-conditioners, and any heating units that bring in air from the outside. Take shelter in the centre of a room that has the least number of windows.

■ **IN CASE OF EVACUATION** Follow the instructions given to you by offical sources on how to travel to an evacuation shelter. Ideally, before you leave, close all doors and windows of your home or accommodation, if travelling, and turn off any heating and ventilation systems. In your car, keep the windows closed and turn the ventilation off.

THE EFFECTS OF EXPOSURE

Gy or 'gray' units measure the dose of radiation absorbed by a person.

MILD EXPOSURE	MILD TO MODERATE EXPOSURE	MODERATE EXPOSURE	SEVERE EXPOSURE	EXTREME EXPOSURE
0.5–1.0 Gy	**1.0–2.0 Gy**	**2.0–3.5 Gy**	**3.5–10 Gy**	**10–20 Gy**
Mild radiation sickness, headaches and nausea. Seek medical advice. Almost certain survival.	Medical treatment required; bone marrow damage likely. Survival rate of around 90 per cent.	Medical assistance urgently required. Survival likely.	Medical treatment essential. At lower levels survival rate around 50 per cent; at higher levels death probable within 1–3 weeks.	Death certain within 2–5 days.

▶▶See also: BURNS AND SCALDS pp112–113

chemical release

Chemical weapons are usually hard to detect as they often take the form of gases or innocuous-looking liquids. They have been used in a number of terrorist attacks, including the sarin gas attack on the Japanese subway in 1995, when 12 people died.

TIME TO ACT The chemical agent may only be known once you show symptoms. Leave the area quickly, covering your nose and mouth. Shield your eyes and cover exposed skin.

be aware

- Chemical agents can be deployed as a liquid or a gas. Many gases are colourless and odourless and the first sign of a release may be the reaction of people around you.
- How and where a chemical weapon is deployed will affect how you should respond. Chemical agents can be spread using an explosive device, some form of aerosol spray or even a crop-dusting aeroplane.
- Similar poisoning can occur from exposure to organophosphates and carbamate insecticides. Organophosphorus insecticides are related to nerve agents such as sarin, tabun and soman.

action

SUSPECTED CONTAMINATION

1 BE OBSERVANT A sudden strange smell, people choking or dizziness are all signs of a chemical release. Move away at once, as you will not be able to help if you become affected.

2 GET AWAY Hold your breath and move as quickly as you can to an exit. If you are in any kind of confined space, move to a larger space if possible. The greater the air volume, the more dilute the chemical agent will be. Get outside the building.

3 CLIMB HIGHER Most chemical agents are heavier than air, so as you make your escape try to move upwards. Take the stairs, stand on chairs, climb on a wall; do whatever you have to do to get higher.

Japanese security forces practise an anti-terrorism drill to deal with the aftermath of a sarin nerve gas attack.

4 **SHUT YOURSELF IN** If escape is impossible, find somewhere that you can shut yourself in, such as a nearby room, compartment or cupboard. Once inside, try to seal it as effectively as you can. Stuff clothing or paper into every crack and block vents and keyholes. Phone someone to tell them where you are and wait for rescue.

5 **PROTECT YOURSELF** Cover as much of your skin as possible, using a scarf, handkerchief or even your shirt as a makeshift mask to protect your eyes, nose and mouth. Depending on the kind of chemical agent that has been released, this could prove to be an invaluable precaution.

6 **DECONTAMINATE YOURSELF** As soon as you are somewhere safe, decontaminate yourself by removing your clothes, which will eliminate up to 90 per cent of contamination. Seek urgent medical advice.

7 **SAFE NOT SORRY** If you think you may have been exposed to a chemical release, seek medical attention immediately. Symptoms such as headache, cough, diarrhoea, skin or eye irritation (which may be delayed) should all be checked.

Chemical agents

There are four basic categories of chemical weapon that may be used in a chemical attack.
● **NERVE AGENTS OR NEUROTOXINS** These act on the nervous system and can kill in 1–10 minutes. They include sarin, a colourless liquid or gas with a faintly fruity odour.
● **BLISTER OR VESICANT AGENTS** Mustard gas is the most well known. These agents burn and blister the skin and damage the eyes and lungs. They can incapacitate or kill.
● **CHOKING AGENTS** These attack the lungs and can cause death within 48 hours. One example is phosgene, a colourless gas that smells like new-mown hay.
● **CYANIDE COMPOUNDS** The most common are hydrogen cyanide (hydrocyanic acid) and cyanogen chloride. Cyanides inhibit metabolism, resulting in asphyxiation.

biological release

The deliberate release of germs or other biological substances can cause mass sickness and terror. It may be aimed at a population centre or at the food supply.

be aware

● Smallpox, plague and anthrax are the three biological agents most commonly feared in a terrorist attack. Smallpox and plague are the most dangerous as they spread rapidly in large populations.
● It may not be immediately obvious that a biological attack has taken place. Health workers may report a pattern of symptoms and alert the authorities.

action

1 **ISOLATE YOURSELF** If you suspect or anticipate a biological release, your best chance of survival is isolation. Either quarantine yourself in your home or escape to as isolated a location as possible.

2 **STAY INFORMED** Public announcements will be made on television and by radio. Listen for information on symptoms and medical advice.

3 **MAXIMISE HYGIENE** Act as you would to prevent the spread of any infection: wash your hands frequently, avoid touching your eyes, avoid contact with infected people, wash surfaces and clothing.

4 **WATCH FOR SYMPTOMS** It may be impossible to know whether you have been affected by a biological agent, so stay alert for symptoms. Many illnesses begin with flu-like symptoms. Skin rashes or boils are also common.

5 **SEEK MEDICAL HELP** If you believe you have become ill as a result of a biological attack, phone the medical services. Contact your regional Poison Control Centre (see page 341). Do not go to hospital or visit your family doctor as you may be contagious.

caught in a **riot**

A large angry crowd can be as unpredictable and dangerous as any natural disaster. If you find yourself caught up in any kind of demonstration, try to keep to the periphery and stay alert. That way you can escape if it turns into a riot.

TIME TO ACT Demonstrators often have a destination in mind, such as a large square or political building. This is where the riot is likely to be most dangerous, so leave the area.

precautions

● Unless you feel compelled to take part in a demonstration, avoid any location where a large rally or protest is being held.

● Keep up to date with news bulletins, even when you are travelling. Riots do not usually happen spontaneously: most large demonstrations require considerable planning and preparation, and there is a legal requirement to alert the authorities.

● When visiting an unfamiliar city or town, carry a map so you can plan an alternative route in order to avoid a demonstration – or an escape route if you find yourself an unwilling part of one.

● Arrange a meeting place if you are travelling with friends or family, in case you get separated.

● Stay back from the front of the crowd. If the police decide to move forward, use batons, rubber bullets or a riot control agent (RCA), such as tear gas, you need to be as far away as possible.

● Watch out for a police signal to use an RCA or for police pulling on gas masks. Some tear gas grenades explode in the air, delivering a hot metal canister that can cause serious injury if it hits you. Exposure to RCAs is painful and debilitating: eyes burn and stream and breathing can be difficult. If you have any respiratory disorders, RCAs can have an even more serious effect.

⚠️ WARNING

● Once you become swept up in a riot, you will appear to be part of it – whether or not you are there intentionally.

● Do not approach police lines, make eye contact or call out to the police while you are part of the crowd. In the heat of a demonstration the police will regard you as a threat and react defensively.

action

CAUGHT IN A CROWD

1 ACT AT ONCE When a demonstration starts to become violent, you need to get away as quickly as possible. Do not wait to see if the situation calms down – it usually only gets worse.

2 GET INSIDE Most of the conflict and violence is likely to be on the streets. If you can shelter inside any kind of building, you will be safer. Once inside, stay away from windows, especially if missiles are being thrown. Try to find a back way out and stay alert for any signs of fire.

3 MOVE SLOWLY If you cannot get out of the crowd, move as slowly and casually as you can, even if things turn violent. Running will draw attention to you – and can make it look as though you are guilty of wrongdoing. Only begin to move away when you can see an escape route. Until then, stay with the crowd.

4 GO WITH THE FLOW People in a crowd move like water, with the centre often moving faster than the sides. Never try to move against the crowd. Flow with it, but as you are pushed forwards a few steps try to take one step to the side. Be patient.

5 WATCH YOUR FOOTING Try to create some space around you so you can stay balanced. If the crowd surges, move with it. Take small steps and if you stumble, grab the person next to you. If you do fall, curl up in a ball and protect your head. If others fall on top of you, stay calm; the crowd is more likely to avoid a number of fallen people than just one.

RIOT CONTROL AGENT USED

1 FLEE THE AREA As soon as an RCA, such as tear gas, is fired, get away as quickly as possible. **Move to higher ground or climb a wall or fire escape, as most RCAs are heavier than air.** Run into the wind if you can.

2 COVER YOUR FACE Use a scarf or piece of cloth soaked in water if you have some, as long as you are sure it has not been contaminated by the RCA.

3 DO NOT RUB YOUR EYES If you have been exposed to an RCA, flush your eyes with cold water repeatedly until the pain subsides.

4 REMOVE CONTAMINATED CLOTHES Wash clothes that have been exposed to RCAs. If a T-shirt or jumper has been severely contaminated, consider cutting it off, rather than pulling it over your head.

5 WASH YOUR SKIN Shower with cool water only for about 10 minutes – hot water will open the pores of your skin. Then shower normally.

6 SEEK MEDICAL ATTENTION If symptoms, such as blurred vision or chest pain, persist, see a doctor.

⚠ TAKE CARE
Remove contact lenses after exposure to an RCA. Do not put them back in your eyes. Seek advice from your optician about cleaning and re-using hard or gas permeable lenses.

Crowd control formations

You may be able to predict the police control tactics by the crowd control formation they adopt.

● **LINE FORMATION** Used to block access to a building or area and to drive crowds back or to pen them into a street or square for containment (a tactic known as corralling or kettling).

● **WEDGE FORMATION** Used to split and weaken a crowd by separating it into sections.

● **ECHELON FORMATION** Used to divert crowds or turn them in a particular direction.

 KEY ▪▪▪ **POLICE** ⠿ **CROWD**

▶▶See also: **INHALING FUMES** pp44–45 ● **POTENTIAL VIOLENCE** pp168–169

fire in a public place

Even in recent years, fires in shopping centres, hotels and railway stations have claimed hundreds of lives around the world. A fire in a public building can be frightening as large numbers of people may be involved, the majority of whom will be unfamiliar with possible escape routes. Your best chance of surviving is to stay calm and act quickly.

be aware

- Make sure that you know all the escape routes in public places that you use regularly. If any of these is a high-rise building, find out which floors link one exit stairwell with another.
- Make sure that your employer has regular fire drills and attend them.
- In unfamiliar buildings, **make a point of establishing two possible escape routes as soon as you arrive.**
- Never ignore a fire alarm.
- A fire escape may be outside (see opposite). Make sure you know how to access it.

action

■ **ACT QUICKLY** Leave at the first sign of fire – a burning smell, smoke or the sound of a fire alarm or shouting. Do not wait until you know that it is definitely a fire and do not stop to collect belongings.

■ **THINK FOR YOURSELF** Do not assume that someone in authority will tell you what to do. Head for the nearest fire exit. Be forceful and determined to get out of the building. Jump over or knock over obstructions if you need to.

■ **MAKE CONTINUAL ASSESSMENTS** If you need to go through a door, feel the door first. If it is hot, do not open it: go to another exit. If it is cool, open it cautiously and check for fire and smoke before going on. Close doors behind you.

■ **AVOID SMOKE** If you encounter thick smoke, turn back and use another emergency exit route, if possible, or drop to the floor where the air is clearer and crawl to the exit. Smoke, heat and noxious gases all rise. If you have a bottle of water, it can be used to dampen clothing to improvise a mask.

■ **USE THE STAIRS** Never use the lift: the electricity supply often gets cut off during a fire.

■ **DO NOT GET SWAMPED BY THE CROWD** If you find yourself in a crowd of people all trying to get out, stick to the periphery so you do not get trampled.

■ **RAISE THE ALARM OR USE YOUR MOBILE PHONE** Only do this once you are safely outside, or nearly outside, the building.

■ **IF YOU ARE CUT OFF BY SMOKE** Take refuge in a room, seal the door with tape or clothing, open a window and lean out. Call for help or attract attention by waving a sheet, curtains or clothing.

 WARNING
Do not attempt to put out a fire unless it is contained (in a waste bin, for example) and is small enough to be put out with a portable fire extinguisher.

lift gets stuck

Although being stuck in a lift for an uncertain length of time is stressful and uncomfortable, it is rarely hazardous. Most lifts are extremely safe; even if one does stop, it is unlikely to stay there for long or to drop suddenly down the lift shaft.

TIME TO ACT Lift safety depends on the owner acting on safety checks, which should be carried out every 6 months. If you experience a malfunction, always report it.

be aware

- Lift accidents are infrequent and rarely fatal. Most injuries involve bruising or broken limbs after a lurch or short fall.
- You are more likely to experience dehydration when stuck in a lift than physical harm. Try always to carry a bottle of water with you when you go shopping or travelling.

action

STUCK AT A FLOOR

1 PRESS DOOR OPEN BUTTON If this does not work initially, try again. Then try all the floor buttons, one at a time, starting with the floor you are on.

2 USE THE EMERGENCY PHONE Report your plight to the lift caretaker or maintenance operative using the emergency phone or intercom. Failing this, press the alarm button or phone the emergency services directly if you can get a signal inside the lift.

3 ATTRACT ATTENTION Bang on the lift door to attract the attention of people outside. Use a shoe or other hard object so you do not hurt yourself.

4 SHOUT LOUDLY If there are other people in the lift, take it in turns to shout loudly. Stop after shouting and listen to see if anyone is responding on the other side of the door. Ask them to press the door open button on the outside of the lift.

 WARNING
If the lift starts to fall, position yourself with your back straight against one of the lift walls and your knees bent to help to absorb the impact. Hold on to a handle, if there is one, to keep yourself upright. Jumping up and down will not help.

STUCK BETWEEN FLOORS

1 DO NOT PANIC Try to stay calm: you are in no immediate danger. If there is a power failure, emergency lighting will come on.

2 USE THE EMERGENCY TELEPHONE Look for the emergency telephone or intercom inside the lift. Try to make verbal contact with the lift caretaker or maintenance operative and let them know where you think you are stuck.

3 PRESS THE ALARM BELL If you cannot reach someone using the telephone or intercom, press the alarm bell. Hold it down or push two or three times in quick succession to get attention. Wait for a minute, then try again.

 WARNING
Do not try to open the lift doors between floors or the maintenance hatch in the ceiling. If the power comes back, you could be crushed between the doors or stranded on top of the lift.

Claustrophobia

Anyone with claustrophobia has a fear of enclosed spaces and crowded situations. Being trapped in a lift might trigger a first panic attack. Symptoms include:

- Sweating
- Accelerated heartbeat
- Accelerated breathing
- Nausea
- Light-headedness or fainting
- Shaking.

In the case of an attack, help the sufferer to sit down and take slow, deep breaths.

▶▶See also: PANIC ATTACK p75

plane hijack

A hijack is arguably every air passenger's worst nightmare. At 10,000m, with no escape possible, it is easy to become paralysed by fear. For the best chance of survival, you need to assess the hijacker's motives and then respond appropriately.

WATCHPOINT Once on the plane, pay attention to the safety briefing. Count the seat rows to the exits both in front and behind you and memorise the number to help you escape.

precautions

● Fly from a secure air hub. The better the airport security, the safer you will be in the air.
● Check with your foreign office whether there are any government warnings about travelling to your destination (see page 340).
● For long flights, try to choose an airline from a country with no political enemies.
● Choose economy class and dress anonymously. If hostages are going to be shot, they are more likely to be chosen from first-class or those wearing military or religious insignia or clothing.
● Watch your bags prior to check in to make sure no one interferes with them.
● Never accept a request to carry something on to a plane from anyone you do not know.

assessment

To decide how to act, try to make a rapid assessment of the hijackers' motives.

● Do they want the plane and its passengers as a bargaining chip? Or do they want to use it as a missile and kill everyone on board?
● The way the hijackers announce themselves and the weapons they have or deploy can tell you a lot about their motives. Note their nationality, any religious or political insignia. Are they simply threatening violence or have they already hurt anyone?
● Keep a close watch on developments. The changing situation will affect the hijackers' mood and their methods. Re-evaluate the situation constantly.

action

YOU ARE HELD HOSTAGE

1 STAY CALM The hijackers will be extremely tense and may behave unpredictably. They will also be looking for ways to exert their control. So in the first few moments you need to stay calm but alert, so you can decide on the best response.

2 COMPLY Release your seat belt and breathe slowly. Keep a low profile. Avoid eye contact. Comply with instructions and do not complain. Try to keep fellow passengers calm. Make requests for water or food respectfully and in a reasonable manner. Ask for what is possible.

3 BUILD RAPPORT The longer you are in contact with the hijackers, the more important it is for you to build some sort of rapport with them. Look for points of personal contact, such as family life, that avoid political or other potentially confrontational topics.

4 STAY POSITIVE Do what you can to stay in the best physical and mental shape. This will help you to be ready should the opportunity arise to escape or challenge the hijackers.

Stockholm syndrome

If the hijackers gain permission to land the plane, negotiations may begin and you may be held captive on the tarmac for several days. In these circumstances, it is common for hostages to come to feel sympathy towards their captors. What begins as a survival mechanism borne out of fear of violence, when any small act of kindness is seized on and given undue importance, can end in perverse feelings of loyalty to the hostage takers.

Elite French troops storm an Airbus on 26 December, 1994. Fundamentalist Algerian hijackers had seized it two days earlier and killed three hostages.

ASSESSING DANGER

■ **USE OF GAS MASKS** If the hijackers put on gas masks, it could mean they are about to use gas in the plane or that they fear the use of non-toxic gas by security forces trying to recover control. Watch carefully; if the hijackers produce canisters, an immediate response may be your only option.

■ **VIOLENT INTENT** If the hijackers begin killing passengers or make it obvious that they intend to crash the plane, you need to fight back at once. The longer you delay, the more control they will have and the more disastrous the consequences.

YOU HAVE TO FIGHT BACK

1 CO-ORDINATE AN ATTACK You are more likely to be successful if you can co-ordinate an attack with other passengers. In this case, you have two possible options: a simultaneous strike by several parties, or a distraction by one group of passengers, followed by an attack by others.

2 USE WHAT WEAPONS YOU HAVE It is unlikely that you will be able to reach the overhead lockers, so attack with what you have to hand. Scalding hot drinks, pens or pencils make useful weapons. Cushions, blankets and ripped-out seats can be used to defend against knives or daggers.

3 SCREAM AND SHOUT Use your voice as a weapon as you attack. If you are going it alone, shout commands to other passengers. A spirited attack will encourage others to join in.

4 IGNORE INJURY Injuries are inevitable. Use your adrenaline to continue your attack even if you become injured. Tell yourself that the consequences of failure will be worse.

5 DIRECT YOUR ATTACK Use your hands, elbows or weapons to attack the hijacker's eyes and throat, particularly the Adam's apple if the hijacker is male (see page 175). Once incapacitated, disarm the hijacker and get other passengers to secure him while you deal with any others.

▶▶See also: PHYSICAL ATTACK pp172–175

bomb attack

Terrorists have long used bomb threats to cause havoc, but in recent years their attacks have become more sophisticated and deadly. In October 2002 a suicide bomb and car bomb killed 200 people in the tourist district of Kuta in Bali and in July 2006 a series of bombs on Mumbai's train network brought the system to a halt, killing another 200 innocent civilians.

be aware

- Keep up to date with the news. If you know where the hot spots are, you can avoid them. Heed government warnings about travelling to certain countries (see page 340).
- When you use public transport, always sit or stand in the emptiest carriage of the train or at the back of a bus.
- When you enter an unfamiliar building, such as a hotel, restaurant, cinema or nightclub, always familiarise yourself with the emergency exits and plan at least two escape routes.
- Take note of the people around you. If you feel something is not right, move away or leave a building. Trust your instincts.

In recent suicide bomb attacks, the explosives were carried in a backpack.

⚠ WARNING

If you find a package tucked under a seat, hidden in a waste bin or that is in any way suspicious, do not touch it. Move away from it at once and warn others.

action

SUSPECT PACKAGE OR BAG

1 ASK AROUND If you see an unattended bag, first look around for its owner. Ask people nearby if it belongs to them or if they saw it being left.

2 ALERT SOMEONE IN AUTHORITY How suspiciously you should treat an unattended bag will depend on where and when it has been left. Ask yourself if the location is a likely target and if there is a high perceived threat of terrorist attack. If you are on a bus, inform the driver at once. If you are on a train, pull the emergency handle only once you have stopped at a station. Then get off the train and tell the driver or guard about the parcel or bag.

3 MOVE AWAY Put as much distance between yourself and the suspect package as possible and let the professionals decide how to deal with it.

SUSPECTED SUICIDE BOMBER

1 SUSPICIOUS BEHAVIOUR If you see someone acting suspiciously or in an excessively anxious manner, look closer. Is he perspiring freely or looking around furtively? He may be constantly thrusting his hands in his pockets or nervously fiddling with belongings.

2 SUSPICIOUS CLOTHING A suicide bomber may be wearing bulky clothing that seems inappropriate for the weather conditions or his apparent body size.

3 INFORM THE POLICE Leave immediately and inform the police of your suspicions.

BOMB EXPLODES

1 MOVE AWAY If you hear an explosion, do not move towards it. Terrorists frequently plant several bombs and trigger subsequent explosions to target security forces and other first responders.

2 AVOID GLASS If you are in a building, move away from the windows in case a second blast shatters them, to avoid being hit by flying glass.

3 GET OUTSIDE If you are in any kind of enclosed space, try to get outside. The pressure of an explosion will dissipate more rapidly outside, so you will be safer should another bomb go off.

4 DO NOT PANIC The panic caused by a bomb blast often causes further injuries. Try to stay calm, look around you and think logically about the safest way you can move to safety.

YOU ARE UNDERGROUND

1 DROP TO THE FLOOR If a bomb goes off underground, there will be a lot of smoke and dust. The air may be clearer lower down. Cover your face with a handkerchief or scarf.

2 ORIENTATE YOURSELF If you find yourself in total darkness, try to orientate yourself. **Use your mobile phone for light.** Keep out of passageways to avoid blocking the emergency services.

3 OFFER FIRST AID If you are uninjured, offer first aid to others who are hurt. Try to reassure them that help is on its way and that you will help them.

4 IDENTIFY THE QUICKEST ROUTE TO SAFETY Find the nearest way out. If you have to evacuate a train when it is between stations, try to remember whether you are likely to be closer to one station than the other and then walk in that direction.

YOU ARE TRAPPED

■ **SIGNAL TO RESCUERS** Use the light, music or an alarm on your phone to signal. If underground, tap on a pipe or wall, or whistle. Only shout as a last resort, as you will inhale dust.

⚠ WARNING

Underground trains frequently draw their power from an electrified third rail and if you touch it and another rail or the ground, you will be electrocuted. However, if all the lights are out it is likely that the fail-safe system has activated and the power is off.

what next?

● Shock often prevents you from feeling pain, so examine yourself for signs of injury. Remain calm and try to apply some first aid to yourself, such as using pressure on a wound to stop the bleeding or lying down and raising your legs if you feel faint.

● Move if you can. Emergency services may take time to reach you, especially if they are unsure whether the area is safe. So if you can move, with or without the help of others, try to get away from the site of the explosion.

● Help others. If you are uninjured and you feel that it is safe to do so, you may be able to offer help or first aid to others (see below).

Helping the injured

In the aftermath of a bomb blast, there will be multiple casualties with injuries of varying severity. Make sure that there is no immediate danger from building collapse or fire before offering help.

● **PRIORITISE CASUALTIES** Stay calm and look around you for those most urgently in need of help. Check quiet casualties first: they may be unconscious or in shock. Then help those with severe bleeding.

● **GIVE FIRST AID** If a casualty is unconscious, clear the airway (see pages 14–15) and apply CPR if necessary (see pages 16–17). Staunch bleeding by applying pressure to the wound, avoiding any objects, such as glass, embedded in it (see page 22). Those who are in shock, with no apparent injuries, may have internal bleeding (see pages 38–39).

● **BE AWARE** Many casualties will be unable to hear you because of perforated eardrums. Stay calm and use reassuring body language.

▶▶See also: ATTENTING TO A CASUALTY pp12–13 • INHALING FUMES pp44–45

suspect mail

Improvised Explosive Devices (IEDs) sent through the mail present a danger not only to the intended victim, but to anyone who might inadvertently touch the package. Terrorists have also been known to send deadly biological agents through the mail. If you handle a lot of mail, watch out for the tell-tale signs that suggest you should treat an item with suspicion.

assessment

How to recognise a suspect package:

GREASE MARKS – are there any grease marks or areas of transparency on the packaging?

METHOD OF ADDRESSING – is there anything strange about the way it is addressed? Is it in handwriting you don't recognise?

OTHER SIGNS

● Is there anything odd about the packaging that makes you suspicious?
● Is the package perforated anywhere or are there any signs of wires either under the packaging or protruding slightly?
● Is the package unusually heavy or lop-sided in shape or weight? An effective letter IED typically weighs between 50g and 100g, making it a little heavier than the average letter.
● Has dry transfer lettering been used, such as Letraset?
● Is the package leaking powder or granules? If so, treat it as a hazardous substance (see page 209).

POINT OF ORIGIN – look at the postmark or name of sender. Is it from an unusual point of origin or a sender you do not recognise?

SMELL – does the package have an unusual smell, such as that of almonds or marzipan?

action

1 PUT IT DOWN Immediately you identify a letter or parcel as suspicious, place it gently on a firm, horizontal surface. Try to shield your face and body as you put the parcel down. If it is leaking powder, don't touch the powder and don't let it spread. If possible, place the package in a plastic bag. Turn off ventilation systems in the room.

2 LEAVE THE ROOM Keep everyone away from the package until you have ascertained whether it is safe. Leave the room and shut the door. Lock the door, if possible, and pass the key to the police.

3 CONTACT THE POLICE If the package is marked with the sender's details, contact them to confirm

that the item is genuine. If you cannot confirm that the item is genuine, contact the police and keep everyone at a safe distance until after they have dealt with it. The police will contact specialists who deal with biohazards, if necessary.

 WARNING

Letter bombs can maim and kill. Along with the explosive there may be nails or glass, designed to maximise injury. **Do not flex or bend an envelope in an attempt to work out what is inside: you do not need to open it to set off the bomb.**

DRIVING EMERGENCIES

witness to a **road accident**

The actions you take at the scene of a road-traffic accident can have important consequences for the casualties involved and other road users. Even if you do not have medical training, there are many ways in which you can help the injured. Stay calm, warn other traffic, and call the emergency services.

assessment

Calmly assess the scene. Give the emergency services as many details as possible.

- Is there an immediate danger of fire and/or are there hazardous chemicals involved (see Warning, below right)?
- How many casualties are there and do they include babies and children?
- If there are multiple casualties, give first aid in the following order:
  – To those who are unconscious and not breathing (see pages 12–19)
  – To those who are bleeding severely (see page 22)
  – To those who are unconscious but breathing (see pages 12–19)
  – To those who are injured and conscious (see pages 28–30).

Highway crash

- **DO NOT ALWAYS STOP TO HELP** Stopping to help can cause delays for the rescue services. But if someone is lying injured on the road or in a vehicle that is on fire it is advisable to stop on the hard shoulder or drive to the next exit to call the emergency services.
- **EXIT CAR FROM NON-TRAFFIC SIDE** Always get out of your car on the non-traffic side and ensure any victims do the same. Leave any animals in the vehicle or, in an emergency, keep them under tight control on the roadside.
- **WALK TO AN EMERGENCY PHONE** Use the markers on your side of the highway to direct you to the nearest emergency phone. These are preferred to mobile phones because they give an exact location. If you do use a mobile phone, refer to the highway sign posts to give your location.

action

INVOLVED IN A CRASH

1 **PARK WELL BEHIND THE ACCIDENT** Use your hazard warning lights to alert other traffic. At night, shine your headlights onto the crashed cars.

2 **SAFEGUARD THE SCENE** Except for a motorway crash, place a red warning triangle at least 45m behind the crashed cars in order to prevent another collision. Ideally there should be a second triangle in front of the cars. If possible, ask someone else to stop or slow the traffic.

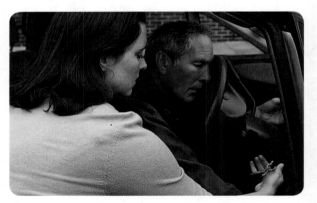

3 **MAKE THE VEHICLE SAFE** Switch off the ignition of the crashed vehicles to reduce the risk of fire, but do not remove the key as this may lock the steering. Check that the handbrake is on. If it is not, put it on.

 WARNING

- If there are any early signs of fire, such as smoke coming from the bonnet, get everyone out of the car and well away. Call the emergency services if the car is on fire; do not try to tackle it yourself.
- **Do not get close to any spillage.** Trucks that carry hazardous materials are marked with codes showing the type of load. Make a note of these symbols and tell the emergency services immediately.

GETTING HELP

1 CALL THE EMERGENCY SERVICES Tell the call-taker how many vehicles are involved, how many casualties there are and whether anyone is trapped. Describe the location as accurately as possible.

2 OFFER TO BE A WITNESS Do not leave the scene of the accident without leaving your contact details. If the police are not involved, offer to act as a witness for the drivers involved.

PEOPLE ARE INJURED

1 DO NOT MOVE THE CASUALTIES Doing so risks making any injuries worse, especially neck injuries where there is a danger of long-term damage to the spine. The only exception is if the injured person is in immediate danger, such as a car being at risk from catching fire (see pages 236–237).

2 CHECK FOR BREATHING Casualties who are quiet are probably the most seriously injured. Ensure they can breathe freely. Carefully loosen any tight clothing around the neck. If they are not breathing, it may be necessary to give rescue breaths (see page 17).

3 CHECK FOR BLEEDING Firm pressure on a wound with a clean cloth will stem bleeding (see pages 96–97). For head wounds, use light pressure as the casualty could have a fractured skull.

4 KEEP THE CASUALTIES WARM Cover the casualties with a blanket or rug to keep them warm and prevent shock. But do not give them anything to eat or drink as they may later need an anaesthetic.

5 REASSURE THE CASUALTIES Be encouraging and tell the casualties that help is on its way. Keep them calm by talking to them.

Being a witness

One of the most valuable ways in which you can help at an accident scene is to offer your services as a witness. In some countries you do not have to give your name and address, but bear in mind that you may have certain responsibilities. Be aware that:

● **THE POLICE MAY BE INVOLVED** The police may ask you to provide a statement if you witness a road traffic accident. If interviewed by the police, you must answer all questions truthfully.

Frequently drivers disagree about the cause of a crash so the whole case can hang on your testimony. Your witness statement may also be used by the insurance company to decide a settlement so it can be crucial in deciding who is held responsible.

● **A COURT CASE CAN FOLLOW** If the case goes to court, you may be summoned to give evidence. You must attend the court. If you fail to attend after receiving a summons, you may be found in contempt of court and punished.

involved in a road accident

Collisions are rarely complete accidents. Two-thirds of them are due to driver error and many others are caused by poor road or driving conditions, or vehicle defects. If you are involved in a road-traffic incident, try to stay calm enough to help others who may be injured and make careful notes of all the information that you may later need to rely on.

action

COLLISION WITH CAR

1 STOP IMMEDIATELY It is an offence not to stop after an accident. You must also stop if you are involved but your car is not damaged.

2 GET HELP Call the emergency services if someone is injured or the road is blocked. Ask for the fire brigade if there is a risk of fire (see pages 236–237). If someone tries to leave the scene without exchanging details take down their car registration number.

3 WARN OTHER TRAFFIC Use any means necessary to alert other road users. Turn on your hazard lights, place warning triangles on the road and try to enlist the help of others to alert oncoming traffic about the collision. It is best not to move any vehicles involved in a collision before the police arrive, if the police are required to attend the accident. In the meantime, note down the vehicles' positions (see step 5).

4 EXCHANGE DETAILS Give your name, address and car registration number to the other motorists or to anyone whose property is damaged. If the vehicle you are driving is not yours, you must give the owner's name. Avoid any arguments and **do not admit liability at the scene of an accident.**

⚠ TAKE CARE
Ensure that the ignition has been turned off in all the vehicles involved in the crash.

5 SKETCH THE SCENE Draw the road layout, pictured from above, showing the cars' positions. Show the direction in which the cars were travelling, the collision points and the road names. Put an X where any witness was present. Compass points are useful as they are often referred to in police reports. You can find the compass points from a map, or print out a map from the internet later, enlarge it and draw on the position of the cars.

6 TAKE PHOTOGRAPHS If you have a camera or a mobile phone with a camera, take photographs of the scene and any damage caused. Take photographs from a variety of different angles.

7 SEEK WITNESSES Write down the names and addresses of any witnesses who would be willing to make a statement either to the police or your insurance company.

COLLISION WITH MOTORBIKE

1 CALL FOR HELP Motorcyclists are far more likely to sustain a serious injury than car drivers because of the lack of protection. Quick action is vital with life-threatening injuries. Call the emergency services as soon as possible.

2 DO NOT REMOVE HELMET Ignore your instincts and leave the helmet on as taking it off can aggravate any head, neck or spine injuries. The only exception is if the motorcyclist has stopped breathing and you need to resuscitate him (see box below).

 TAKE CARE

● As a road user, look out for motorcyclists, especially when you are turning at an intersection. The most common accidents occur at T-intersections where the motorist fails to see a motorbike.
● Bends are a danger area for motorcycles – many accidents occur on a curve or corner.
● As a motorcyclist, you can reduce accident rates by wearing fluorescent clothing and a brightly coloured helmet to make yourself as visible as possible. Dipped headlights in the daytime also aid visibility.

COLLISION WITH PEDESTRIAN

1 STOP IMMEDIATELY Legally you have to stop if someone is injured and give details of the accident. Stop even if you are uncertain whether an injury occurred. Protect the scene with warning triangles and redirect traffic around the injured pedestrian.

2 CALL FOR HELP The pedestrian is the first priority. Call the emergency services and inform them that someone is injured. Do not move the casualty, but reassure him that help is on its way. To prevent him going into shock (see pages 38–39), keep him warm by covering him with a rug or coat.

3 GET WITNESSES Try to find witnesses who are willing to testify on your behalf. This is especially important in cases where a personal injury claim is possible. Write down all names and addresses at the scene as it is easy to lose contact with witnesses in the confusion following a collision.

If you need to resuscitate

If the casualty is talking, it means he is breathing, so do not remove his helmet. The only circumstances in which you should remove a motorcyclist's helmet is if he is not breathing and you need to resuscitate him (see pages 14–17). To remove the helmet carefully you will need help. One person should support the casualty's head and neck, while the other carefully undoes the strap.

1 SUPPORT NECK AND JAW Place your fingers, spread wide, under the base of the helmet to support the casualty's neck and hold his jaw firmly.

2 CAREFULLY REMOVE HELMET Get your helper to tilt the helmet clear of the chin, then clear of the base of the skull. He should then lift the helmet off slowly while you continue to support the neck and jaw.

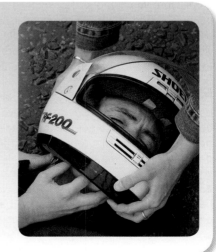

after the accident

Sorting out the paperwork following an accident can be time-consuming but it is worth doing immediately. Fill in the accident report supplied by your insurance company as soon as you can so that you do not forget key pieces of information. Do not admit liability, even if the accident appears to be your fault. The issue of blame is best left to the insurers – and the courts – to sort out.

REPORTING THE ACCIDENT

1 INFORM THE POLICE **You must report the incident to the police as soon as possible or at least within 24 hours** if it has caused injury or damaged another car or property, or if alcohol or drugs were involved.

2 DO NOT ADMIT LIABILITY Never admit liability even if you think you are in the wrong. If you admit liability, you are prejudging the issue and this may affect any insurance claim.

3 SEEK MEDICAL HELP Following the forceful jerk of a collision, you could suffer whiplash or other injuries. Do not ignore even minor aches and pains as these can turn into chronic complaints in the weeks ahead. Remember that doctors' records are extremely important in any compensation claim.

4 GET A REPAIR ESTIMATE Get at least two estimates for repairs. But do not have any repairs done if you intend to get the insurance company to pay for them. The insurers may want to assess the damage themselves.

5 DRIVE AGAIN Many people do not want to get back behind the wheel after having a road accident. The only way to conquer your fear is to drive again. Ask someone to be a passenger if you lack confidence.

SETTLING YOUR CLAIM

1 CONTACT YOUR INSURER Inform your insurer within 24 hours of the accident. Ask them to send you an accident and claim report. Check your entitlement: you may be allowed a replacement car for the time it takes to repair yours or have personal injury cover.

2 DECIDE WHETHER TO CLAIM Telling the insurer does not mean that you have to claim. That will depend on the costs of the repair and the effect on your no-claims bonus. The insurer will explain how much of your no-claims bonus you will lose if you make a claim. Check your excess as well as this will affect how much you have to pay.

3 RECORD YOUR EXPENSES Keep a careful record of all extra spending, including taxi receipts, transport costs and prescription charges, as these can often be reclaimed on your insurance policy.

How to make a claim

- **ACCIDENT REPORT** Fill in and return the accident report from your insurance company.
- **GATHER EVIDENCE** Note down anything else you think is relevant. A sketch of the accident scene and/or photographs (see page 222) are good evidence to support a claim.
- **DO NOT CORRESPOND WITH THE OTHER DRIVER** Pass on any letters straight to your insurer. Do not correspond with the other driver's insurer.
- **POLICE PROSECUTION** Let your insurer know if you receive a police prosecution notice.
- **CAR VALUATION** The insurance company may pay 'market value' for any written-off car, but it is likely to be less than the replacement cost. Talk to your motoring organisation if you are unhappy with the valuation – the insurers may improve the offer if you dispute it.

unable to stop

Although it rarely happens with modern cars, it is possible for an accelerator to jam and for the brakes to fail. There are specific driving skills that can help to prevent serious accidents and possible injury in this emergency situation.

TIME TO ACT Alert other drivers by sounding your horn and flashing your lights. In extreme emergencies, phone the police who may be able to clear the road ahead.

action

ACCELERATOR GETS STUCK

1 **TAP THE PEDAL** Depress the pedal slightly – it may come unjammed. If that does not work, hook your toes under the pedal and try to lift it up. Ask a passenger to see if anything is stuck under the pedal, such as the floor mat, and to remove it.

2 **USE THE BRAKES** If the accelerator is still jammed, leave the vehicle in gear and brake to a stop.

3 **DO NOT TURN OFF IGNITION** Turning off the engine could disable the power steering, making the car extremely difficult to manoeuvre. Some older or diesel-powered cars may not respond to this. If it is imperative, turn the key one notch to kill the engine and allow the car to decelerate. Do not turn the key so far as to engage any steering lock.

4 **SHIFT TO NEUTRAL** This action should be a last resort as it can cause the car to over-rev, which can destroy the engine, but it should slow the car down.

BRAKES FAIL

1 **PUMP THE BRAKES** Press down the brake pedal, lift your foot and press it down again. Keep pumping. You cannot usually pump anti-lock brakes, but it may sometimes work in the case of brake failure.

2 **SHIFT TO LOWER GEAR** Change down to a lower gear – second or third – bringing the clutch up slowly and smoothly. This will slow the vehicle down and allow you to use the handbrake to slow down. In cars with an automatic gearbox, select L or 2.

3 **APPLY HANDBRAKE** As the car slows, use your handbrake to help stop the car. Keep a firm grip on the steering wheel as the use of the handbrake may cause the rear wheels to lock and the car to skid.

4 **DO NOT TURN OFF IGNITION** As tempting as it may be, this will only make matters worse because you will not be able to use the engine to slow down the car as you shift to a lower gear. The steering could also lock if you switch off the ignition.

5 **LOOK FOR AN ESCAPE ROUTE** If all other action fails, the only option is to use a slope or a bank to help stop the car. Drive gradually up at an angle to prevent rolling the car. Scraping along a hedge or a fence may also slow you down.

⚠ WARNING

● **Never ignore a warning light on the dashboard.** If the brake system alert comes on when you are driving, get the brakes and fluid levels checked as soon as possible.

● The moment you start to slow down, signal to show that you intend to pull over as the car could decelerate rapidly once you take action.

▶▶See also: CAR BREAKDOWN pp232–233

car jacking

If you live in or are travelling through a country where car jacking is prevalent, be on the alert. There are things you can do to lessen your chances of being a target, but if someone tries to steal your car by force, always put your safety first.

WATCHPOINT Even if you are getting out for just a moment, lock your car and take the keys with you. Most insurance companies refuse to pay if the keys were left in the car.

precautions

- When driving, always keep the doors locked and the windows never more than partially open, especially when driving through urban areas. Make sure that your boot is also locked.
- Anticipate traffic conditions that might force you to stop. Move to a middle lane if there is one, and brake early, so you can keep rolling for as long as possible. If you have to stop, leave sufficient space for you to manoeuvre around the car in front, should you need to drive away.
- If a stranger asks for directions or help, talk to him through a partially open window and keep your doors locked.
- If you suspect that you are being followed, drive to a police station. Or drive to a safe public place and then use your mobile phone, or a landline, to call the police.
- A car jacker may bump a vehicle from behind. When the driver gets out, the thieves strike. Although you should always stop at the scene of an accident, if you are suspicious, or fear for your safety, drive to the nearest police station.

action

How you react to a car jacking will depend on whether the car jacker is armed. If he is, do not take risks. Stay calm and comply with his demands. Remember that possessions can be replaced, a life cannot. Put your safety first.

CAR JACKER APPROACHES

1 DRIVE AWAY If someone you suspect to be a car jacker comes towards your car, drive away quickly.

2 MAKE A NOISE Sound your horn to attract the maximum amount of attention. Then report the attack as soon as possible to the police.

be aware

- Be extra alert at 'ambush sites' or places where you have to slow down, such as intersections that are controlled by traffic lights or pedestrian crossings.
- Car jackers may loiter near cash machines, roadside shops, petrol-station forecourts and car-wash facilities as many motorists leave the keys in their cars when at these sites.
- When returning to your car, stay alert. Walk confidently, key in hand, get in quickly, lock the doors and drive off as soon as possible.
- Never leave children or pets alone in your car, even when loading or unloading.
- When selling a car think twice before offering a test drive. Take someone else with you and do not leave the keys in the ignition when changing seats. Do not let the keys out of your sight in case they are copied or switched.

CAR JACKER GETS IN

1 GET OUT AND AWAY If a car jacker gets into your car or orders you out with a weapon, get out or away from the vehicle at once. Do nothing to stop him taking the car.

2 IF YOU CANNOT GET AWAY Remain calm and listen to the car jacker. Don't make any sudden moves and avoid eye contact. Proceed as if in a hostage situation (see pages 294–295). If ordered to drive, do so responsibly.

3 ONCE RELEASED As soon as you are sure the car jacker has driven off, report the incident to the police. You may find that you need to seek counselling for trauma.

road-rage attack

Once behind the wheel of their cars, many people behave with uncharacteristic aggression. If you find yourself in a threatening encounter with another road user, it is always best to take defensive action and prioritise your safety.

 WATCHPOINT If you are being followed or feel threatened, call the police on a hands-free mobile or from a safe public place. Give your location and direction of travel.

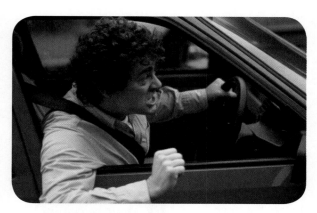

action

FOLLOWED BY ANGRY DRIVER

1 DRIVE NORMALLY Do not let the other driver's actions make you lose concentration. Focus on driving safely. **Avoid making eye contact with the other driver** as this only personalises the conflict.

2 TAKE A DETOUR If another driver persists in following you, try to deter them by taking a small detour. But stick to busy areas (see box, below).

3 DRIVE TO A PLACE OF SAFETY If the other driver continues to intimidate you, drive to a police station. Or drive to a place of safety and then use your mobile phone, or a landline, to call for assistance.

Escape manoeuvres

If another driver is angry enough to try to force you to stop or to drive you off the road, your priority should be to get to somewhere safe. Stick to main roads that are likely to have plenty of witnesses and CCTV cameras. Heavy traffic will provide witnesses and will allow you to put cars between you and the other driver.

CAR HIT BY ANGRY DRIVER

■ **DRIVE AWAY** Although by law you must report all accidents, if you suspect you were hit deliberately, or fear for your safety, do not stop or get out. Keep your doors locked and drive to the nearest police station or place of safety.

■ **STAY IN YOUR CAR** If your car is undrivable or you are boxed in and the other driver gets out of his car, stay in yours. Depending on how threatening the behaviour is, try to appease the angry driver through a partially opened window. Alternatively, sound your horn and activate your hazard warning lights to attract attention, and phone the police immediately for assistance.

■ **MAKE A STATEMENT** Report a road-rage incident to the police and give them as much information as you can about the offender and/or vehicle.

 WARNING

If someone is following you and behaving in an aggressive manner, do not drive to your home. You do not want them to know where you live.

for next time...

● Some drivers seem to enjoy provoking conflict. Be alert for signs of erratic or aggressive driving and make an effort to keep out of the way, even if it delays your journey by a few minutes.
● Keep your own emotions under control. If you react aggressively with an offensive gesture or a long blast of the horn, you may provoke a violent response.
● If you make a driving error, raise a hand to acknowledge it and apologise.

▶▶See also: **KIDNAPPED OVERSEAS** pp294–295 **227**

tyre emergencies

Punctures and blow-outs are less common in modern tyres but flat or damaged tyres are still the second most common reason for calling out a breakdown patrol. Check all your tyres regularly for signs of wear and tear and know what to do if a tyre bursts while you are driving or you need to change one in an emergency.

precautions

- Regularly inspect your tyres for cuts, cracks and bulges. These can all cause blow-outs.
- Check for any nails, stones or anything else piercing the tyre casing. Change the wheel and repair any tyre damage.
- Check for uneven tread wear on all four tyres. Uneven tyre wear could be a sign of faults in the braking, steering or suspension systems, or that the wheels are not properly aligned.
- Always ensure that your spare wheel is adequately inflated. Make sure that the jack and wheel brace are in good condition.
- Fit reinforced 'run-flat' tyres. Many cars now have these as standard. While more expensive to replace, these should allow you to continue driving for up to 50km if you have a puncture.

- Always keep tyres at the pressure recommended by the manufacturer. Check them when the tyres are cold before you set off, as **warm or hot tyres can give a misleading reading**.
- Change your tyres before the tread depth is worn down so that you keep a good grip on the road. Check your road safety code for legal tread depths.
- Check the pressure and tread every 2 weeks, and always before a long journey.

action

FRONT TYRE BURSTS

1 AVOID BRAKING If a front tyre bursts, the car will pull heavily to the side on which the tyre has burst. Grip the steering wheel tightly and do not change gear. Ease off the accelerator and, if possible, try to avoid braking. The aim is to let the car lose speed naturally.

2 COUNTER THE PULL To slow down, take your foot off the accelerator and clutch and turn the steering wheel smoothly to counter the pull. If you do use your brake, apply it very gently.

3 PULL OVER When you have slowed sufficiently, signal and steer the car to the side of the road to pull up. Try to stop on hard ground rather than soft as you need a firm base to change the wheel. Put on your hazard warning lights.

BACK TYRE BURSTS

1 BRAKE GENTLY If a back tyre bursts, the back of the car may slide to one side. The car will have a tendency to weave, especially at speeds over 80km/h. Brake gently; if you brake hard, you may lose control of the car. Changing to a lower gear will help in a front-wheel-drive car provided you can control the steering with one hand.

2 MAINTAIN A FIRM GRIP Keep looking ahead and keep a firm grip on the steering wheel to maintain a straight course. If you do have to brake quickly, be prepared to counter a slide at the back.

3 SLOW DOWN SMOOTHLY The aim is to slow down gradually, pulling up as soon as it is safe to do so. Park the car well off the road if you intend to change the wheel yourself. Put on your hazard warning lights.

EMERGENCY TYRE CHANGE

1 SWITCH OFF ENGINE Put the handbrake on, put the car in first gear or park for an automatic. Remove any heavy luggage and the spare wheel. If necessary put on your hazard warning lights.

2 LOOSEN WHEEL NUTS Remove the hubcap, if necessary, and loosen the wheel nuts by half a turn before attempting to use the jack.

3 DEACTIVATE AIR SUSPENSION If your car has air suspension, check the manual for how to deactivate it before jacking up the car, or you will not be able to raise the car high enough to remove the wheel.

4 JACK UP CAR Check the manual to locate the wheel bolts and the correct places to put the jack. Use the jacking point nearest the wheel you want to change (usually just behind the front wheel or just in front of the rear wheel). Wind or pump up the jack.

Using a jack safely

Jacking up a car is the single most risky part of the whole operation. For your own safety:

● **ENSURE SURFACE IS LEVEL** Only ever use a jack on a firm, level surface.
● **POSITION SECURELY** Make sure that the jack is securely positioned before raising the car.
● **EMERGENCY USE** The jacks supplied with most cars are for emergency use only and not designed for working underneath a car. Never get under a car that is supported only by a jack.

5 REMOVE WHEEL Remove the nuts completely, taking the top one off last and ensure they do not roll away. Remove the wheel with the deflated tyre.

6 REPLACE WHEEL Fit the spare wheel. Replace the nuts, tightening them up by hand. Work on opposite pairs at the same time so that the wheel goes on evenly. Tighten the nuts clockwise with the wheel brace. Lower the car with the jack and tighten the nuts completely. Place the hubcap back on, if you have one. Check that the nuts are at the correct torque at a garage as soon as possible.

 TAKE CARE

● In very hot weather, as the temperature outside rises, air pressure in the tyres increases. Over-inflation can lead to loss of grip so check your tyres are correctly inflated.
● If you are not confident about changing a tyre, call your breakdown service. They will have no objection to carrying out this procedure.

controlling a **skid**

Loss of control from skidding usually results from driving too fast for the road conditions. The tyres lose grip, leaving the vehicle in a seemingly uncontrollable slide. How you react depends on which wheels are causing the skid. Keep a cool head because a violent or sudden reaction can be extremely dangerous.

action

FRONT-WHEEL SKID

In a front-wheel skid, the car keeps going straight on even though you have turned the wheel to navigate a bend.

1 SLOW DOWN The natural reaction is to slam on the brakes. Do not do this as it could cause the rear wheels to skid as well. Instead, ease off the accelerator, look well ahead and, if in a manual vehicle, push in the clutch.

2 STRAIGHTEN THE WHEELS Reduce the amount that you have turned the car to help you regain grip on the front wheels. It will feel as if you are running wide of the corner.

3 REGAIN CONTROL Once you have regained grip, you can steer gently in the direction that you originally intended. Do not oversteer or you risk losing control of the car again.

REAR-WHEEL SKID

In a rear-wheel skid, the back of the car feels as if it is breaking away and could even spin round.

1 STEER INTO THE SKID As the rear tyres lose grip on the road, the back starts to swing out. Turn the steering wheel in the direction that the rear wheels are sliding. So, if the back is sliding to the left, you should steer to the left. Look well ahead and, if in a manual vehicle, push in the clutch.

2 DO NOT OVERREACT Do not turn the wheel too far. If you steer too hard into a skid you could easily set off a secondary skid in the opposite direction, causing complete loss of control.

3 BRING THE STEERING BACK As you regain control, you will feel the wheels gain traction and you can bring them back smoothly towards the centre.

⚠ TAKE CARE

Front-, rear- and four-wheel drive vehicles behave slightly differently in a skid, but the basic principles of controlling the skid are the same. Familiarise yourself with the way your vehicle handles and read the owner's manual for further information.

DIRECTION OF SKID

4 DRIVE ON As the car moves back on course, accelerate gently. Maintain reduced speed until you have complete control and drive according to the conditions.

4 ACCELERATE GENTLY When all four wheels are in line, gradually increase speed again. Keep your speed down until you have full control of the car.

precautions

● Recognise the danger signs. Pay particular attention to the weather conditions and road surface: ice, snow or standing water are all especially dangerous. Black ice (see page 245) is a major risk because it is so difficult to spot.
● **Take special care when rain falls after a long dry period. Oil and dust mix with the water to create a lethal slippery surface.**
● Heavy acceleration, sudden braking and sharp changes of direction all cause the tyres to lose grip. Smooth, calm, steady driving is the best way to avoid skidding in the first place.
● Look after your car carefully. Worn tyres, badly maintained brakes or poorly aligned steering can cause, or aggravate, a skid.
● Many drivers react too slowly because they fail to recognise the signs of a skid until it is too late. If you are concerned or frequently drive long distances, consider taking an advanced driving course at a driving school.

Four-wheel skid

Harsh braking can cause all four wheels to lock, leaving the car to slide forward at speed. The only way to regain control is to release the brakes then reapply them more gently.

● **STOP BRAKING** Release the brakes until the tyres start to roll again and re-establish their grip on the road. **Do not push down the clutch.**
● **PRESS SMOOTHLY** Most vehicles are now fitted with anti-lock braking systems (ABS), which ensure that the wheels will not lock when you reapply the brakes. Instead, ABS automatically 'pumps' the brakes to guard against wheel lock. If you have ABS, simply press down on the brake pedal in a smooth motion and keep the pedal depressed until the skid is under control.
● **BRAKE GENTLY** If you do not have ABS, reapply the brakes with a pumping action, repeatedly pushing them on and off in order to avoid locking the wheels again. This is known as 'cadence' braking. Look well ahead.
● **STRAIGHTEN THE WHEELS** When you regain control over steering, straighten up the wheels. This should allow you to get back on course.

car **breakdown**

Breakdown services are called out to thousands of stranded drivers every day. A breakdown can be an emergency, especially if you are alone or in an exposed or dangerous position close to fast or heavy traffic. Your first priority should always be your own – and your passengers' – safety, then you can move on to dealing with the problem with your car.

precautions

- Know your car. Keep your owner's manual in your car. It will tell you everything from the jacking points for changing a wheel to what the warning lights mean. A basic car maintenance manual is also handy for routine checks.
- Keep a set of jump leads. A flat battery is a very common cause of callouts for breakdown patrols.
- Each time your car has a service, check that the battery terminals have been cleaned and protected from corrosion.
- Motoring organisations say that 90 per cent of callouts are due to inadequate servicing, so regular checks are advisable. Ensure that your car is fully serviced annually, or according to the mileage or at the frequency stated in your driver's handbook, in addition to any legally required roadworthiness checks.

action

BREAKDOWN ON MAIN ROAD

1 **STOP AT FIRST HINT OF TROUBLE** Look for a safe place to stop the moment a dashboard warning light flashes or odd noises start coming from the engine. Get your car off the road and into a lay-by or service station forecourt if possible. Finding a safe place to stop is far better than having to stop on the highway.

2 **GET OUT OF DANGER** Get everyone out of the car first, by the non-traffic side where possible. Warn other traffic by using your hazard lights and place a warning triangle (if it is safe to do so) at least 45m behind your vehicle. **Never stand between your vehicle and oncoming traffic.** At night, turn on the sidelights and wear a reflective jacket if you have one.

3 **LOCATE THE FAULT** If it is something simple, like running out of petrol or a puncture, you may be able to get back on the road without help. But never attempt to fix a puncture on the driver's side when you are parked by the side of the road.

4 **CALL A BREAKDOWN SERVICE** If you cannot fix the fault yourself, call a breakdown service (see page 339). Even if you are not a member of a motoring organisation, most will allow you to join on the spot – though you may have to pay a supplement.

 TAKE CARE
- Carry a light-coloured waterproof coat in the car and a high-visibility jacket in case you break down at night or in bad weather and have to go for help. A torch (flashlight) is also an essential part of any emergency kit (see box, opposite).
- If you are driving in bad weather and are likely to encounter snow and ice, assemble a winter survival kit (see page 244).

BREAKDOWN ON MOTORWAY

1 PULL OVER Leave the motorway at the next exit or pull into a service station if you can. If forced to use the hard shoulder, pull over as far as you can and near an emergency phone if possible.

2 LEAVE CAREFULLY Turn on your hazard warning lights and sidelights and leave the vehicle by the non-traffic door. Make sure your passengers do the same. If you have a reflective jacket, put it on.

3 KEEP ANIMALS IN THE CAR Any animals should be left in the car, but leave a window slightly ajar. If it is essential to let them out of the car, keep them under tight control on the verge.

4 CALL FOR HELP Locate the nearest emergency phone. On motorways, they are spaced at regular intervals. Use these phones to report your breakdown rather than a mobile phone as they contact the highway agency directly and give your exact location.

5 DO NOT ATTEMPT ANY REPAIRS Return to your car and wait near your vehicle well away from the motorway and the hard shoulder. Up on the bank, or behind the barrier is the safest option, in case other traffic crashes into your immobile vehicle.

Emergency kit

Having the right equipment can make all the difference between being stuck beside the road for hours and getting to your destination quickly. Consider carrying these items.

Essential:
- Torch (flashlight)
- Basic tool kit
- Jack and wheelbrace
- Jump leads
- Duplicate ignition key
- Warning triangles
- Reflective clothing
- First-aid kit.

Useful:
- Owner's manual
- Tow rope
- Duct (gaffer) tape
- Water-repellent lubricant
- Fire extinguisher
- Blanket
- 5-litre petrol can
- Spare bulbs
- Spare fuses.

If you do not have the right equipment, here are some good ways to improvise.

- **DUCT (GAFFER) TAPE** Temporarily stops leaks in cars and is ideal for patching up holes in radiator hoses while you drive to a garage.
- **WIRE** Carry a small coil of thin insulated wire for electrical repairs or for tying up loose parts, such as trailing wires.
- **BATTERY CONNECTIONS** If the battery connections are corroded, clean them inside and out with glass or paper.

 WARNING

If you feel at risk from another person, even if they appear to be trying to help, return to your car by the non-traffic side, fasten your seatbelt and lock all doors. Do not try even the simplest repairs. Wait for professional help to arrive. If you feel threatened, use your mobile phone to call the police.

▶▶See also: **DRIVING IN ADVERSE WEATHER** pp240–242 • **MOTORING PROBLEMS OVERSEAS** p289

shattered **windscreen**

Almost all modern cars are now fitted with laminated glass that will crack or chip rather than shatter completely. But even a cracked or chipped windscreen requires prompt repair as it can obscure your vision and cause an accident. It may also be illegal to carry on driving depending on the size or position of the chip.

precautions

- Fit laminated glass on an older car. This multiple layered windscreen has a plastic film sandwiched in between the glass to prevent the screen from shattering. No matter how hard they are hit, these kinds of screens should only crack or chip and not shatter.
- Drive slowly on a newly surfaced road to prevent loose chips hitting the windscreen. Maintain a good distance from the car in front.

- Do not ignore a chip because it can weaken the glass and allow water to seep between the layers, causing long-term damage to the windscreen.
- A chip can also cause a vehicle to fail its mandatory roadworthiness checks.
- Check your insurance policy to see whether it covers windscreen repair. Many insurers will cover the cost of repairing chipped glass (or shattered windscreens) with no risk to your no-claims bonus.

action

WINDSCREEN SHATTERS

1 **PULL UP** The first priority is to stop safely at the side of the road. **Avoid the temptation to punch out the glass as by doing this you risk cutting your hand.** Instead slow down and lean forward to get as good a view of your surroundings as you can and then find a safe place to stop. You may be able to steer by looking through the side window.

2 **CLEAR THE GLASS** Stuff rags or newspapers down the heater and demister vents to prevent shards of glass getting into the heating system. Spread newspaper or a blanket on the bonnet. Protect your hand with gloves or rags and push the glass out onto the bonnet. Alternatively, gently tap the glass out with a spanner or jack handle.

3 **GET A NEW WINDSCREEN** Drive slowly to the nearest service station. If you do drive on, make sure that all the glass fragments have been removed from the windscreen surround as these can get blown into your face. Alternatively, call a specialist to fit an emergency windscreen at the roadside, although this can be expensive at night and on weekends. Check your breakdown service as it may offer a discount.

Repairing a chip

Chips can be repaired but get professional advice first as many windscreen repairs are covered by car insurance.

- **SIZE OF CHIP** A chip larger than about 2.5cm across is likely to be too big for repair. You will need to replace the windscreen.

A car with a chipped windscreen will fail its roadworthiness check depending on the position and size of the chip, particularly if it affects the driver's critical vision area (CVA).

locked out of car

The cost of replacing lost car keys rises sharply each year as car-entry and anti-theft systems become more sophisticated. Always keep a spare set of keys and choose a breakdown recovery service with lockout cover.

WATCHPOINT Opt for a breakdown or car insurance policy that has a 'keycare' option. This covers you against locksmith charges and the cost of replacing a lost key.

precautions

- Make sure that you know the whereabouts of your spare key. Calling out a locksmith can be very expensive.
- If you do not have a spare set, get one cut. Copies of modern keys that have chips to operate the alarm and immobiliser system can be expensive but avoid the cost and inconvenience of having to break in to your car.
- Conceal your keys in a safe place at home as burglars may take them and also steal your car.
- Keep a copy of your keycode as this will save time and money if you need a replacement. Technology is developing all the time for car keys. Some modern anti-theft systems have rolling keycodes that switch each time you use them. Older cars, with remote-entry systems, tend to have fixed keycodes.
- Check your breakdown policy carefully. Some insurers will tow you to the nearest service station while others will refuse to do anything other than call a locksmith for you.

 TAKE CARE

If you are buying a secondhand car, make sure that it has a spare key.

 WARNING

Replacing the master set of keys for a modern car, with a sophisticated alarm and immobiliser system, can entail reprogramming – or even refitting – the car's computer system. This can be time-consuming and very expensive.

action

LOST KEY

■ **CALL YOUR BREAKDOWN SERVICE** Phone your breakdown service in case they can help. They may be able to tow you to the nearest service station, which could have tools for getting into locked cars.

■ **PHONE A LOCKSMITH** Get quotes from three locksmiths as prices vary greatly, especially at night and on weekends. They will need to know the model number and the registration date to give you a quote. Some are able to cut keys at the roadside.

■ **CONSIDER BREAKING IN** If you are forced to break a window – because a child or animal is trapped in the car, for example – make sure it is a side one, as these are cheaper to replace. Check if your insurance covers you for such an action.

FROZEN LOCK

■ **USE A HAIR DRYER** If you are at home, a hair dryer is probably the most effective way to defrost a frozen lock, providing you can get a safe extension cord to the car. Alternatively, you could heat the end of the key with a match or a lighter before inserting it into the lock.

■ **LUBRICATE** Squirt a few drops of lubricant into the door. Anti-freeze or lighter fuel may also work. Once open, to prevent the lock from refreezing, squirt a drop or two of oil on the key and turn it in the lock a few times to coat the interior.

 WARNING

Most side windows are still made of toughened glass. As an anti-theft measure in new cars, motoring organisations recommend replacing this with laminated glass as it is more difficult to break.

car fire

Every year there are thousands of vehicle fires, mainly as a result of mechanical and electrical faults. In a worst case scenario, where the fire spreads to the fuel tank, the whole car may explode. Motorhomes are particularly vulnerable to electrical fires and – as with all vehicles – regular maintenance is the key to spotting potential problems.

precautions

- As well as regular maintenance and replacing faulty parts, check your vehicle for worn fuel pipes. Fuel leaks in the vehicle's engine are a common cause of fire. All fuel lines should be inspected regularly.
- Take particular care where you park. **Many fires occur when a vehicle is parked in long grass.** The catalytic converter on the underside of a car gets extremely hot and can cause grass or piles of dry leaves to ignite.
- Carry spare fuel only in an approved container. Secure it in an upright position to prevent it sliding around in the boot.
- Do not use heat, exposed flames or welding tools near the fuel tank or feed pipes.

Fire extinguishers

- Carry a fire extinguisher. Fire experts recommend a dry-powder extinguisher with a capacity of at least 1.5kg. A bigger, bulkier fire extinguisher can also make a useful escape tool as it can be used to smash a window.
- Make sure that the fire extinguisher is stored securely in an easily accessible place, such as under the dashboard or fixed under the driver's seat. Never keep extinguishers in the boot.
- Be wary of smaller car fire extinguishers. Some last for just eight seconds, which is probably not enough time to put out a fire.
- Most extinguishers require an annual inspection by the manufacturer to ensure that they are functioning properly.

action

CAR ON FIRE

1 SWITCH OFF IGNITION If you are driving pull up by the side of the road at the first sign of fire. Turn off the ignition to shut down the fuel pump. Do not remove the key or you could lock the steering.

2 KEEP THE BONNET CLOSED Do not be tempted to open the bonnet (hood) as this will cause the flames to flare up. But do pull the bonnet release catch to enable the fire brigade to access any fire.

3 GET PASSENGERS TO SAFETY Get everyone out of the car and well away from the vehicle. If you have stopped at the roadside, their exit should be from the non-traffic side of the vehicle. Take particular care with petrol-fuelled vehicles as they are more explosive than cars fuelled by diesel, which is more difficult to ignite.

4 GET HELP Call the fire brigade and ask passengers to flag down any passing vehicles – especially trucks – as they may have a fire extinguisher. Even if you already have one, two extinguishers are better than one.

5 TACKLE ONLY SMALL FIRES Only tackle a fire in its very early stages and if you believe it is safe to do so. A small fire, such as smouldering upholstery or wiring, can be tackled with a fire extinguisher or smothered with a fire blanket before the flames take a significant hold. If the fire is under the bonnet, aim the extinguisher through the radiator grille or under the edge of the bonnet. If the fire is under the chassis and threatens to reach the fuel tank, abandon any attempt to fight the fire and get well clear of the vehicle.

6 CHECK THE DAMAGE Do not drive the car again until it has had a full safety check by an auto electrician or a qualified mechanic.

GET HELP The fire brigade offers safety advice to prevent car fires occurring. Call them for advice on which type of fire extinguisher is suitable for your vehicle.

TIME TO ACT Take particular care in the danger zone behind the fuel tank (usually at the rear, but do not assume that). If the tank explodes, the blast may reach up to 30m.

WATCHPOINT Unattended cooking is the main cause of fires in caravans and motorhomes. Never leave a cooking appliance unattended while it is in use.

USE A FIRE EXTINGUISHER

1 **PREPARE THE EXTINGUISHER** Ideally, you should have checked how to use the extinguisher when you first installed it. Prepare the extinguisher carefully, following the instructions. Make sure that the extinguisher is always maintained in line with the manufacturer's instructions.

2 **AIM AT THE BASE OF THE FIRE** **Direct the extinguisher at the base of the fire.** Be methodical. Start at the edge of the fire closest to you and sweep the extinguisher back and forth until the fire is out. Do not spray aimlessly at the flames as this will waste the contents.

3 **WATCH FOR FLARE-UPS** Remember that fires can often flare up after they seem to have been put out. A common mistake is to use the entire contents of the extinguisher in one frantic first effort to put out the flames. Try to save some of the contents to tackle flare-ups.

4 **CHECK THE VEHICLE** Even if you think you have put the fire out, call the fire brigade to check over the vehicle and ensure that the fire is fully extinguished.

Motorhomes

The presence of propane gas for cookers makes motorhomes especially prone to fire incidents. There is also a greater risk of electrical fires in motorhomes because of their complex wiring systems.

● Make sure that you have smoke and gas detectors fitted.
● Ensure that all the equipment is installed and inspected by a qualified technician.
● Be careful about what you cook. Stove-top fires are a major risk in caravans and motorhomes due to low ceilings.
● Purchase a large-capacity fire extinguisher as flames can take hold quickly in the confined space. Know where it is kept and how to use it, especially if you are renting the vehicle.
● Only keep the gas cylinders that you need rather than storing several in the motorhome.
● Never smoke or use candles in a motorhome because of the heightened risk of fire.

sinking car

If your car plunges into water, you must escape quickly. You have between 30 seconds and 2 minutes before the car sinks. Once it is submerged, you can survive for only 3–5 minutes without oxygen so you must act fast.

TIME TO ACT Cars usually sink engine-end first, leaving an air pocket at the other end of the car. If the car sinks, put your head in the air pocket while you try to escape.

be aware

- Most instances of cars sinking occur in lakes and rivers. Driving in low-lying countryside where there are roadside drains is another danger.
- Speeding or unsafe driving is another factor in most water fatalities so keep your speed down near lakes or rivers.
- Listen carefully to weather warnings, especially when driving at night in flood-hit areas or places prone to flash floods.

action

1 DO NOT WASTE TIME Do not phone for help – rescuers are unlikely to be able to reach you in time. Wait until you are back on dry land before calling the emergency services.

2 TURN ON LIGHTS Unbuckle the seat belts and turn on the interior and exterior lights. Do not turn off the engine. Car electrical systems are built to withstand water so should keep working. Lights will help rescuers find the car and prevent the occupants from panicking.

3 TRY TO OPEN A WINDOW Tests show that windows represent your best chance of escape, as water pressure holds the doors shut. Even if you did manage to open a door, the rush of water into the car would cause the car to sink very quickly. Open the window as soon as possible. Keeping your engine running means that electric windows should continue to work, even when the car is sinking.

4 WAIT FOR PRESSURE TO EQUALISE Wait until the car fills with water and the water pressure equalises between the inside and the outside. Try not to panic and keep calm as the car fills. Hold onto the open window edge, or the door handle so you do not get disorientated if the car sinks at an angle.

5 SMASH A SIDE WINDOW If the window jams, kick it as hard as you can to smash the glass. Side windows are usually weakest; try the corners first where the glass is easiest to break. If you have a centre punch or wheel nut lock these may also be effective to break the glass. Expect a rush of water when you open the window.

6 LEAVE THE CAR Take a deep breath just before the water rises almost to the roof, then you may be able to open a door or window. Expect some resistance as you push a door against the water outside. Push off from the car and swim to the surface.

■ **IF THERE ARE CHILDREN IN THE CAR** Get any children out of their car seat or seat belt and into the seat next to you. Once you have the window open and the pressure has equalised, push them out of the escape window first before following them to the surface.

 WARNING

Prepare and discuss an escape plan with your family. If everyone in a car keeps calm and follows an agreed plan, escape and survival from a sinking car is possible.

stuck on a **level crossing**

Every year people die on rail level crossings. Car driver error causes the majority of accidents. Never rush to beat the lights or take risks for the sake of gaining a few minutes. Take extra care on unmanned or open crossings. If you are unlucky enough to stall or break down on a level crossing, save yourself rather than the car.

be aware

- Level crossings are considered the biggest safety risk on the whole of the rail network. Every year vehicles get hit on level crossings. The chances of a motorist surviving such a crash are minimal.
- Approach all level crossings with care at a moderate speed. Only drive onto a level crossing if you can see that the exit ahead is clear.
- Do not park on the approach to a level crossing.
- Never overtake on a level crossing.
- Never think about jumping the

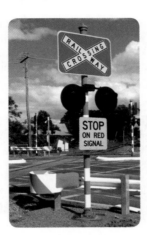

barriers. There can be as little as 27 seconds between the lights starting to flash and the train crossing.
- Know your barriers. Most have traffic-light signals with twin flashing red stop lights, and a sound alarm such as a clanging bell to warn pedestrians of approaching trains.
- Some level crossings have full barriers; some half barriers (barriers that extend over one lane on each side). Open level crossings with no barriers, gates, lights or attendants are by far the most dangerous.

action

BREAKDOWN ON CROSSING

1 GET AWAY FROM THE CAR Get everybody out of the car and away from the level crossing as quickly as possible. Make sure that you are all a safe distance from the crossing.

2 CALL THE POLICE There may not be a phone at the barrier, so use your mobile phone to call the police. Never try to move your car before contacting the train control.

BARRIERS COME DOWN

1 ABANDON THE CAR If you are caught on the crossing and the lights start flashing and the barriers come down, the first priority is to abandon the car. With modern crossings there is only a matter of seconds before the train arrives with potentially devastating consequences when it hits the car.

2 GET AWAY FROM THE TRACKS Stand well clear of the tracks. If you are too close, you could be in danger of being injured by the car wreckage.

MOVING CAR OFF CROSSING

1 PUSH THE CAR FREE If there is no train approaching, you may be advised by the train control to try to move the car off the tracks. If the engine will not start, take off the handbrake, put the car in neutral and push it out of the way.

2 USE THE STARTER MOTOR In a manual car, try using the starter motor to move the car. Put the car in first gear, take your foot off the clutch and turn the ignition on. Keep your right hand on the ignition as you steer with the left. The car should lurch forward.

3 INFORM THE TRAIN CONTROL Let the train control know that the obstruction has been cleared the moment you succeed in moving the car.

driving in **adverse weather**

Heavy rain and strong wind, especially when combined, can cause hazardous driving conditions, and floodwater adds significantly to the risk. Do not travel in adverse weather unless your journey is essential. If you do have to drive, go equipped for the worst of the elements and adapt your driving techniques to the conditions.

be aware

- Keep abreast of weather changes. Internet access on some mobile phones provides up-to-date satellite images, and local radio can help. If you find yourself on the road in storms or floods, it is vital to keep a close eye on the weather.
- Do not continue if you are uncertain about the depth of water on the highway. Any water level above 30cm could damage the engine. Look for the kerb – if it cannot be seen the water is at least 15cm deep and caution is required.
- Drive with extreme caution. Motoring organisations say that drivers tend to underestimate the dangers of wet weather.
- Stopping distances are substantially longer in wet weather (see page 246). Keep at least a 2-second gap between you and the nearest vehicle under normal conditions. In the wet, this should

be at least doubled and increased further under icy conditions.
- Always use dipped headlights, even in daytime, as these allow others to see you more clearly.
- Flooding is most likely in low-lying areas by rivers and lakes, in dips and under bridges. Take particular care when driving in these areas or where there are signs warning of flooding.
- Do not drive at night during flood alerts as it is nearly impossible to judge the depth of water.

 WARNING
Never try to drive through fast-moving water.
Cars are surprisingly buoyant and can be swept away all too easily. A car can float in as little as 60cm of water.

action

STORMY CONDITIONS

1 TURN WIPERS ON FULL Turn your wipers on to the fastest speed. Dip the headlights to lessen the glare and turn on the demister to combat condensation.

2 TURN BACK IF NECESSARY Stop if you are unsure and turn back along familiar roads if the weather worsens. Turning off a main road into a minor road to escape a storm can expose you to danger as secondary roads are more prone to flooding.

3 HEAD FOR SHELTER If driving conditions worsen, you have no option but to seek shelter. Service stations or multistorey car parks are ideal shelters for a car if you can reach one. In really treacherous conditions, you should abandon the car and seek shelter for yourself in a nearby building.

BLIZZARD CONDITIONS

1 SWITCH ON THE WIPERS The easiest test of whether there is any point in continuing the journey is to switch on the windscreen wipers. If they cannot push aside the snow accumulating on the glass, then you have no option but to seek shelter.

2 PREPARE A RETREAT At the first sign that you cannot continue, find a safe place to turn and head back. Retreating may allow you to outrun the storm. Look for potential shelter, such as a service station or restaurant.

3 ACT NOW Do not push ahead in the hope that you will find somewhere. Blizzards can close roads in a matter of minutes. If you have to shelter in your car by the side of the road, do not risk venturing out as you may become stranded (see pages 244–245).

TIME TO ACT Watch the cars in front to see how they cope with the driving conditions. They can give you a good idea of what lies ahead and whether you should turn back.

WATCHPOINT Rain is most dangerous after a dry spell. The roads will have accumulated deposits of oil and rubber in the cracks. These mix with water to produce a slippery surface.

WINDY CONDITIONS

1 STEER FIRMLY Keep both hands on the wheel at all times particularly on exposed stretches of the road and on bridges, or when overtaking.

2 MIND THE GAP Other vehicles may be blown off course. Keep at least a 2-second gap from other vehicles, taking particular care near caravans, cyclists, motorcyclists and horse riders.

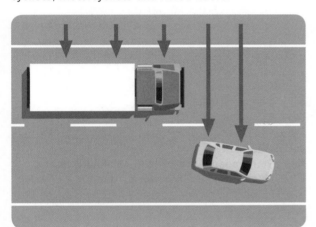

3 EXPECT SUDDEN GUSTS Be prepared for unpredictable gusts of wind on open stretches of road, when passing vehicles or gaps in hedges, or when overtaking high-sided vehicles. If you are caught in a gust, hold the wheel tightly to maintain control. The car may be rocked by the wind, but winds seldom have the strength to blow the car off the road.

4 WATCH FOR DEBRIS Drive carefully on country roads, especially at night or in the early hours of the morning when you are most likely to encounter branches or trees on the road. Watch out for twigs and small branches – these could indicate larger branches around the next corner.

TORRENTIAL RAIN

1 SLOW DOWN In wet weather drivers tend to underestimate the dangers caused by rain and drive at their normal speed. In reality, the combination of poor visibility and slippery, rain-sodden roads can make torrential rain one of the most risky driving situations. Keep your speed down and double your stopping distance (see page 246).

2 TEST YOUR BRAKES One of the main dangers of heavy rain is wet brakes, which can dramatically increase the car's stopping distance. To keep them dry, occasionally press lightly on the brake pedal. The heat from the friction should help to remove any moisture.

3 GET A GRIP If the steering becomes unresponsive, then it probably means that water is preventing the tyres from gripping the roads. This can cause aquaplaning (see below). If you lose grip, ease off the accelerator and slow down gradually.

CAR STARTS TO AQUAPLANE

1 REDUCE SPEED Aquaplaning is caused by the rain being so heavy that the tyres lose all grip and you lose steering control. It can also be the result of inadequate tyre tread. Braking will have little or no effect. The only answer is to take your foot off the accelerator and slow down gradually.

2 STEER STRAIGHT Hold the steering wheel firmly, anticipating the moment that the tyres regain their grip. The car may swerve when this happens so maintain a firm hold on the wheel to enable you to steer out of trouble.

driving in a **flood**

Flooding is often localised, and as flash floods can occur in an instant, they can be difficult to anticipate. Never take the risk of driving through any water if you are unsure of how deep it is. A depth of as little as 60cm of water can cause a car to float away. Beware, too, of the risk of stalling in floodwater as it can cause irreparable damage to the engine.

action

FLOOD CONDITIONS

1 DRIVE SLOWLY Driving through floodwater, even at slow speeds, creates a wave of water called a bow wave at the front of the car. Keep your speed down to limit the size of the wave, which can obscure your vision and swamp your engine. In a car with a manual gearbox, drive in first or second gear; in an automatic, opt for L or 1. Drive slowly but keep the revs high. The flow of exhaust gases will help to stop water entering the exhaust and the engine stalling.

2 KEEP THE ENGINE REVVING To avoid stalling, maintain steady pressure on the accelerator while slipping the clutch by pushing the clutch pedal down a little. All cars are susceptible but turbo-charged and diesel engines are the most vulnerable.

3 STAY IN THE SAME GEAR Do not change gear as any change in engine speed runs the risk of sucking in water and damaging the engine.

4 TEST YOUR BRAKES As soon as you leave the floodwater, test your brakes. Lightly press down on the brake pedal several times to check the brakes are pulling evenly on all the wheels. To dry them out, drive slowly pressing lightly on the brake pedal.

■ **IF THE CAR STALLS IN STANDING WATER** You have no option but to get out and push the car clear. Do not try to restart the car – you will just compound the damage to the engine. Be careful as there is a further risk that the airbag may be accidentally deployed due to water in the electrical system.

■ **IF THE CAR IS FLOODED OUT** Bail out the water with a bucket. Dry out the car as best you can, mopping up any water with rags or towels. Take out damp carpets and underlay. A professional dehumidifier and air blower can speed up the drying process. Get a mechanic to check over your car thoroughly before driving it again.

⚠ WARNING

Keep your speed down even in shallow water as there might still be a bow wave. The surge of water may swamp the engine compartment and cause the engine to stall.

stuck in mud

In this situation, do not try to power your way out by revving the engine. Patience and perseverance are required. Utilise something, be it carpets or tree branches, to provide traction. Be prepared to rock or push your way back onto the road.

WATCHPOINT Stand well clear if the car is being pulled out using tow ropes. If they become loose, there is a risk of the tow hooks flying off the car and hitting someone.

precautions

- In muddy conditions, drive in as high a gear as possible while keeping your speed low. This will reduce torque on the wheels and will decrease the risk of wheel spin.
- Keep your speed down on country roads and other roads with ditches. Cars that end up mired in mud or stuck in ditches are usually going too fast for the road conditions.

- The best protection from getting stuck is to travel in pairs of cars if you know you will be driving through muddy terrain. That way one can pull the other if you do get trapped.
- If you are renting a car for a holiday in a remote area with rough terrain, it is worth opting for a four-wheel-drive vehicle with a high ground clearance, which will avoid many problems.

action

1 GET A GRIP Straighten your wheels and pack something under the driving wheels to provide grip. Sand, gravel, sacking, old carpets, even tree branches can work. On a front-wheel drive, the grip is needed on the front wheels so place the material here; on a rear-wheel drive on the rear wheels; on a four-wheel drive do the front wheels first, then the back wheels if you have sufficient material.

2 ACCELERATE GENTLY Push the accelerator gently, starting in second gear to reduce wheel spin. Try to move the car gently forwards, using the clutch as necessary to keep the engine going; do not rev too hard. Enlist the passengers to help push the car.

3 ROCK THE CAR If the car is stuck in a rut or a ditch, first clear any obstructions then try rocking it out. Move forwards a few inches in first gear, then while it is as far forward as it will go, quickly switch to reverse so that it moves slowly backwards. Repeat the movements in a gentle rhythm that will, hopefully, rock the car out of its rut.

4 USE TOW ROPES
Towing the car out is the last resort. Check the position of the chassis to ensure that you will not damage the underside of the car. Phone for a professional tow truck if you have any doubts. **Make sure that you attach the tow ropes to the frame of the two vehicles – the bumper is not strong enough –** and ensure that you have the right straps. You need recovery straps (see above) rather than towing straps as they are less likely to snap.

 TAKE CARE
Once you have released your vehicle, drive slowly to a firm surface. Do not stop to let passengers back into the vehicle until you can feel sufficient grip.

driving in **snow** and **ice**

Only make a journey in heavy snow if it is absolutely vital. If you do have to travel, make sure that you have appropriate survival equipment and supplies in case you have a breakdown or get stuck. With frostbite and hypothermia being a real danger in extremely cold weather, it is important to stay warm and keep fully awake.

precautions

- Keep an eye on weather forecasts for warnings of snow. Do not drive if there are warnings unless your journey is essential.
- Do not attempt to drive in a blizzard. Driving is impossible if the snow has reached a depth of more than 30cm.
- Ensure that the car battery is working well as flat batteries are a leading cause of winter breakdowns. A load test by a mechanic will tell you if the battery is sufficiently charged.
- Do not forget blankets. Cars can provide shelter but only limited warmth.
- Make sure that you have your winter survival supplies with you (see box, right).
- Carry snow chains with you or consider fitting 'winter' tyres, which provide better traction in snow and ice.

⚠ TAKE CARE

Check that your tyres are properly inflated as under-inflated tyres can seriously impair steering. **Tyres lose pressure in freezing conditions – around 1psi of pressure for each 6-degree Celsius fall in temperature.**

Winter survival kit

- Scraper and de-icer
- Fully charged mobile phone
- Shovel and long-handled brush
- High-energy food and drinks
- A vacuum flask with a hot drink
- Warm clothing and blankets
- Torch (flashlight) and spare batteries
- Sacking to provide tyre grip in icy conditions
- Jump leads for the car.

For more extreme conditions:
- Snow chains
- Can of spare fuel
- Tow rope.

action

DRIVING IN SNOW

1 CHOOSE YOUR ROUTE CAREFULLY Stick to major roads, which are likely to be gritted and cleared during winter weather. If you can, avoid minor country roads and steep hills, which are particularly treacherous. Take care when overtaking gritting vehicles, especially if you are riding a motorcycle.

2 ACCELERATE GENTLY Avoid harsh acceleration that can cause the wheels to spin and get the car bogged down in the snow. If the car does get stuck, do not accelerate hard to pull away. Clear the snow, pack something under the wheels to provide grip, and pull away gently, using the same techniques as when a car is stuck in mud (see page 243). Try driving in a higher gear while keeping the revs down.

WATCHPOINT Keep a careful eye on the car exhaust. Ensure that the area around the exhaust pipe is kept clear so that the fumes can escape when you use the heater.

TIME TO ACT Slow down and take particular care when the ice starts to melt, as a thin layer of water forms on the road, which can make it even more slippery.

DRIVING ON ICE

1 SLOW DOWN Steer gently and avoid all sharp turns, braking or acceleration. Stopping times are much longer in icy weather so leave a 10-second gap between your car and the next vehicle.

2 USE A HIGH GEAR Motoring experts recommend pulling away in second gear to avoid wheel spin. Drive in as high a gear as possible to limit wheel spin and prevent skidding. Make sure that this does not result in your speed creeping up.

3 BRAKE GENTLY When braking you should get into a low gear earlier than usual as this will allow the speed of the car to fall. If you do not have an anti-lock braking system (ABS), gently apply pumping pressure to the brakes to slow down.

4 CORNER CAREFULLY When cornering, allow the speed to fall well before the bend by easing off the accelerator gradually.

5 WATCH THE GRADIENT Do not try to power up hills. Use a low gear and try to get a bit of momentum before reaching the hill and let this carry you up. Reduce speed once you reach the top of the hill and drive down in a low gear as slowly as possible.

TRAPPED IN SNOW

1 SHELTER IN THE CAR The main priority is to stay warm and keep awake to protect against frostbite and hypothermia. Use the car for shelter. Do not risk going for help as there is a serious risk of exposure.

2 CONSERVE YOUR FUEL Running the engine all night to power the heater can empty the tank. To conserve fuel, turn on the engine and the heater for only 15 minutes per hour. Leave a window open slightly to let fumes escape.

3 KEEP WARM Use blankets, rugs and coats for warmth. Newspapers can also conserve body heat if wrapped around limbs or stuffed down clothes. Wear a hat, scarf and gloves as well.

4 STAY AWAKE Try to stay awake. If there is a group of snowbound vehicles, join forces with other motorists. Teaming up in one vehicle saves fuel, provides warmth and will boost morale.

5 AWAIT RESCUERS If the car becomes completely buried, open a window and poke an air hole through the snow with an umbrella or torch. To move the car out of deep snow, provide traction with carpets and rock the car free (see page 243).

Black ice

Dark patches caused by water freezing on the roads are notoriously difficult to spot and pose one of the biggest dangers in icy weather. One sign is frozen puddles by the side of the road; another is a feeling of light steering or a lack of noise coming from the tyres on the roads. To reduce skidding, drive more slowly in lower gears and ease off the accelerator when you want to reduce speed, rather than hitting the brakes.

▶▶See also: HYPOTHERMIA pp46–47 • DRIVING IN ADVERSE WEATHER pp240–241 • STUCK IN MUD p243

driving in **fog**

As well as reducing visibility, fog causes drivers to lose the sensation of speed by muffling sounds and blotting out familiar landmarks. Use your lights to make sure that you are seen by other drivers and leave plenty of time and space for braking.

WATCHPOINT Fog lights dramatically enhance visibility in foggy conditions, but they must be switched off if conditions improve to avoid dazzling other drivers.

precautions

- Know how to switch your fog lights on and off and when to use them.
- Drive with your window partly open to help you to listen out for traffic, especially at intersections.
- Fog makes the roads more slippery so increase your stopping distance (see below).
- Follow the kerbside or near-side verge as a guide to your road position.
- Switch on your windscreen wipers and demisters to improve your vision.

⚠ **WARNING**

- Fog is patchy and often comes in pockets so keep driving carefully even if you think you have hit clearer weather.
- Low-lying areas, valleys and wooded areas on cool autumn and winter mornings are most susceptible to foggy conditions.
- If you have to pull over, try to ensure that you park off the road.

action

1 DIP YOUR HEADLIGHTS Drive with dipped headlights during the day or night. Sidelights are not bright enough and full-beam headlights dazzle because they reflect off the fog particles. Turn on your fog lights when visibility is seriously threatened.

2 SLOW DOWN Reduce your speed so that you can stop within the distance that you can see ahead. Do not accelerate if the car behind is too close. You could easily end up too close to the car in front.

3 KEEP YOUR DISTANCE Maintain at least a 2-second gap with the car in front; 4 seconds in heavy fog. It is a mistake to get too close to the car in front in order to stay in sight of its tail lights; this is a major cause of multiple pile-ups.

4 TURN OFF HIGHWAY WITH CARE Signal in good time, wind down the window completely and listen for traffic before crossing the other lane to turn off, or at major intersections.

Stopping distances

In wet and foggy conditions, allow extra space between cars for braking.

Thinking distance

Braking distance

STOPPING DISTANCE IN DRY CONDITIONS AT 50km/h

9m   14m

= 23m
8 CAR LENGTHS

STOPPING DISTANCE IN WET CONDITIONS AT 50km/h

9m   18m

= 27m
9 CAR LENGTHS

driving in a **remote area**

Driving in remote areas exposes you to more risk and requires preparation. Before you leave, make sure that your vehicle is in a sound condition and appropriate for the terrain you will encounter. Check that you have the correct equipment and supplies in case of a breakdown and be sure to inform someone of your plans, including timings.

precautions

- Study the owner's manual before going off-road, especially if your vehicle is rented.
- Be aware of changing weather conditions and be especially cautious of fast-running water when crossing rivers or streams.
- Make sure that you have all the right equipment for emergencies (see page 233).
- Ensure that your vehicle is up to the task. A four-wheel-drive vehicle is recommended for difficult terrain.
- Check the tyres, water level (in radiator), oil level and battery condition before you leave.
- Carry a 406MHz personal locator beacon (PLB), preferably one that provides a GPS location. When activated, the beacon sends out a distress signal that is picked up by passing satellites, alerting rescue services.
- For remote, off-road trips, travelling in two or more vehicles is a good idea as there will be someone to tow you or to go for help if there is a problem.

action

FUEL RUNS LOW

1 DRIVE AT A STEADY PACE Keep to a speed of about 40–50km/h in top gear in order to conserve fuel for longer. Avoid unnecessary stops and starts. If possible, turn off the air-conditioning.

2 ACCELERATE GENTLY When approaching hills, build up speed first, then change down so that you can keep going without having to press hard on the accelerator.

YOU BREAK DOWN

1 STAY WITH YOUR CAR Do not risk getting lost or injured by setting off on a fruitless hike for help. The only exception is if you know that there is definitely somewhere within walking distance.

2 RAISE YOUR BONNET This instantly signals to other road users that you have broken down and hopefully encourages them to stop.

3 CONSERVE SUPPLIES Take provisions for at least 14 days and at least 4–5 litres of water per person per day if driving in hot, remote places. Carefully ration supplies if you are stranded.

 TAKE CARE
If you must leave the vehicle, attach a note to the steering wheel showing your proposed route. If you are in a hot area, move at night when it is cool and mark your route so that you can be followed.

⚠️ **WARNING**
- Tell someone your route and expected return time. Arrange a call-in time when you are due back so the alarm can be raised if necessary.

hitting an **animal**

Every year many animals die and motorists are injured in animal collisions. Take particular care on rural roads, especially at night, and know the correct procedure if you should accidentally hit an animal.

WATCHPOINT Many animals, including kangaroos and rabbits, are crepuscular. This means they are most active at twilight and likely to stray onto the roads.

be aware

- Take special care at night when the majority of collisions occur. Animals get mesmerised by the glare of headlights and tend to freeze in the middle of the road.
- Remember that animal warning signs on roads are there for a reason. Even if you cannot see any animals, they may well be lurking around the bend or over the brow of the hill.
- When you see one animal, expect others. Animals rarely travel alone.

- In areas where wildlife tends to stray onto the roads – in woods or bushland, for example – alternate your headlights between dipped and full beam to scare animals out of the way.
- If you are travelling in an area that is prone to deer on the road, attach a deer whistle or siren to the grille of your car. These can be heard by the animal but not by the human ear.
- Be aware of local laws and customs. For instance, in India killing or maiming a cow is an offence.

action

1 DO NOT SWERVE Instinctively, you will want to swerve or slam on the brakes, but sudden manoeuvres increase the risk of an accident because you could hit a tree or another vehicle. Generally, it is safer to slow down and continue on your normal track when an animal strays into your path as it may well move out of your way.

2 PULL OVER Stop as soon as you can after an impact. Check to see if the animal is dead or injured.

3 APPROACH WITH CARE **An injured animal is likely to be in a distressed state.** Approach slowly, talking soothingly. Be especially wary of wild animals.

4 MOVE IT If the animal is small, try to move it to the side of the road to reduce the danger for other drivers. A blanket makes a good improvised stretcher for smaller animals.

5 HELP THE ANIMAL If the animal is injured, take it to a local vet or contact an animal protection organisation, such as the (R)SPCA. They will give you advice on how best to help the animal. See page 339 for contact information.

6 CALL THE POLICE Although it is not always a legal necessity, it may be worth calling the police as they may help either to move the body or to find treatment for an injured animal.

OUTDOOR INCIDENTS

drowning

Every year tens of thousands of people get into difficulties in water, mainly in inland waters as well as in the sea. A significant proportion of these victims are people who drown while attempting to rescue someone else. Follow these rules to keep yourself safe in water, and if you do see someone who may be drowning know how to help them safely.

be aware

KEEP YOURSELF SAFE IN WATER

- Always swim with others and ideally where there is a lifeguard.
- Do not dive into water unless you know the depth and what lies below the surface.
- Do not swim out of your depth unless you are a confident swimmer.
- Pay attention to tides and water currents that may carry you into deep water.
- Take care not to exhaust yourself in open water, where it is easy to misjudge distance.
- Do not float on lilos or large inflatable rings when the tide is going out or there is a strong offshore wind.
- Always wear a personal flotation device when participating in any kind of water sport.
- Never let children swim unattended. Fence or cover unattended pools, spas and ponds.
- Ensure that your children learn how to swim and lifesave.

RECOGNISE WHEN TO RESCUE

- Look for the signs that someone is drowning, rather than fooling around. Typically, his head is back, his mouth open, his arms waving frantically but he is making no sound. He is vertical in the water and his head is submerging periodically.
- **Always attempt a rescue from land first** to avoid putting yourself at unnecessary risk. Remember the mnemonic: **'reach or throw before you go'.**

⚠ TAKE CARE

If you are reaching out to pull someone in from the side of a swimming pool, lie down on the edge, otherwise you may end up in the water yourself. Encourage them to climb out unassisted if they are able to.

Surviving in water

Known as 'drownproofing', this technique enables you to float in open water when you have no life jacket.

1 HANG IN THE WATER Use your body's natural buoyancy to float just below the surface of the water. Extend your arms in front of you and put your face in the water to hang in a relaxed position and conserve energy.

2 LIFT YOUR HEAD OUT OF THE WATER When you need to take a breath, raise yourself up by pushing your arms down and kicking your legs. Exhale completely as your head breaks the surface, then take a deep breath in.

3 RETURN TO THE REST POSITION With your lungs full of air, close your mouth and return to the rest position (see step 1, above). If you stay relaxed and get into a rhythm of rising, breathing and resting, you can stay afloat indefinitely without getting tired.

- **In cold water you may want to adopt the HELP posture to conserve heat (see page 255).**

action

RESCUE FROM LAND

1 SHOUT AND SIGNAL Call out to the person: encourage him not to panic and to swim if he can.

2 THROW A BUOYANCY AID This could be anything that floats – such as a life jacket or ball.

3 PULL TO SAFETY Throw him a line to grab hold of, tying a loop in it first if you can. A line with a lifebuoy is the best option. An electrical extension lead or a tow rope could be used or something rigid enough to pull him to safety, such as an oar, fishing rod or branch.

4 WADE OUT As a last resort, wade out, staying within your depth, with a lifebuoy that you can throw to the person. Two buoyancy aids would be even better. If the person is too far out, consider entering the water with a flotation device that the person can hold on to while you tow him to safety.

⚠ TAKE CARE
A drowning person may grab hold of you in panic and pull you under the water. To escape his grip, actively swim down deeper; he should then release you.

⚠ WARNING
● When back on shore, if the victim is not breathing, perform CPR at once (see pages 16–17).
● If the water is cold, remove the person's clothing and wrap him in blankets. Give a conscious casualty a warm, but not very hot, drink.
● In every case of near drowning, seek medical advice urgently as lung complications are common.

Life-saving skills

Only those with a life-saving qualification should attempt the following techniques to rescue a drowning person from the water.

1 TOW WITH AN EXTENDED ARM If you do not have a flotation device and the water is calm, cup the person's chin to raise his head out of the water and then swim back.

2 USE A CROSS-CHEST TOW To keep the victim's face higher out of the water in a rough sea or choppy conditions on a lake or river, reach over his shoulder and hold him into your side, gripping his belt so you have a firm hold. Alternatively, grip him under his arm between armpit and waist. Use side stroke to bring him to safety.

▶▶See also: **ATTENDING TO A CASUALTY** pp12–13 • **CPR** pp16–17 • **HYPOTHERMIA** pp46–47 **251**

falling into a river

The power of a fast-flowing river is frequently underestimated. Even a small stream in full flood can knock an adult off his feet. Whether you are attempting a crossing or strolling along the bank, a few straightforward guidelines will keep you safe.

WATCHPOINT Rivers can be unpredictable and water levels can rise dramatically. Heavy rain or snow melt in distant mountains may result in a rapid rise in water levels downstream.

precautions

- If you plan to walk near a river or need to cross one, consider the depth and speed of the water, the risk of collision with rocks and the temperature of the water. Always try to find a bridge to cross before resorting to wading through the water.
- Watch out for warning signs that a river is in flood. These include discoloration of the water, the sound of small rocks and boulders being rolled along the riverbed and large branches or other debris floating quickly past.
- Do not walk too near the water's edge, especially on the outside banks of bends. These are often undercut by the river, which flows most quickly here, and are prone to collapse.
- Use a map to decide where a river can be safely crossed. Identify the location of hazards such as weirs, waterfalls or dams.
- Insist that children wear a life jacket and wear one yourself if you plan to spend time on or near a major river.

action

YOU SEE SOMEONE FALL IN

■ **STAY ON LAND You are more likely to be of help if you stay on the bank** and attempt a rescue from there. If the person is moving rapidly downstream, try to run ahead of him along the bank. Shout and signal for help as you do so.

■ **THROW SOMETHING BUOYANT** So that he can stay afloat, throw him something buoyant (see box, opposite) that he can cling to until he is rescued.

■ **THROW A LINE** Keep a lookout for a point where you may be able to reach him with a line or a long branch and pull him to safety.

■ **ROW OUT** If you are confident of handling a rowing boat or canoe, row or paddle out. Do not try to haul him on board unless you are rescuing a child or you have someone else to balance the rowing boat. Instead, throw him something buoyant or get him to hold on to the side and tow him to safety.

Emergency river crossing

Before fording a river that is knee high or deeper, spend some time looking for the best place to cross. Try to get above the river so you can look down and take note of deep channels or hazardous rocks. Do not cross near rapids or waterfalls.

■ **IF YOU ARE CROSSING ALONE** Improvise support. Find a stout stick about 2m long and hold it diagonally across the front of your body. Push the stick into the riverbed about a metre upstream from your feet, then lean on the pole as you step forwards. Once you have a secure footing, reposition the pole and repeat the process.

1 TO CROSS AS A GROUP Line up along the bank so you have the strongest individuals at the upstream and downstream ends and the rest of the group in between. Rope yourselves together, interlock your arms or grasp each other's backpack straps.

2 ENTER THE WATER TOGETHER Step off the bank and into the river simultaneously. Walk slowly across the river, crossing in a line parallel to the bank and making sure that you stay in line with the current at all times.

YOU FALL IN

■ **CALL FOR HELP** If there are people nearby, call out as loudly as you can to attract their attention. Keep your backpack on as a flotation aid.

■ **TRY TO REACH A SAFE PLACE** If you can touch the riverbed easily, try to use it to push yourself – in a series of small jumps – towards the safety of the bank or a large rock that you can climb onto. If the current is strong and the water is above your thighs, work with the flow of the water, not against it, even if this carries you downstream. It is safer to swim or crawl than try to stand, as you may get a foot trapped on the riverbed.

■ **PROTECT YOURSELF** If you are out of your depth and find yourself being swept along by the flow, lean back and try to float feet first. Keep your knees slightly bent and be ready to use your booted feet to push yourself away from rocks or any other hazards. Try to steer using your hands and arms as paddles.

■ **WATCH OUT FOR RIVER DEBRIS** A floating log might provide a useful lifesaver, but a submerged tree or large branch might cause you injury. If you spot a potential hazard in the water, try to swim round it or, if you have to, over it.

■ **PROTECT YOUR HEAD** If you find yourself heading towards a waterfall or weir, try to roll into a ball and use your hands and arms to protect your head.

■ **SWIM TO SAFETY** As soon as you encounter slower-moving water, flip onto your front and swim front crawl as strongly as you can. Swim diagonally across the current towards the bank. Get out of the centre of the river as soon as you can and avoid the outside of bends, as this is where rivers flow fastest.

DOG FALLS IN

■ **STAY ON THE BANK** Dogs are good swimmers and are unlikely to come to any harm. Try to follow the dog from the bank and encourage it to come out of the water. If possible, get ahead and drag the dog to safety with a branch or an oar.

■ **USE A BOAT** If there is a boat you can use, row out to the dog and either haul it in, kneeling in the boat to avoid capsizing, or tow it by the collar.

 WARNING
Do not swim out to rescue a dog. It may panic and resist rescue, putting you in danger of drowning.

Makeshift life savers

In an emergency, many everyday items can be used to make an improvised life saver.

● **PLASTIC-COVERED CUSHIONS** While not very buoyant, foam cushions may float for long enough to win you sufficient extra time to effect a rescue.
● **FOOTBALL** Although not easy to hold on to, plastic footballs float well and can be thrown or kicked a long way.

● **EMPTY PLASTIC PETROL CAN** Many people keep plastic petrol cans in their cars. When empty, they make good buoyancy aids.
● **LARGE PLASTIC BOTTLES** Empty 5-litre containers with screw tops provide an ideal impromptu life saver. If possible, tie a line to the handle and pull the person to safety. Throwing a container to the person to hold against his chest may help him to float.

caught in a rip current

Getting caught in a rip current, also known – less accurately – as an undertow or rip tide, can be a frightening and occasionally life-threatening experience. It can usually be avoided if you learn to identify the warning signs, both out at sea and on the beach. If you find yourself in one of these currents, escape is possible, provided you use your strength effectively.

action

1 TRY TO GET OUT OF THE WATER If a strong current knocks you off your feet, try to stand up and get out of the water as quickly as you can.

2 DO NOT FIGHT THE CURRENT If you find yourself out of your depth, do not fight the current as you will only become exhausted. If you cannot swim well, try to signal for help at once. Wave both your arms and shout as loudly as you can.

3 SWIM IF YOU CAN Try to see which way the current is pulling you and swim at right angles to this. Rip currents are seldom more than 30m wide, so even if you are carried a little further out to sea, it should not take too long to swim clear of the current.

4 REST If you get tired, float on your back and continue to shout and signal for help.

5 SWIM BACK TO SHORE Rip currents usually weaken 100–150m from the shore. Once you are out of the rip current, make for the shore, swimming diagonally away from the current to avoid re-entering it.

be aware

- Rip currents can occur wherever there is surf. **Look for a tell-tale 'dead spot' in a line of otherwise white breakers.** The water in a rip current may be slightly discoloured due to the sand or silt it is carrying.
- Remember, the bigger the surf, the stronger the potential rip current will be.
- Look out for warning signs on beaches that are known to be prone to rip currents.
- Test the water. If, when you walk into the surf, you can feel a powerful current pulling you away from the shore, walk along the beach to find a safer spot to enter the water.
- Avoid swimming within 30m of piers or jetties, as permanent rip currents often form near such structures.
- Try to swim where there are lifeguards. Where there are no lifeguards, seek out local knowledge about the safety of a beach.

Discoloured, churning water often indicates the presence of a rip current.

A second disturbance in the line of breaking surf indicates a second rip.

Powerful backwashes (left and far right) drive the current out to sea.

cut off by the tide

You need to take particular care if you are following a path along the shore. High cliffs and high tides can prove a dangerous combination for the unwary walker or for anyone on a day out on a beach.

GET HELP If you have a phone, call the emergency services immediately and ask for the coastguard. Give them your position and the number of people in your party.

precautions

● Check your route on a map before setting out if you intend to follow a coastal footpath for any distance. Where the sea meets high cliffs there is often a severe wave action against the cliffs, so avoid this part of the beach at all costs.
● Try to estimate the time it will take to complete each leg of your route and plot a timeline of the walk. Most people can manage about 5km/h on all but the roughest terrain. Check the local tide tables to see what time the tides are at their height and compare these with your timeline.

● When taking an unplanned stroll along a beach, pay attention to warning signs, such as visible evidence of high tide lines, and note whether the sea is receding or approaching.
● Allow plenty of leeway in your timing. Leave potentially dangerous bays or headlands before low tide – do not wait for the tide to turn.
● Be especially cautious when exploring rocky coastlines and caves. Always plan an escape route in case you find yourself cut off.
● Listen to local advice about coastal dangers.

action

1 HEAD FOR SAFETY If you are a long way from the shore, you are unlikely to be able to outrun the tide. Do everything you can to get off the beach or, as a last resort, look for rocks, or sand or shingle banks that are higher, to give you more time to be rescued.

2 RAISE THE ALARM If you can, phone for help. Alternatively, attract the attention of anyone nearby in a boat or on the cliff top. Shout or give six long blasts on a whistle or six long flashes with a torch (flashlight), repeating the sequence at intervals of one minute. This is an internationally recognised distress signal to which you may receive three long whistle blasts or flashes of light in response.

3 LOOK FOR USEFUL ITEMS As you make your way to your chosen point of safety, pick up anything you can find that floats, such as large pieces of wood, polystyrene packaging or large plastic bottles.

4 PREPARE FOR THE WATER Before the sea catches up with you, remove bulky clothing that is likely to hinder swimming, but keep on woollens that will conserve heat. Once the sea is deep enough, swim calmly towards your destination.

■ THE HELP POSITION
If you find yourself in open water with a makeshift lifesaver and little hope of reaching the shore or a place of safety, relax in the water and adopt the HELP position (Heat Escape Lessening Posture) – keep your arms crossed, hugging yourself and draw your knees towards your chest. Hold any buoyant object you have close to your body.

 WARNING
Large flat bays and beaches can be especially dangerous because the tide can come in extremely quickly. Within seconds you can find yourself in deep, turbulent water, a long way from the shore.

▶▶See also: HYPOTHERMIA pp46–47

sailing boat/canoe **capsizes**

If you go sailing or canoeing, sooner or later you will almost certainly experience a capsize. How serious this is will depend on how you capsized and the depth, temperature and roughness of the water you find yourself in. Controlled capsize practice in a dinghy or canoe will give you the confidence to deal with the real situation and help to keep you safe in the water.

precautions

- Do not sail in conditions beyond your ability, such as in high winds or heavy seas.
- Never sail or canoe alone.
- Always canoe in waters that are within your ability. If white-water canoeing, check the difficulty of a particular river before entering it.
- **Make sure you have practised a capsize drill repeatedly** under controlled conditions before taking on more challenging waters.
- Always wear a life jacket or buoyancy aid when sailing or canoeing.

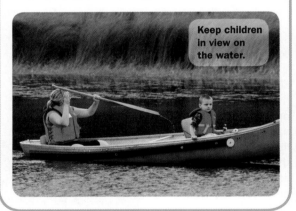

Keep children in view on the water.

action

BOAT CAPSIZES

■ **STAY WITH THE BOAT** When you capsize any kind of boat – dinghy, rowing boat or inflatable – your first priority should be to stay with the boat. If your attempts at righting it are unsuccessful and you need to be rescued, the boat is bigger and easier to spot than a swimmer in the water. The boat will float, so if you can, climb onto the hull and signal for assistance from other boat users.

RIGHTING A DINGHY

1 **CHECK THE BOAT** Uncleat and loosen any sheets (the ropes attached to the sails) so that the boat does not start sailing by itself once righted. Check for any tangled lines and make sure that the centreboard, if retractable, is fully down.

2 **GET IN POSITION** If there are two of you, the strongest or heaviest person should swim to the hull, holding the end of the main sheet as a safety line. The second crew member should hold on to a seat or crossbeam inside the boat so that he is lifted into the boat as it is righted.

3 **USE YOUR WEIGHT** Once in place, the heavier crew member should drop the main sheet, pull on the upper jib sheet and lean, then stand on the centreboard to bring the boat up. (Lean, rather than stand, on a wood centreboard or it may snap.) The crew member inside the boat kneels and helps the person in the water back into the boat by pulling on the shoulders of his life jacket.

■ **SAILING SOLO** The process is similar if you are alone. To get on board, swim to the widest part of the boat, pull down on the side and 'swim' into the boat. Sort out the sheets and tiller before sailing.

WATCHPOINT Make sure you wear appropriate clothing for the water conditions. If the water is cold you will need a drysuit or wetsuit of an appropriate thickness.

TIME TO ACT Multiple capsizes will be physically tiring. Take note of your physical condition and come off the water before you become exhausted or cold.

GET HELP If someone is injured or a dinghy is disabled, signal for help. Attract attention by raising and lowering your arms over your head or by setting off a distress flare.

CANOE CAPSIZES

1 KEEP HOLD OF YOUR PADDLE Try to hold on to your paddle as you capsize so that you can paddle once you retrieve your canoe.

2 PROTECT YOURSELF If you are in fast-flowing, dangerous waters, focus first on self-protection. In water deeper than knee high, float on your back and travel downstream feet first (see page 253).

3 QUICKLY ASSESS THE SITUATION If the water is dangerous or if there is a weir ahead, your priority must be to reach safety first and retrieve your canoe second.

4 RECOVER YOUR CANOE If the water is quite calm, try to recover your canoe. If it is within reach, grab it from the upstream end.

5 GET BACK IN In a river it is usually easier to swim the canoe to the bank and get back in. In the sea or a lake, if you are a long way from shore, you should right the canoe (see right) and try to get back in.

What to do in a kayak

● **ENLIST HELP** If you capsize in a kayak, call for help from another kayaker. He can paddle his kayak so he is perpendicular to the bow of yours – making a T-shape – then haul your kayak up and across the bow of his kayak to drain it. Once emptied, it can be flipped back over and pulled alongside the other kayak.
● **GET BACK IN** As you pull yourself back in, the other kayaker can keep the craft balanced by putting as much weight as possible onto the nearside of the cockpit.
● **DO NOT KAYAK ALONE** If you get thrown out of your kayak when it turns over, it is difficult to drain the boat and get back in alone. Do not venture out alone unless you are experienced.

RIGHTING A CANOE

1 GET UNDER THE CANOE First lift one edge out of the water to ensure that there is air under the canoe. Then swim under the canoe.

2 LIFT THE HULL Once you have got your breath back, hold firmly on to the hull, lift it clear of the water and flip it away from you to one side. If there are two or more of you, make sure that everyone pushes towards the same side at the same time.

3 PULL YOURSELF IN Once the canoe is righted, grasp a far edge and pull yourself diagonally into the boat. Try to get as much weight across the canoe as quickly as possible to prevent a further capsize. If there are two of you in the water, one person should hang on to the opposite side of the canoe as you climb in, to keep it level on the water.

boat emergencies

Running aground remains a common sailing hazard and a serious leak can quickly become an emergency. A fire on a boat must be dealt with urgently due the flammable nature of the craft. Make sure the crew are drilled in safety procedures.

GET HELP Seek immediate assistance. Call Mayday on Channel 16 VHF, giving your position, number of people on board the boat and the nature of your emergency.

precautions

- **Always be aware of your position, especially when you are in unfamiliar waters.**
- Make sure you have up-to-date charts, a good compass or a GPS. If you are at all unsure of your position, slow down.
- Carry an Emergency Position Indicating Radio Beacon (EPIRB). When activated, it sends out a distress signal that is picked up by passing satellites, alerting rescue services.
- When in tidal waters, make sure that you know the tide times and the tidal range.
- Consider joining a towing organisation and keep their details in a safe place on the boat.
- Prepare a 'grab bag' of essential items you need in a life raft. Include a first-aid kit, handheld VHF and GPS, torch, water and food.
- Ventilate the cabin, engine compartment and bilges regularly to prevent a build-up of gas.

action

BOAT RUNS AGROUND

1 ASSESS THE SITUATION First find out whether anyone is hurt, whether the hull has been damaged and what kind of obstacle you have hit. What did the collision sound like?

2 CHECK YOUR CHARTS If you are in tidal waters, check where you are in the tide cycle. Are you likely to float off on a rising tide? Locate the closest deep water. Although you may know that deeper water lies behind you, there could be a channel even closer.

 WARNING
Stow belongings carefully below deck before setting sail. Objects flying across the cabin can cause serious injuries.

3 USE AN ANCHOR If there is any chance that the wind, waves or current will drive your boat further aground, set a kedge (auxiliary) anchor behind you in deep water. Set it as far from the boat as possible, using a tender (small boat) if you have one.

4 BACK OFF If you have run aground on a soft spot, try backing off slowly. It may help if someone goes over the side and rocks the boat as you do this.

5 GET A TOW If you cannot back off, enlist help from another boat. You may need a combination of reverse engines, a rising tide and the tug of another boat or winching against the anchor to pull you free.

Heeling the boat over

Only attempt to heel the boat over if you have been trained to do so. This technique will help to reduce the boat's draught (its depth below the water line) and may help free it. Use the weight of the crew on one side or drop the mainsail on a sailing boat and weight the boom with a crew member – wearing a life jacket and safety harness – on one side.

Fuels and flammable solvents set ablaze by a spark are a frequent cause of on-board fires.

BOAT SPRINGS A LEAK

1 **TURN ON THE PUMPS** If you discover water in the bilges, turn on the pumps immediately.

2 **FIND THE LEAK** It could be a failed seal, a split seam, a leaking stern gland on the propellor shaft or a puncture through the hull. If the pumps are not coping with the influx of water, start bailing as fast as you can.

3 **BLOCK A HOLE** Use cushions or towels wedged in place with lengths of timber. Small holes can be sealed with bungs or filled with marine epoxy.

4 **SEAL OFF THE AFFECTED AREA** Consider whether the leak can be isolated. Is there a way to seal off the affected area to limit the spread of water?

5 **USE YOUR RADIO** Make sure the rising water is not about to compromise your boat's batteries. Send a distress call while your radio is still working or set off your EPIRB (see 'Precautions', opposite).

6 **PREPARE TO ABANDON SHIP** Put on life jackets and get your grab bag with emergency supplies (see 'Precautions', opposite). Make sure the life raft is accessible. Only abandon ship if you are sure that it is about to sink.

FIRE ON BOARD BOAT

1 **GET TO SAFETY** Get everyone as far away from the fire as possible. If you are in a smoke-filled cabin, drop to the floor where the air is cleaner. If you cannot exit through the hatches, smash a window, covering it first with a blanket to minimise injury.

2 **PREPARE TO ABANDON SHIP** Ensure everyone is wearing a life jacket, that the life raft is accessible and you have your grab bag (see 'Precautions', opposite). Send a distress call (see box, below).

3 **FIGHT THE FIRE** Without compromising your safety, aim fire extinguishers at the base of the flames. Seal all hatches and vents to starve it of oxygen.

Sending a distress call

- **CALL MAYDAY** Make sure that all crew members know how to send a Mayday message on Channel 16 VHF. Give the boat name, your position, the nature of the emergency and number of people on board.
- **ACTIVATE YOUR EPIRB** (see 'Precautions').
- **SET OFF A RED FLARE**
- **CALL EMERGENCY SERVICES** If you have a mobile phone, use it. Put it in a sealable plastic bag and keep it inside the bag while you use it.

▶▶See also: BURNS AND SCALDS pp112–113 • INHALING FUMES p44–45

storm at sea

A storm at sea in a small boat can be dangerous, even for an experienced sailor. Thousands of people have to be rescued every year. Yet there is much you can do to stay safe, by keeping your boat in good order and preparing for the worst.

GET HELP Seek immediate assistance. Call Mayday on Channel 16 VHF, giving your position, number of people on board the boat and the nature of your emergency.

be aware

- Monitor the weather constantly. If a storm is forecast, stay in port or alter your course to avoid it, if possible.
- Ensure your boat is absolutely seaworthy. Any small failing, such as an ill-fitting hatch or an unreliable engine, could be disastrous in storm conditions.
- Make sure that the crew have practised a 'storm drill' and are confident that they can handle a boat in storm conditions.
- Ride out the storm in deep water if you are at sea when the storm hits. It is far safer than trying to enter port in bad weather.

Lightning precautions

Lightning can strike nearly 10km from a storm, so if you see a flash and can count to less than 30 before you hear the thunder, you are in range. Most sea-going boats have some form of lightning protection device, but if you are unsure, move to the centre of the boat, crouch down as low as possible and avoid touching anything that conducts electricity.

 TAKE CARE

Ensure everyone is wearing foul-weather clothing and life jackets. Crew above deck need harnesses.

action

1 KEEP WATER OUT Seal and fasten all hatches, close ventilators and turn off the seacocks (valves) to sinks and the toilet to make the boat watertight.

2 PUMP THE BILGES DRY This empties the bilges of water and ensures the pump will work in the storm. Clear cockpit drains so water can drain out quickly.

3 PROTECT GEAR Make sure all equipment is stored securely where it will not be damaged or be a danger to the crew. Tie down anything loose on deck, such as the tender. Fasten cockpit lockers. Check emergency equipment, such as first-aid equipment, radio, flares and torches.

4 DELEGATE Give each crew member a specific job or responsibility for the duration of the storm.

5 DEPLOY A SEA ANCHOR Use this or a drogue (a conical-shaped device that is dragged behind a boat to reduce speed) to help stabilise the boat and keep the bow into the wind. Turn on your navigation lights.

6 SLOW YOUR SPEED Reduce your sail in good time before the storm hits. Slow your speed and head the boat into the wind, turning the boat at an angle, approaching 45 degrees, as you take each wave to reduce the chance of crashing down from the top. Take the same approach if motoring.

7 USE THE PUMPS Keep the bilges as dry as possible by pumping them out regularly throughout the storm. Extra weight here will increase the vessel's tendency to roll.

person **Overboard**

A person can fall overboard at any time and in any conditions but it is a particularly serious emergency if the water is cold as hypothermia can swiftly set in. Whatever craft you are sailing, take precautions and practise a 'man overboard' routine regularly so that your response is automatic whether it is you that falls in, or you need to rescue someone else.

action

SOMEONE FALLS OVERBOARD

1 **SHOUT 'MAN OVERBOARD'** Select a crew member to keep the person in the water in view and point at him throughout the rescue.

2 **REDUCE POWER** Cut the engine or reduce the sail, maintaining enough speed to manoeuvre.

3 **MARK THE POSITION** If possible, throw the person a lifebuoy and line. Use an underarm throw for greater distance and accuracy. Fenders or cushions can also be used. If the boat has satellite navigation with a 'Man Over Board' (MOB) function, use it to mark the position of the accident.

4 **USE FLARES** At night set off flares as necessary to locate the person in the water.

5 **RAISE THE ALARM** Even if you make a recovery, the person may need medical help.

6 **APPROACH THE PERSON** Turn the boat around so the course is 180 degrees from the original course.

7 **HELP THE PERSON OUT OF THE WATER** If you have a boarding ladder, help the person up the steps. Otherwise, attach a halyard (a rope that hoists the sails) to his life jacket or harness, or throw him a line with a loop in the end to secure under his arms, then pull him back onto the boat.

 WARNING

● Send out a distress signal (see page 259) as soon as someone falls overboard in case you lose sight of him in the water or are unable to make a rescue.
● Do not attempt to recover a person overboard using a stern ladder in rough seas, because of the danger posed by the engine's propeller. Recover them from the side of the boat using a halyard.

YOU FALL OVERBOARD

1 **STAY CALM** If the water is cold you will initially go into cold shock and your breathing will speed up. Tread water and try to get your breathing under control. Turn your back to the waves and tighten any wrist or ankle closures on your clothing to reduce heat loss.

2 **SHOUT AND WAVE** Attract the attention of the crew on the boat with your whistle and light, if you have one, so they can get a clear fix on your position.

3 **HOLD YOUR POSITION** Do not try to swim after the boat. Save your strength, look for a lifebuoy that may be thrown and let the boat come back to you.

 TAKE CARE

If you are motoring towards someone in the water, approach slowly, bow or side on: never back towards him. When close by, put the engine into neutral.

Safety on a boat

● Always wear a buoyancy aid or life jacket.
● Never overload a boat or carry more people than its safe capacity.
● Take care when moving about in a small boat, as changes to the weight distribution can easily make the boat tip.
● Wear life jackets and harnesses in rough water and at night. Carry a whistle and light.
● Ensure all guard rails are sturdy and in good order. Treat slippery surfaces with non-skid paint or grip strips.

▶▶See also: HYPOTHERMIA pp46–47

caught in lightning

Lightning is one of Nature's more dramatic special effects. But if you are out in the open, it can pose a real hazard; thousands of people are killed by lightning every year. Taking the right action can reduce your chances of a strike.

> **WATCHPOINT** If you are part of a group, spread out so that you are at least 6m apart. This means that if anyone is struck there should still be someone to offer first aid or call for help.

be aware

- Lightning occurs most frequently in the tropics, as this is where most thunderstorms occur. Check the weather forecast before setting out on a walk; don't go out in a thunderstorm.
- If you are caught in a storm, seek shelter in a safe place, such as a building or vehicle, as soon as you hear thunder. Lightning can strike as far as 16km away from a thunderstorm and can literally come out of a clear blue sky.
- Obey the 30–30 rule. If thunder follows lightning within 30 seconds, the storm is less than 10km away and you need to get inside urgently. Do not go out again until 30 minutes after the last thunder clap.

Person struck by lightning

Anyone struck by lightning will need urgent first aid. There is no risk to you from touching the casualty so check that he is breathing and give CPR if necessary (see pages 16–19). Keep him warm. Treat burns as you would those from any other source (see page 23).

 TAKE CARE

- Once inside a building, stay away from the plumbing, electrical appliances and the telephone.
- Avoid smaller structures with no plumbing or wiring to direct lightning to earth as they may draw a strike without affording you sufficient protection.
- Vehicles can offer protection, but once inside, take care not to touch any metal parts.
- If sheltering in a tent, stay as far as possible from metal poles. Choose a campsite where tents are not erected on the highest land.
- Motorbikes and bicycles also attract lightning. Get off and shelter until the storm is over.

action

■ **IF YOU ARE IN, ON OR NEAR WATER** Get out and move away from the water at once. Swimmers are at extreme risk from lightning as even if they are not struck directly, water is such a good conductor that they risk electrocution if lightning strikes nearby.

6m

■ **IF YOU ARE NEAR A TALL OBJECT** Lightning will generally hit the highest good conductor. Make sure that it is not you: crouch or lie down and move well away from tall trees, rock spires or metal fences. Once lightning has hit something, the bolt of electricity can either jump sideways or run along the ground so **leave at least 6m between you and another person, or any higher object.**

■ **IF YOU ARE PLAYING GOLF** Golfers are frequently struck by lightning as they are often out in the open with metal clubs and umbrellas, which turn them into excellent conductors. Stop playing at once. If you cannot make it to the club house, abandon your clubs and crouch down in a bunker with your head tucked in.

■ **IF YOU ARE RIDGE WALKING OR RUNNING** Immediately move to lower, less open ground. Although single tall trees should be avoided, sheltering among a plantation of more or less equal height trees is safer than remaining out in the open.

falling from a **height**

Cliffs, banks and steep-sided tracks are often prone to collapse, making them hazardous to climb and unsafe to walk along. If someone falls, knowing how to respond will be critical and will ensure you do not become a casualty too.

GET HELP Call the emergency services immediately if someone has fallen down a cliff or mountain. They will organise the rescue, including a helicopter, if necessary.

action

YOU FALL OFF A CLIFF/BANK

■ **IF YOU LOSE YOUR FOOTING** Try to twist your body so that it faces the cliff or bank and reach for anything solid that you can hold on to. Call for help.

■ **IF YOU ARE FALLING** Try to keep your limbs as loose as possible to reduce injury. If you have any control over your movement, try to slow your fall by grabbing at anything you can, such as any bushes or roots that might protrude from the cliff.

■ **REACHING THE BOTTOM** Try to roll and tumble. Although this will not protect you from injury, it may reduce the severity of a hard impact. Protect your head with your arms and hands.

■ **MAKE YOUR POSITION SECURE** Once you have stopped moving, try to make your position safe by finding more secure finger and foot holds. If the cliff face is soft, try to excavate these holds by gouging or kicking the cliff face. If you have a pocket knife, use it to make deeper, more effective hand holds.

■ **STAY CALM** Once you are secure, try to relax and decide on your next action. If you are uninjured and fit, your best option may be to climb up or climb down. If you are injured or are not a competent climber, stay put and await rescue.

SOMEONE ELSE FALLS OFF

1 DO NOT RUSH TO THE EDGE If possible, lie down some way back and ask someone to hold your ankles as you crawl towards the edge.

2 TRY TO LOCATE THE PERSON Shout out to him if possible, to see if he is conscious.

3 TRY TO PULL HIM UP If he is stuck just below the edge, try to hold out something you can pull him up with, such as a branch, a dog lead, wire fencing or an item of clothing. But make sure that someone else is holding you or that you are tied to something secure – a tree, for example. If the person is too far down, try to find out if he is injured and tell him that you will get help.

4 CALL THE EMERGENCY SERVICES If you cannot pull him up or he has fallen to the base of the cliff, call the emergency services. Tell them exactly where the accident has occurred.

5 THROW A LIFE LINE If you can find some rope or wire, make a large loop in the end and lower it down to him. Get him to put his arms through the loop and tighten it. Even if you cannot pull him up, by tying the rope to something secure, you can help ensure that he remains safe until rescued.

precautions

● Plan your trip carefully and the amount of time you can reasonably expect it to take.
● Tell someone your plans and when they should raise the alarm if you haven't made contact.
● Be aware of the weather, check the forecast and be prepared for weather changes.
● Take sufficient supplies. Make sure you have enough food, water, clothing and equipment. Take an appropriate means of communication.
● Be alert to your surroundings: do not follow paths blindly. If the path is crumbling or appears unstable, move inland at once.
● Don't be too ambitious: challenge yourself within your physical limits and experience.

▶▶See also: **CPR** pp16–17 • **MAKING FURTHER CHECKS** pp28–30 • **BACK AND NECK INJURY** pp84–85

stranded on a mountain

Every year rescue teams attend to hundreds of people who get into difficulties while climbing a mountain. Even the best equipped hikers and climbers can suffer an injury or become separated from their party. To prevent a mishap – whether a twisted ankle or a sudden change in the weather – from becoming a life-threatening emergency, plan and prepare thoroughly.

precautions

- Plan your route carefully, from maps, photographs, accounts from other hikers and climbers, and the internet.
- Get the most accurate weather forecast you can and check with other climbers on unusual local conditions you might expect.
- Never rely on a GPS device alone. Always take a map and compass.
- Do not hike or climb in the mountains alone. Make sure that you tell others where you are going and when they can expect you back.
- Always be ready to change your plans. Do not 'carry on regardless' to the summit or next waymark, if it would be dangerous to do so. Safety must always be your first priority.
- Ensure your mobile phone is charged in case you can get a signal. In remote areas your phone may not work so consider hiring a satellite phone or mountain radio.
- Carry a 406MHz personal locator beacon (PLB). When activated, the beacon sends out a distress signal that is picked up by passing satellites, alerting rescue services.

WHAT TO TAKE
- Sufficient food and water for approximately twice as long as you expect the hike to take. The colder the conditions, the more food you should take.
- Iodine water-purifying tablets or water filter
- First-aid kit
- Head torch (flashlight) and spare batteries
- Spare clothes, waterproofs, warm hat, gloves
- Emergency shelter and sleeping bag
- Fire-lighting equipment
- Knife, rope and a means of communication.

 WARNING

Weather in the mountains can change dramatically from one hour to the next and even one hill to the next. Check your local weather service for mountain area forecasts. These include risk levels for snow, wind, chill effect, rain and thunderstorms.

GET HELP Call the emergency services if you can. Try to give details of your location (including a grid reference if possible) and details of injuries.

 TIME TO ACT Keep an eye on the time and the light. Night can fall fast in the mountains and it may become bitterly cold very quickly.

 WATCHPOINT Make sure that you allow time to make your way down from anywhere that is high or dangerous before the light goes. Walking in the dark is extremely hazardous.

CANNOT DESCEND MOUNTAIN

1 MAKE A DECISION The most important action is to accept when it is safer to remain on the mountain than to continue walking in the dark, through very bad weather or with an injury.

2 KEEP WARM Depending on your location and the time of year, keeping warm is likely to be your top priority (see box, below). Be aware of signs of hypothermia (see pages 46–47), which include shivering, feeling cold and confusion.

3 DESCEND IF POSSIBLE If conditions permit, descend as far as you can before darkness falls or the weather closes in. It will be warmer lower down. As you walk, look for a sheltered site for your camp.

4 CONSERVE ENERGY Walk as steadily as you can to conserve energy and avoid perspiring too much. When resting, do not sit directly on snow or ice.

5 DRINK WATER If you run out of water, drink from a stream in preference to eating snow. Purify it first, if possible, as it could harbour germs.

Keeping warm

- **COVER YOUR HEAD** Wearing a hat is essential as you can lose more than 50 per cent of your body heat from your head.
- **FIND SHELTER** Get out of the wind to reduce wind chill or erect an emergency shelter (see page 267).
- **LIGHT A STOVE** A stove will warm a small shelter quickly. Heat water to make a warm drink, which will raise your core temperature.
- **REASSESS YOUR CLOTHING** If you have a damp layer next to your skin, replace it with dry clothing which will make you feel warmer.

PERSON WITH HYPOTHERMIA

1 STOP AND FIND SHELTER Protect the casualty from the cold and wind, ideally inside a shelter or a tent. Replace wet clothing with dry if you have any. Do not give him your clothes as you need to stay warm.

2 PROTECT THE CASUALTY FROM THE GROUND If you cannot find shelter, lay the casualty on a layer of dry material, such as leaves, to insulate him from the ground. Wrap him in a sleeping bag and/or blanket to keep his head and body warm. Hug him gently using your body heat to prevent further heat loss.

3 WARM UP GRADUALLY If there is no danger of the casualty getting cold again, warm him up gradually. Give him a warm (not hot) drink or energy-giving carbohydrates, such as chocolate, to eat.

4 GET EMERGENCY HELP The casualty will need to be taken to hospital by stretcher. If you are in a remote place and cannot call the rescue services, someone may need to go for help. If possible, one person should stay with the casualty and two should go together for help. If there are just two people in the party, make the casualty as comfortable as possible, make a note of his location (see page 268) and go for help.

▶▶See also: **HYPOTHERMIA** pp46–47 • **LOST IN A WILD AREA** pp268–269

surviving a **night outside**

When conditions force you to spend an unplanned night outdoors, finding shelter will rapidly become a top priority. If you have a tent, bivouac or tarpaulin with you, you will have a head start. If not, then you must look to your environment to furnish you with adequate protection from the elements.

precautions

- Make sure that your kit contains a knife, cord, some fire-lighting equipment and a torch (flashlight), as well as a first-aid kit, whenever you venture out into the open countryside.
- Include a survival bag. This lightweight sack is waterproof and has some thermal insulation. It can be used as a groundsheet or as an improvised tent and can help to prevent (or treat) hypothermia (see pages 46–47).

assessment

- Assess the climate. What poses the biggest threat: cold, rain, wind or all three? Work out the wind direction so that you can build your shelter in the lee of a slope or rock face.
- Assess your environment. Check for dangers, such as rockfalls and dead trees, and for animal hazards, such as ticks, ants, hornets – or scorpions or snakes.
- Use the lie of the land to make a shelter. Look for a natural shelter, such as a safe cave or crevice. Add rocks or snow (and your backpack) to raise the height of a small ridge or bank. Avoid valley bottoms and deep hollows, which are colder and liable to frost and mist, and dry riverbeds, which may be prone to flash floods.

⚠ WARNING

If there are large predators, such as bears, in the area and you have food with you, put the food in a bag – preferably sealed – and hang it from a high branch well away from your camp. See page 310.

action

NIGHT IN THE WOODS

1 CHOOSE YOUR SITE Choose a dry, sheltered site that is not in an area that is boggy. Align your shelter so that its back faces the prevailing wind.

2 MAKE AN A-FRAME Find a long, sturdy branch for a ridgepole and two shorter branches to push into the ground to form an 'A'. Push one end of the ridgepole into the ground and tie the other on top of the 'A'.

3 CREATE WALLS Fix more branches to the ridgepole at intervals along each side then weave long flexible twigs and branches between them. Fill in the gaps with a thatch of leafy evergreen branches, heather or dried bracken or grass. Cover the floor with ferns or conifer branches for warmth.

NIGHT IN THE SNOW

1 FIND A SITE FOR A SNOW CAVE Look for an established snow drift with a firm crust near a ridge or trees. The drift needs to be at least 1.2–1.5m deep. Avoid freshly fallen or powdery snow.

2 DIG AN ENTRANCE TUNNEL Use a shovel, snow shoe or your hands to dig a 1m tunnel into the snow drift on the leeward (sheltered) side of the drift.

3 EXCAVATE A SMALL CAVE Make a lower entrance, where cold air can collect, and a higher ledge that is large enough for you to sit on. Keep the walls at least 45cm thick and create a smooth, domed roof for strength and to prevent meltwater dripping.

4 MAKE AN AIR HOLE Use a stick or ski pole to make a vent in the roof at least 5cm in diameter. Line the floor of the ledge with conifer boughs for warmth and mark your snow cave with branches, skis or clothes placed outside to make you visible. Block the entrance with your backpack.

 TAKE CARE

When you build a snow cave, always consider the avalanche risk (see pages 192–193). Do not shelter on, or near the base of, a slope of 30–50 degrees, especially in moderate to high winds after a snowfall, in rain or when overnight temperatures rise above freezing.

MAKING A FIRE

■ **OUTDOOR FIRE** Locate your fire close to your shelter where it is not a fire risk to your shelter or trees. Build up the fire in the shape of a tepee with dry grass, wood shavings or pine needles as tinder, then small twigs as kindling. Set light to the tinder and, once the fire is going, add fuel that burns more slowly, such as dry logs or dried animal dung.

■ **USING A STOVE** A stove will quickly warm a snow cave. Place at the lower level (see left), but make sure that your ventilation hole stays open and never go to sleep with the stove still lit.

Makeshift shelters

● **A-SHAPED TENT** A rectangular tarpaulin, emergency blanket or poncho take up little space in a pack and can quickly be transformed into a shelter. Simply lay a tarpaulin or blanket over a line tied between two trees and peg out the lower edges to create a simple tent (above). Most tarpaulins have eyelets for this purpose. Use a Mylar sheet as a groundsheet for warmth.
● **USE A SURVIVAL BAG** Find somewhere sheltered, then put the survival bag over your head, cut small air holes at head height so you can breathe and sit upright inside it. Sit on your backpack to insulate your body from the ground.

▶▶See also: HYPOTHERMIA pp46–47 • FROSTBITE p47 • ENCOUNTERING A BEAR pp310–311

lost in a wild area

Walkers and hikers are drawn to isolated woodlands, mountains and outback areas to test their mental and physical strength, but losing your way 100km from the nearest settlement can have disastrous consequences. Survival in this situation comes down to making a few simple decisions correctly.

precautions

- Planning, preparation and practice are all crucial to your safety. If you are new to wilderness walking, take as much expert advice as you can. Plan and check your routes, research the weather conditions, make sure that you have all the equipment and clothing you will need – and ideally rehearse all your skills, from map reading to fire lighting, in a safe location.
- Make sure key pieces of equipment – such as maps, compasses and GPS devices – are at least duplicated within the party. Never keep them together in the same bag or tent.

- **Do not travel alone and make sure someone knows where you are going** and when you expect to arrive so that they can raise the alarm if you fail to arrive within a given period.
- Keep a note of the time and distance you have walked, and check your position frequently.
- Turn around every so often to get a feel for how the path looks from the other direction.
- Take photographs with your mobile phone or with a digital camera of the path and waymarks of interest that you pass in case you have to find your way back along the route.

action

LOST YOUR WAY

1 STOP As soon as you realise that you may have gone the wrong way, stop. The next decision you make may well be the most important. So take your time. Stop for a drink, a rest or a meal or even camp for the night. Consider your position carefully.

2 LOOK FOR LANDMARKS
If you still have your map and compass, look around and try to identify two or, ideally, three landmarks, such as mountain peaks, that you can find on your map. Circle them with a pencil. If you are travelling in a group, make sure that everyone agrees that you have correctly identified the features on the map.

3 TRIANGULATE YOUR POSITION Align your map and compass to north, and then turn the base of your compass so its direction of travel arrow points to your first landmark. Now draw a line on your map from the landmark at this angle. Repeat the process for the other landmarks. The triangle where the lines cross shows your position.

4 GUESS INTELLIGENTLY If you cannot triangulate your position, think back to when you were last certain of where you were. Average walking speed is 4.5km/h, so draw a circle around your last position with a radius that is the number of kilometres you could have travelled from that point. Try to locate a linear landform on the map, such as a river or ridge that you can see, and walk towards it.

GET HELP A mobile phone is unlikely to work in remote areas. If you plan to spend time in this kind of place, consider renting a satellite phone or mountain radio.

 TIME TO ACT In wilderness areas, night can fall very quickly. It is better to make camp early rather than risk getting lost or injured by carrying on in poor light.

NO COMPASS

1 USE YOUR WATCH AND THE SUN Where the sun is visible, set a watch that has a face and hands (rather than a digital watch) to true local time, taking daylight savings into account. If you have a digital watch, make a drawing of the time showing a traditional watch face and hands.

2 FIND DUE NORTH In the Southern Hemisphere, point the numeral 12 at the sun. Due north is found mid-way between 12 and the hour hand. In the Northern Hemisphere, point the hour hand at the sun. Due south is found mid-way between the hour hand and the numeral 12.

USE SHADOWS TO NAVIGATE

1 USE A LONG STICK AND THE SUN Find a long stick and push it into the ground. Ideally, it should be at least 1m long and upright. Mark the end of the stick's shadow with a stone. Wait for 3 hours and mark the end of the new shadow with a stone.

2 DRAW YOUR COMPASS POINTS Draw a line between the two stones to give you an east–west line. To find north–south, mark a line at 90 degrees to the east–west line, taking it through the centre of the line and the middle of the stick.

Emergency signals and codes

If injury or other circumstances make it impossible for you to carry on, one option is to stay put and signal for help. This strategy makes most sense when you have informed someone of your journey, who will raise the alarm when you do not arrive. Most search and rescue missions in remote areas are done from the air. There are several actions you can take to help the search.

● **MAKE YOURSELF VISIBLE** Select a location where you will be seen, such as a rocky outcrop or open hill top.
● **BUILD A SIGNAL FIRE** By day, throw damp vegetation onto the fire to produce smoke. At night, use drier wood that will burn brightly.
● **USE A MIRROR** Signal to passing aircraft using a mirror to reflect sunlight.
● **USE FLARES** Set off smoke flares to identify your location to passing aircraft.
● **LAY OUT LARGE MESSAGES** Use whatever contrasting materials are to hand to lay out signals on the ground. SOS is the universal distress signal but where space or materials are limited, a simple I means someone is injured, while an X means you are stranded and unable to move; F means you need food and water. A triangle is also recognised as a distress symbol.

 TAKE CARE If you are travelling in remote areas, don't rely on a mobile phone for communication. It is better to hire a satellite phone or mountain radio. Also consider carrying a 406MHz personal locator beacon (PLB). When activated, the beacon sends out a distress signal that is picked up by passing satellites, alerting rescue services.

▶▶See also: **HEAT-RELATED ILLNESS** pp48–49 • **DEHYDRATION** pp50–51

poisonous plants

A common cause of accidental poisoning is the consumption – usually by children – of poisonous plants. A surprising number of familiar plants contain dangerous poisons. It is worth learning to recognise the common culprits, including deadly nightshade and daphne, and the symptoms they produce.

precautions

- When out and about try to keep children well away from potentially poisonous plants. This is particularly important if the plant produces attractive fruits.
- Teach children not to eat anything that is not a recognised food.
- Never pick or eat wild mushrooms. It is difficult to identify mushrooms accurately and some cause death very quickly and have no known antidote.
- Cover up when working near plants known to be a skin irritant. Wear long-sleeved tops, trousers and gloves.
- Familiarise yourself with the symptoms of plant poisoning (see chart, opposite) so that you can seek medical advice promptly.

Stinging nettle

There are many varieties of stinging nettle (Urtica), all bearing the same characteristic stinging hairs on their branches, stems and leaves. Contact with the skin can cause burning pain, itching and numbness. In some people, the stings can induce a severe allergic reaction known as anaphylaxis (see page 54).

1 CLEANSE Wash the affected area with water. If a large area of skin has been affected, seek medical advice.

2 SOOTHE Pain and itching may be relieved by applying an ice pack or moistened cloth to the affected area.

3 SEEK HELP In severe cases, especially if the casualty shows signs of anaphylaxis, seek medical help as soon as possible.

action

POISONED BY A PLANT

1 ASSESS THE SITUATION If an adult or child appears to have eaten a possibly poisonous plant, make sure that any remaining plant material is removed from his mouth. **Keep whatever you extract or get him to quickly identify the plant he has eaten.** Before going to hospital, collect a sample in a container to help medical staff diagnose the problem. It is also helpful to take any prescribed medication that the casualty is taking.

2 MAKE SURE THE PERSON IS SAFE If he is conscious and breathing normally, sit him down with a receptacle in case of vomiting and call your regional Poison Control Centre (see page 341), which will be able to give you medical advice.

3 CALL THE EMERGENCY SERVICES If the person is drowsy or unconscious, put him in the recovery position (see page 15) and call the emergency services immediately. You should also call the emergency services if he has swelling of the mouth, face or tongue.

4 PROVIDE INFORMATION If possible, tell the emergency services the name of the plant eaten, when it was ingested and how much was eaten, and whether the person is conscious. Take their advice and while you wait for help, monitor the casualty's condition.

■ IN CASES OF SEVERE SKIN IRRITATION Go to your doctor or local Accident and Emergency Department with a sample of the plant or plants you suspect may have caused the reaction.

RECOGNISING POISONOUS PLANTS

Many plants contain poisons, which cause symptoms from contact dermatitis to vomiting, diarrhoea, heart or respiratory problems, headache, hallucinations, coma and death. These are some of the most common.

PLANT NAME	DESCRIPTION
Castor oil plant *Ricinus communis*	A woody shrub with glossy, star-shaped green/bronze leaves. Its bean-like fruits, produced in clusters at the top of the plant, contain the poison ricin. A few seeds can be fatal.
Daphne *Daphne sub-species*	A genus of deciduous and evergreen shrubs notable for their fragrant flowers and poisonous berries.
Deadly nightshade *Atropa belladonna*	A branching perennial with purplish stems, large leaves and dull purple flowers followed by black berries. All parts are poisonous. One leaf or 2–5 berries can be fatal for a child.
Foxglove *Digitalis purpurea*	Spikes of colourful tubular flowers are carried on plants 30cm to 2m tall. The leaves can cause irregular heartbeat and digestive upset.
Hemlock *Conium maculatum*	1.5–2m tall with green stems, lacy leaves and umbels of small white flowers. Can be mistaken for parsley, fennel or wild carrot. All parts are poisonous, causing muscle paralysis.
Common thorn apple *Datura stramonium*	1m tall plant with long, violet or white trumpet-shaped flowers. The chambered seed pods are round and spiny. All parts of the plant are poisonous but especially the roots and seeds.
Oleander *Nerium oleander*	A shrub or small tree with straight, dark green leaves and red, pink, white or yellow flowers. Produces brown seedpods. All parts contain a heart stimulant similar to digitalis. The smoke from burning oleander is highly toxic.
Rosary pea *Abrus precatorius*	This climber produces pods of seeds, which are bright red with a black spot at one end. Often used in jewellery, the seeds contain abrin, which is more toxic than ricin. Just one seed can be lethal.
Rhubarb *Rheum rhaponticum*	Red-stemmed perennial grown for its edible stems. The large green leaves contain oxalic acid and can cause convulsions and coma.
Wisteria *Wisteria sub-species*	A woody climber with pendulous purple or white racemes. Its seeds are produced in pods and are capable of causing severe digestive upset.
Rhus *Toxicodendron succedaneum*	Grows up to 8m tall and has 7–15 pairs of leaflets on each stem, which turn bright red in autumn. Produces creamy-white flowers and clusters of pale-brown berries. Contact with the skin can cause severe blistering and dermatitis.

DAPHNE

DEADLY NIGHTSHADE

COMMON THORN APPLE

OLEANDER

WISTERIA

RHUS

▶▶See also: UNCONSCIOUS ADULT/CHILD/BABY pp14–19 • ACCIDENTAL POISONING pp114–115

breakdown in the desert

The desert landscape is a hostile environment for people. There is very little water, temperatures can be extreme – both hot and cold – and settlements are few and far between. So if you're taking a trip that involves driving through a desert, you need to take every precaution to avoid breaking down – and know how to cope if you do.

precautions

• Make sure that your vehicle is thoroughly serviced. Ensure that the tyres, including the spare, are in good condition and inflated to the recommended pressure for desert driving (usually slightly lower than normal driving).

• Take tools and a spares kit, including a powerful torch (flashlight), fan belt, radiator hoses and a second spare tyre. Carry a shovel in case blown sand blocks the road.

• Pack extra food and water – ideally twice as much as you expect to need for the trip. In desert conditions you should allow 5 litres of water per person per day.

• Pack a large sheet of thin polythene and a 2m length of tubing in case you need to build

a solar still (see box, opposite). A sheet measuring 2 x 4m is enough for two stills.

• Take a first-aid kit with extra sun block and Mylar emergency blankets, which have a reflective surface that will help to keep you cool. Take appropriate clothing, hats and sunglasses.

• Make sure that your phones are fully charged (carry a car or solar charger for back-up).

• Carry a 406MHz personal locator beacon (PLB). When activated, the beacon sends out a distress signal that is picked up by passing satellites, alerting rescue services.

• Tell someone when and where you are going and an estimated arrival time so that they can alert the emergency services if you do not make contact.

action

VEHICLE BREAKS DOWN

1 **STAY WITH YOUR VEHICLE** You are more likely to be rescued if you stay put. Drive or push your car to a place of safety beside the road.

2 **PUT THE BONNET UP** This is a clear sign that you have broken down. At night, if you have sufficient battery power, keep the hazard flashers on.

3 **CREATE AS MUCH SHADE AS POSSIBLE** Wedge towels, sheets or your emergency blankets along the top of the doors and then stake out the lower edges or secure them with rocks to create shelter.

4 **USE A MYLAR BLANKET** If your car is a dark colour, securing a silver Mylar blanket on the roof will help keep it cooler by reflecting the sunlight and it will make it easier to spot. Drape a brightly coloured garment over the boot or bonnet to make your vehicle more conspicuous.

STRANDED IN THE DESERT

■ **FIND SHADE** Your overriding priority is to stay cool and help your body to conserve water. Stay in the shade, limit physical activity until after dark, wear long-sleeved clothing and a head scarf to absorb sweat and cool your skin, and sit on a cushion or improvised seat instead of the hot ground.

■ **STAY HYDRATED** Although you may need to ration your water, you do need to drink regularly to avoid dehydration. **Sip water at regular intervals; do not wait until you are thirsty as you will already be dehydrated.** Your body needs about a litre of water per hour in temperatures above 38°C (100.4°F). Build a solar still to provide water (see box, right).

■ **CONSERVE WATER** If water is in short supply, eat less food to limit the amount of water you need for digestion and moisten your lips and mouth before swallowing. To conserve as much bodily moisture as possible, keep your clothes on, move about as little as possible during the day, eat less and do not smoke or drink alcohol.

■ **LOOK OUT FOR SANDSTORMS** Keep your nose and mouth covered and wear goggles if you have them. Stay in your shelter and wait for it to pass.

 WARNING

Do not be tempted to drink the water from your car's cooling system unless you know that it only contains water. The cooling systems of most modern cars are filled with a mixture of water and anti-freeze all year round – and anti-freeze, despite being sweet tasting, is highly poisonous.

TAKE CARE

● If you do not drink enough water you are likely to get heat exhaustion (see pages 48–49), heat cramps and heatstroke, which can be fatal.
● Monitor your urine colour: if it is light, you are drinking enough fluid; it if is dark, you need to increase the amount of water you are drinking.
● Recycle your urine in a solar still to produce more drinking water.

Building a solar still

A solar still will generate valuable drinking water. Make sure that you carry the equipment needed (see 'Precautions', opposite).

1 SELECT A SPOT IN DIRECT SUN Look for a dry riverbed (wadi), sandy wash or depression where water might collect and dig a few sample holes. Check for moisture in the subsoil.

2 DIG A HOLE Once the sun goes down, extend the hole to 1m across by 1m deep, with gently sloping sides. Lay any vegetation on the sides, urinate in the hole and add dirty water: the still will only capture pure, evaporated water.

3 INSERT A CONTAINER Fix a cup or bowl in the centre of the hole. Run a length of tubing from the container out of the hole to allow you to drink without dismantling the still.

4 COVER THE HOLE Stretch polythene over the top and secure the edges with sand to make the still airtight. Put a small, smooth stone in the middle so that it dips down to a point just above – but not touching – your container.

5 WAIT FOR THE SUN The sun will evaporate the moisture in the hole so it condenses on the plastic sheet and drips into the container. Once the hole has become dry, repeat steps 1 to 5.

▶▶See also: **HEAT-RELATED ILLNESS** pp48–49 • **DEHYDRATION** pp50–51 • **SEVERE SUNBURN** pp52–53

falling through **thin ice**

Entering onto frozen bodies of water is extremely hazardous and should be avoided at all times. Every year many people drown or have to be rescued after falling through ice. Children are particularly at risk. Much of the danger comes from the water's freezing temperature, which can swiftly lead to hypothermia.

precautions

- Never venture onto ice unless you are absolutely sure it can support the weight of a person. In most cases it can't, so be cautious.
- Educate children about the dangers of ice.
- Ice over salt water is always potentially weaker than ice over fresh water.
- Be aware that ice under snow is potentially weakened.
- If you are visiting a region where people regularly skate on ice, such as northern Europe or Canada, seek local knowledge for places that are considered safe. Dress appropriately, wearing layers of clothing for maximum warmth. Make sure that you take spare clothes, an emergency blanket, a vacuum flask with a hot drink and the means to light a fire.

 WARNING

The more pressure you put on the ice, the more likely it is to crack. Pressure is the effect of weight divided by area: if you stand on one leg, you double the pressure on the ice. **If you feel the ice beneath you cracking, lie down immediately and roll back the way you came.**

 TAKE CARE

Many of the fatalities due to falling through thin ice are the result of someone attempting to rescue another person or a dog. Never follow a dog onto ice as they are often able to scramble out on their own. Avoid throwing sticks or balls to dogs near frozen water.

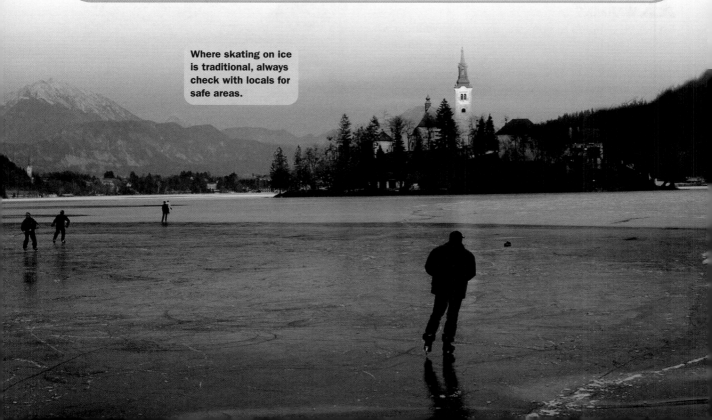

Where skating on ice is traditional, always check with locals for safe areas.

action

YOU FALL IN

1 **TRY NOT TO PANIC** On contact with the icy water your body will go into cold shock and you will begin hyperventilating. Try to stay calm. Do not immediately try to get out. Tread water and lean back. Concentrate on keeping your head above the water and getting your breathing under control. You have plenty of time.

2 **DITCH HEAVY ITEMS** Remove a backpack, if you are carrying one, or anything else that is likely to pull you down. Do not remove clothing.

3 **TURN** Once your breathing has begun to normalise, turn to face the way you came, towards the ice that originally supported your weight.

4 **TRY TO PULL YOURSELF OUT** Lift your arms onto the ice and try to pull yourself as far out of the hole as you can. If you do not have enough strength to get all the way out, rest on your elbows and let some of the water drain off you as this will make you lighter. If you still cannot lift yourself out, try to swim out by kicking hard with your legs both to raise your body to the horizontal and provide extra propulsion. If possible, use a makeshift 'ice pick', such as car keys, a knife, a pen, or any other object on your person that would help you to grip the ice.

5 **ROLL AWAY FROM THE HOLE** Once out of the water, do not immediately try to stand up. Instead, roll on your side away from where the ice has cracked. The further away you roll, the safer you should be.

⚠ TAKE CARE

● If you cannot get out of the water, lift as much of your body out as possible. You will lose less heat to the air than the water. If you hold your arms in one position on the ice, they should freeze in place and hold you up. Although you may lose consciousness, if you can avoid drowning you can survive for up to an hour – increasing the chance of rescue.

● When off the ice, return to a shelter or vehicle at once. Try to keep warm and phone for help.

SOMEONE ELSE FALLS IN

1 **STOP** If you follow someone who has fallen in, you may end up in the water with him. Shout and signal for help and try to get him to pull himself out and onto the ice (see left). If you have a phone, call the emergency services.

2 **FIND A RESCUE PROP** If the person is having difficulty getting out of the water, try to find a way of pulling him out. If there is a house nearby, try to find a ladder, a rope or a long electrical extension lead. A coat or a long branch may also suffice.

⚠ WARNING

A human chain, where a group of people lie down on the ice and inch forwards carefully with each person holding the ankles of the one in front, should only be attempted on ice that is known to be thick and able to withstand the weight. If a chain is attempted, the strongest, heaviest members of the group should remain furthest from the hole so they can pull everyone back should the ice begin to crack.

▶▶See also: **UNCONSCIOUS ADULT/CHILD/BABY** pp14–19 • **HYPOTHERMIA** pp46–47

stuck in quicksand

The thought of being slowly sucked down into a bottomless pit of quicksand is, for many, the ultimate nightmare scenario. Fortunately, this fate is largely a figment of the imagination. Quicksand is real enough and it can exert a powerful pull, but it is seldom more than waist deep. So even when it cannot be avoided, escape is possible as long as you know how.

precautions

- Check your map for indications of boggy or waterlogged ground when you are planning a walk through an unfamiliar area. Organise your route to avoid these areas.
- If you are walking near water where there might be quicksand and carrying a pack, undo the waist or chest straps so you can slip out of it quickly should you need to.
- Avoid walking along unfamiliar trails when you are alone.

- Carry a long stick so that you can check how firm the ground is in front of you.
- Ensure you always have a means of calling for help, such as a whistle, which you can wear around your neck so it is always to hand.
- For quicksand to form, sand or similarly granular soil must become waterlogged. Keep a lookout for quicksand when you are walking near riverbanks, lake shores, beaches, marshes, springs and streams.

WARNING
Soft Sand & Mud

action

YOU GET STUCK

1 **SIT DOWN** If you take a step onto ground that instantly swallows up your boots, you may be able to save yourself if you immediately sit down or fall backwards. With your upper body still on dry land and less weight on your feet, it should then be easy for you to slowly pull your legs free.

2 **DO NOT PANIC** Even if you find yourself sinking deeper into the quicksand, try not to panic. The more you thrash about, the deeper you will sink and the more tired you will become. If you are wearing a backpack, try to remove it.

3 **MOVE SLOWLY** Your body is less dense than the quicksand. Try to stay relaxed and move slowly, as if you were swimming. If you lean back and slowly paddle your legs, you should find that you can push yourself gradually backwards.

4 **DO NOT STAND UP** Once you have released yourself, monkey crawl – army-style on your stomach, using your forearms and knees to propel you along – until you are on firm ground.

SOMEONE ELSE IS STUCK

1 **TRY TO STOP THE PERSON PANICKING** If he is carrying anything heavy, tell him to discard it.

2 **REACH OUT** Lie down at the edge of the firm ground and extend your arm or a branch for the person to hold on to. Get him to lean forwards on the surface of the quicksand and ease himself gradually out as you pull him slowly with a long, steady pull.

⚠ TAKE CARE

Quicksand forms where water saturates a sandy soil to the extent that the particles of sand are forced apart. This reduces the friction between the particles to the point where the sand behaves like a thick liquid. If you try to move quickly, you will find yourself fighting both the weight of the liquid sand and the suction effect caused by its viscosity. **Long, slow movements are always the most effective way to release yourself from its grip.**

TRAVEL
EMERGENCIES

airport crises

A delayed or cancelled flight is stressful and can play havoc with your travel plans, while missing a flight or losing your luggage can ruin the start of your holiday. But it is possible to reduce the impact of these events, or even avoid them.

WATCHPOINT Try not to book the last flight of the day because if it is cancelled there are fewer alternative flights. Early flights also tend to have fewer delays than later ones.

precautions

- Different countries have different regulations about how much assistance airlines are required to give their passengers. Find out what you are entitled to before you book so you know what to expect in an emergency.
- **Make sure you buy comprehensive travel insurance to cover you in the event of a delay or cancellation. It is also worth checking whether you are covered in the event of a natural disaster or political unrest.**

action

DELAYED FOR HOURS

1 TIME THE DELAY For short-haul flights, you may be entitled to meals, refreshments and phone calls for delays of more than 2 hours; on long-haul flights, entitlements usually begin after 4 hours.

2 BE INSISTENT If a delay extends beyond 5 hours, you may be able to demand a refund. Check your ticket conditions. Airlines sometimes try to avoid paying, citing 'extraordinary circumstances' such as weather or 'safety reasons'.

Making complaints

Complaints are best resolved at the airport where staff can offer upgrades or give vouchers for meals or accommodation. If this fails:

- **WRITE TO THE AIRLINE** Include all flight details and copies – never the originals – of tickets, receipts and documents to back up your claim.

3 AVOID A MISSED CONNECTION Make sure that the airline knows that you have a connecting flight. You can give yourself some breathing space and avoid stress by allowing more than the standard 2-hour check-in time between connecting flights.

4 CARE FOR CHILDREN There are generally no special conditions for children who are victims of delays. If you have children flying with you, make airline staff aware of this and tell them about any requirements the children might have, such as special foods.

CANCELLED FLIGHT

1 SEEK AN ALTERNATIVE FLIGHT First ask the airline for a suitable alternative flight. Check your ticket for information about where you stand regarding refunds. The airline may be duty bound to find you a replacement flight.

2 IGNORE THE EXCUSES Do not accept excuses such as maintenance problems or crew shortages. Stand your ground. If a suitable replacement flight is not provided, ask to be transferred to a different airline.

3 MAKE A COMPLAINT If you are unhappy with your treatment, write to the airline.

4 CONSIDER COURT ACTION If you are unhappy with the airline's response, you may be able to take the matter to court for compensation. It depends on the laws of the country where you bought your ticket. Seek legal advice if you are considering court action and remember to consider the cost of legal proceedings. Do check your travel insurance to see whether you are covered for flight delays or cancellations.

⚠ TAKE CARE

Arrive in good time to check in; the different airlines have different rules about this. Late check-ins, even by minutes, can result in you being denied boarding.

FLIGHT OVERBOOKED

1 CONSIDER OFFERS Airlines routinely offer free flights, upgrades or mileage bonuses to those who agree to a later flight so consider accepting an offer.

2 INSIST ON BOARDING It might be worth a try to insist on boarding, but airlines can deny boarding to ticket holders if not enough passengers volunteer to catch a later flight. Know your rights: in some countries, airlines are obliged to offer compensation plus another flight, but this is not generally the case.

MISSED FLIGHT

■ **NEGOTIATE WITH STAFF** It is up to you to get to check-in on time. You have no rights if you are late. Try to get on the next flight. Airlines often allow even passengers with cheaper, restricted tickets to switch flights. If later ones are fully booked, ask to fly to an alternative airport. Most airlines charge a flat 'rescue' fee for switching a flight plus the difference in fares. These fees are negotiable, so try to persuade check-in staff to waive the fee if you have a valid reason (see below) for missing your flight.

■ **CHECK YOUR POLICY** Make sure you read the small print, as insurers may only pay out if you have missed the flight in particular circumstances, such as a public transport failure or car accident.

LOST LUGGAGE

1 SEE IF BAGGAGE TURNS UP Airlines have effective systems for tracking luggage – a high percentage of misplaced bags are returned to users within hours.

2 REPORT THE LOSS Do this at the airport. Fill out a form even if the airline says the bag will be on the next flight. Make sure the airline agrees to deliver the bags to your address free of charge.

3 CLAIM FOR EXPENSES Most airlines will pay any reasonable expenses you incur while you wait for missing bags. Negotiate exactly what these are in advance as you may only be able to make this claim at the airport.

4 FILE A CLAIM If your luggage is not recovered within a certain time (which may differ between airlines), it is deemed officially lost and you will have to fill out a more detailed claim form. It is worth checking the policy of your particular airline. If you are not happy with the settlement, complain to the airline in writing.

 WARNING

Bags are most likely to be lost on a transfer between connecting flights so fly direct if you can. Fix address and flight details inside and outside the bags.

▶▶See also: **HOLIDAY DISASTERS** pp280–281

holiday **disasters**

We have all heard stories of airlines going bust and hotels taking bookings when they are not even built. Fortunately such incidents are rare; more common are unacceptable room standards or a mix up over reservations. You can do much to reduce your risk of a holiday disaster by taking some simple precautions and finding out where you stand before you buy.

precautions

- Look for a travel agent that is affiliated to a self-regulating body as this usually means members have to follow a code of conduct. Should you be unhappy with the travel agent, you can complain to the regulating body. Examples include TAANZ (Travel Agents' Association of New Zealand), AFTA (Australian Federation of Travel Agents and TAFI (Travel Agents' Federation of India).
- **Make your travel bookings by credit card.** Although credit card companies vary in their rules and conditions, in general they offer a measure of security because you can ask them to mediate in a dispute. Check with your credit card provider; some only offer this protection on purchases over a certain amount. Whenever you use a credit card be on the alert for credit card fraud (see pages 184–185).
- **Buyer beware.** Find out what the conditions of sale are before you purchase your flight or holiday. Ask about refunds, cancellations and compensation. Most reputable companies will be happy to provide the information. **Make sure you read it.**

HOTEL BOOKINGS
- Pay with a credit card.
- Confirm the hotel booking in writing.
- If booking online, use only reputable companies.
- Find out what to expect. Read internet reviews or, even better, get advice from people you know who have been to that destination.

FLIGHT BOOKINGS
- Take out comprehensive travel insurance. Good policies include airline failure coverage.

action

AIRLINE GOES BUST

■ **TRAVEL AGENTS** If you bought your tickets through a reputable travel agent or tour operator (see Precautions), they may be able to provide an alternative flight or a refund, as applicable.

■ **OWN FLIGHT BOOKING** If you bought the tickets direct from the airline, you have no protection apart from a possible credit card or insurance claim.

■ **CLAIM ON YOUR CARD** If you bought the ticket on your credit card, you may be able to recover a refund. Check your credit-card provider's conditions.

■ **CHECK YOUR INSURANCE** Some travel insurance policies include cover for scheduled airline failure. If you have this in your policy, you should be able to claim a refund.

HOLIDAY FIRM GOES BUST

■ **BOOKED BY A TRAVEL AGENT** If you booked through a licensed travel agent that belongs to a self-regulating body, you are more likely to be able to receive a refund if the holiday company goes bust. How much compensation you are entitled to varies, however, and you should ask your travel agent for information before you make a booking.

■ **SELF BOOKED** If you booked the holiday directly you may be protected if you used a credit card. If you didn't, you might have to consider court action, in which case you will need to keep a record of all correspondence and transactions with the company. Keep in mind you might not get all your money back if you sue. You will be competing with others who are owed money and there might not be enough to go around.

TIME TO ACT Call or email to confirm your hotel booking the day before you arrive. Like airlines, hotels tend to overbook assuming that someone will not show up at the last minute.

WATCHPOINT It is best to use a credit card when booking online. The card company can mediate for you and you may be able to obtain a refund if the supplier fails to provide the services you paid for.

UNACCEPTABLE HOTEL

1 BE CALM AND POLITE Report problems at once. Explain the problem clearly and concisely to the front desk staff. Do not exaggerate. Just be straightforward about how you want the fault rectified. A smile and a clearly stated solution will get the best results.

2 TALK TO SOMEONE IN AUTHORITY Determine whether the person you are talking to can resolve the problem. If not, ask to speak to the manager. Most hotels will readily arrange a room swap if they have space. Your travel agent may be able to transfer you to a different hotel.

Substandard facilities and noisy building work can be grounds for complaint.

3 GATHER EVIDENCE Keep a photo diary and send it to the tour operator or travel agent when you return with details of your complaint. Any compensation you get will depend on the extent to which your enjoyment of the holiday was spoiled by the problems you have recorded.

NO RESERVATION AT HOTEL

■ **CHECK YOUR BOOKING** Make sure that it is not a simple mistake such as a name misspelled in the register. It is essential to carry and show written confirmation of your booking.

■ **DEMAND A ROOM** Do not leave the front desk. Politely but firmly ask a manager for a room. Find out what alternative options are on offer.

■ **ASK FOR AN UPGRADE** Ask if there are any other types of rooms, such as suites, available, but do not pay more than your original guaranteed room rate even if you are given a better room.

■ **MOVE HOTEL** If the hotel wants to accommodate you at a nearby hotel, make sure it is not simply providing you with a cheaper alternative. It should agree to pay the cost of transferring to the hotel and any difference between room rates at the two hotels. It should reimburse you if the hotel you are moved to is a cheaper one.

■ **COMPLAIN IN WRITING** Write to the hotel management or booking agent upon your return setting out your full case together with all the evidence, including booking details. State that you intend to write about your experiences on travel review sites such as www.tripadvisor.com. Make sure that what you say on such a site is true, and you can back it up with evidence. If what you say is false and damaging, then you might be successfully sued for defamation or libel.

 WARNING
You have far less financial protection if you book your own flights and hotels online. You will have to look to your insurer or credit-card provider if things go wrong.

▶▶See also: AIRPORT CRISES pp278–279

lost ticket or passport

If you do not have a ticket to fly, you may be turned away at the airport, while a lost passport will mean that you cannot book into many hotels, change money or even travel home. With careful planning you can minimise the impact of such losses, while ever-improving communications usually allow tickets and passports to be quickly replaced.

action

LOST PAPER TICKET

■ **PLEAD YOUR CASE** Test the goodwill of the check-in desk by arguing your case. **They might allow you to travel without a ticket if you can prove your identity and address, especially if you have a photocopy of the original ticket.** If they follow the rules, though, you will have to buy a new ticket.

■ **BUY A NEW TICKET** This may cost more than your lost ticket if you buy it just before you fly. You should be able to claim a refund for a higher-priced ticket when you file a lost ticket claim with the airline.

■ **SEEK A REFUND** Fill in a lost ticket application with the airline. Refunds can take anywhere between 30 days and as much as a year to come through.

■ **NEGOTIATE OVER FEES** Airlines vary in their policies but there is usually a processing charge. This may be worth challenging, especially if there are mitigating circumstances, such as the ticket being lost in the post.

■ **CONTACT YOUR INSURER** Depending on your travel insurance policy, your insurer may pay for any loss.

precautions

TICKETS

● Buy an electronically issued e-ticket. You just need to prove your identity at check-in. Keep your confirmation number for a fast check-in.
● Photocopy all tickets. If it is an e-ticket, keep a paper receipt.

PASSPORTS

● Keep a photocopy of your passport. It will speed up the process of getting a replacement.

LOST OR STOLEN PASSPORT

1 **GO TO THE POLICE** Report the loss at once to the police. Make sure you get a police report.

2 **GATHER YOUR ID** Before you can get a passport from a consul (see box, below), they will need verification of your identity. Take along as much identification as you can, but expect the consul to make further checks. This can delay travel plans. A photocopy of your passport can speed up the process, as can a photocard driving licence.

■ **EMERGENCY PASSPORT** To obtain an emergency passport, valid for one journey, call the nearest consulate and take the police report plus two passport-sized photos and identification. Consulates may offer out-of-hours services to provide an emergency passport but this will involve an extra fee. Reclaim replacement costs on your insurance.

■ **PERMANENT PASSPORT** A consulate should be able to replace a permanent passport relatively quickly if you have sufficient identification.

Contact your consul

First locate your home country's embassy (or High Commission in the case of Commonwealth countries), which is often in a nation's capital. Look for a listing in the phone book or online. There you will be put in touch with a consul, an official representative of your state, who can help with various emergency matters. Services include the replacement of lost passports and help for subjects who have been detained or imprisoned, fallen ill or been the victim of a crime. See page 340 for some web addresses to help you locate your consul.

money problems overseas

If you are suddenly deprived of funds when cash is lost or stolen, or the bank blocks a credit card, it can ruin your holiday and leave you surprisingly vulnerable as you will not even be able to pay for essentials. But it is now very straightforward to get money transferred in an emergency – and there are a number of ways to safeguard your cash.

action

LOST OR STOLEN WALLET

1 RETRACE YOUR STEPS Once you report a missing credit card, the process cannot be reversed, so first check that the card really is lost. Do not delay. Quickly look over places that you have been and thoroughly search through all your belongings.

2 CALL YOUR INSURER OR BANK Most good insurers accept reverse-charge calls and will – while you are on the phone – cancel your cards and have new ones issued. If they are unable to do that, or you do not have the right travel insurance, phone your bank or credit-card company to cancel cards. Most have toll-free numbers. If you do not have the numbers use the internet or call the local directory enquiries.

3 FILE A POLICE REPORT Go to the nearest police station and file a police report. Make sure you get a copy – the insurance company will require one.

4 WIRE FUNDS If your insurer, bank or credit card company cannot provide emergency cash, you can get money wired from your bank through transfer companies such as www.westernunion.com. The service is not cheap, but it can be set up in minutes.

CREDIT CARD REFUSED

1 FIND OUT WHY Call the card company (carry the number with you when you travel) to find out why the card has been blocked. Be aware that some cards are refused even when users have phoned to say they are going abroad (see For next time, right).

2 GET THE CARD UNBLOCKED Insist that the card is unblocked immediately. Much depends on the bank and the attitude of call-centre staff. Talk to a supervisor if you do not get results. Try to call on a toll-free number as phone charges can mount up.

Emergency money

Most consulates (see box, opposite) can give you advice on how to get funds transferred from home, but will not make cash payments unless it is an extreme emergency.

 TAKE CARE

Keep your money safe when you are out and about. For daily use, a money belt under the waistline of your trousers is the safest option. Do not carry all your money and cards in one place, such as in a handbag where it can be easily stolen, but spread them across several pockets, all with zips or Velcro.

for next time...

● Let the card company know you are going abroad. This may stop the card being blocked due to 'unusual' overseas transactions.
● Before you go on holiday, if you have access to webmail, email yourself your insurance policy number and all the credit card contact telephone numbers and account numbers. You can access the webmail at an internet cafe if you have lost all your papers.
● Do not keep all your cash in the same place. Keep an emergency supply of cash or travellers' cheques in the hotel safe.
● Make sure the bank has your up-to-date contact details, including mobile phone number. Banks are supposed to call before blocking.
● Take spare cash and credit card or traveller's cheques as a back-up. You can now buy prepaid money cards, available from several banks, which carry just the amount of money you put on them and can be used much like a credit card. Remember to leave back-up cash or cards somewhere safe when you are out.

medical help overseas

Getting medical help overseas can be traumatic. Language problems, difficulties finding a doctor, paying for treatment and worries about getting home, all add to the stress. Even if you have comprehensive health insurance, there are steps you can take to improve the situation. If you are not covered by insurance, you still have options, albeit limited.

action

GETTING A DOCTOR

1 CALL THE EMERGENCY SERVICES For a serious injury or health problem, get medical help at once by calling the emergency services. For a list of emergency phone numbers, see page 338. Get to a hospital as fast as you can. If you are in a remote area, get to a major city, where you may find better health care, as soon as possible.

2 CONTACT YOUR TOUR GUIDE OR TRAVEL AGENT If your condition is not serious, but you still need help, contact your tour guide or travel agent. If you arranged the holiday yourself, talk to the hotel front desk or call the consular service (see page 282).

You could also contact your insurer. All of these should have contact lists of doctors or other local medical services.

3 FIND AN EXPERT The consular service can provide a contact list of doctors who speak your language, as well as clinics and hospitals and their areas of expertise. Another useful source of information is the International Association for Medical Assistance to Travelers (IAMAT) www.iamat.org. This maintains a worldwide network of doctors who speak English.

4 GET IT IN WRITING Get written details of any treatment you have and any test results so you can show these to your family doctor at home.

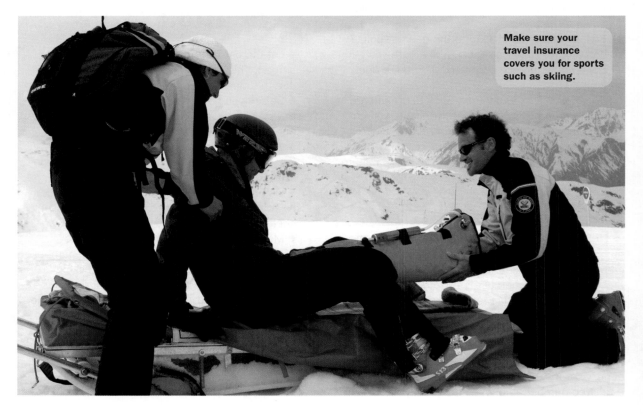

Make sure your travel insurance covers you for sports such as skiing.

TIME TO ACT When travelling at high altitudes, you may get altitude sickness. If symptoms such as a headache, tiredness, dizziness and vomiting occur, it may be best to descend.

WATCHPOINT Time differences may require an adjustment in your medication schedule, especially with drugs such as insulin. Ask your doctor for advice.

PAYING FOR TREATMENT

■ **CONTACT YOUR INSURER** Call your insurer before going for treatment if possible. Do not assume you will be covered in private clinics. Depending on your policy, there may also be an excess to pay.

■ **CARRY YOUR POLICY DOCUMENTS** If using travel insurance, give your policy details to the hospital. Some doctors will charge you upfront and ask you to reclaim fees; others will recover costs themselves.

■ **RECIPROCAL CARE** Some countries have reciprocal agreements to provide emergency medical care for each other's citizens. Check before you go on holiday whether this applies to your destinations.

■ **GET RECEIPTS** Use these for insurance claims.

GETTING HOME

1 **ASK FOR HELP** Contact your tour guide or travel agent, or call the airline direct, who may agree to waive the fees for switching flights to return home early on compassionate grounds.

2 **CONTACT THE CONSULAR SERVICE** In serious cases, the consular service (see page 282) can contact your friends or family, and may visit you in hospital and help to arrange your repatriation.

3 **CALL YOUR INSURER** Liaise with your insurer on anything that is likely to result in a claim, especially extra payments for getting you home early.

what next?

● Show all your medical notes to your doctor when you return home.
● If travelling overseas soon afterwards, declare the medical incident on any travel policies you take out as failure to do so could invalidate the policy.

 TAKE CARE
Ask your doctor for extra supplies of any prescribed medicines. These should be carried in your hand luggage. If you forget or lose your medicines, contact the consular service (see page 282). Ask your doctor for a letter listing your medications by their generic name and giving the dosage. Take the phone number of your doctor in case you need to call him.

Medical cover

● Make sure your vaccinations are up to date and appropriate for all your destinations and check whether you need to take precautions against malaria. Getting all your shots may take time so start the process about 6 months before you travel. A travel medicine clinic can give you the latest advice on what you'll need.
● Comprehensive travel insurance can be a life – and bank balance – saver. Health care bills can run to hundreds of thousands of dollars when overseas. Check exactly what will be covered, including sporting injuries and a medical escort home. A good insurance policy will cover the costs of flying relatives out.

for next time...

● Consider having both a dental and a health check-up before you go.
● Take a letter from your doctor about any pre-existing medical conditions. Find someone to act as a translator if you cannot find an English-speaking doctor.
● Drinking contaminated tap water can cause sickness. Try to stick to bottled water if you are at all unsure of the local supply. Ice may also have been made with contaminated water and is best avoided.

car accidents overseas

Driving overseas is more dangerous than driving in your own country. You may be driving in a strange car on the 'wrong' side of the road in an unfamiliar environment. Ensure that your insurance policy covers you for every eventuality and familiarise yourself with national conventions before travelling. Never drive if there is a possibility of jet-lag.

precautions

- Take frequent breaks when driving long distances. Stop the moment you feel sleepy.
- Watch your speed, especially in countries where speed limits are higher than you are used to. Do not be forced by other traffic to speed up so that you feel out of control.
- Drive within the regulations and conventions of the country you are visiting (see page 288). Your chances of a fatal accident are far higher

overseas. This is not only due to your own unfamiliarity, but because driving standards may be lower than in your home country.
- Talk through your insurance policy with your car insurer before you leave so you know exactly what is covered. You may be able to take out additional cover. Ensure you have adequate breakdown cover to provide roadside assistance and rescue should you require it.

action

AVOIDING CRASHES

■ **DRIVING ON WRONG SIDE OF ROAD** If you are driving on the opposite side of the road, take extra care when you resume driving after a break. To avoid pulling off on the wrong side, stick a note somewhere where you cannot avoid seeing it, such as on the steering wheel, stating clearly which side of the road you should be driving on.

■ **WHEN OVERTAKING** Take extreme care when overtaking, especially in a right-hand-drive car in a country where they drive on the right as your ability to see oncoming traffic will be impaired.

■ **AT ROUNDABOUTS** At a roundabout, the driver inexperienced at motoring overseas may find the flow of traffic confusing and go the wrong way round. When driving on the right, go right at roundabouts.

When you are driving on the opposite side of the road to normal, take special care at roundabouts. Follow the directional arrows.

GET HELP Immediately call the emergency services – see page 338 for a list of numbers – if anyone involved in an accident has been injured, no matter how slightly.

 WATCHPOINT If you do not speak the local language, insist on an interpreter in police interviews. If arrested, you are entitled to seek help from your consul (see page 282).

AFTER A CRASH

1 STOP AT THE SCENE Get the other driver's full details, and names and contact details of witnesses. Photograph damage for use in any insurance claim.

2 CALL POLICE In most countries, police have to attend accidents involving foreign vehicles. You may be asked to sign an accident statement, which is designed to help drivers exchange facts. Do not sign if you are not happy with, or do not understand, the statement: it can be legally binding; ask your insurer if unsure.

■ **HIRE-CAR DRIVERS** Report the accident. Tell the police, your rental car firm and your own insurer. If the accident was not your fault, make sure this is clearly stated in the accident reports.

 WARNING

Before you hire a car, find out what the insurance covers. The basic package is usually only the legal minimum and may leave you liable for injury claims. Even extra insurance from the hire firm can still leave you liable for some damage to the car. It can be cheaper to take out separate hire-car cover before you go – speak to your insurer.

YOU HIT A PEDESTRIAN

1 CALL EMERGENCY SERVICES The first priority is to help the victim, so call the emergency services (see Get Help, above). Protect the scene with warning triangles and get someone to redirect traffic around the injured pedestrian. Do not move the victim, but give reassurance that help is coming.

2 STAY AT THE SCENE You must stop at the scene of the accident and give your details if asked to do so.

3 GET WITNESSES Try to find people who saw what happened and are willing to testify on your behalf. Write down all names and addresses at the scene so that you can contact the witnesses later.

4 FIND A TRANSLATOR Ensure a translator is present at all police interviews. The consular service (see page 282) will have a list of English-speaking lawyers. Make sure they are used to dealing with road accident and personal injury claims.

Take your documents

Make sure you pack all the documents required for driving overseas, but do not leave them in your car in case it is stolen.

● **FULL DRIVING LICENCE** Provisional licences are not valid overseas. Take the paper counterpart as well if you have a photocard licence.
● **VEHICLE REGISTRATION DOCUMENT** Required in some countries if you are taking your own car.
● **MOTOR INSURANCE CERTIFICATE** Make sure that it covers where you are driving.
● **BREAKDOWN COVER DOCUMENTS** Take these with you in case you have to call for roadside help or help with repairs.
● **INTERNATIONAL DRIVING PERMIT** Required for hiring cars in some African and Asian countries.

▶▶See also: **MOTORING PROBLEMS OVERSEAS** p289

car accidents overseas

As if the trauma of an accident is not bad enough, there can be the added complication of dealing with an uninsured driver. Find out what you can do to get recompense in such a situation.

As insurance is a legal requirement almost everywhere you drive, you do have the law on your side, but there is specific action that you must take at the roadside.

action

HIT BY UNINSURED DRIVER

1 GET THE DRIVER'S DETAILS Write down the vehicle's registration number, make, model and colour. Ask for the driver's name and address, although these often prove to be fake for uninsured drivers.

2 GATHER EVIDENCE Take as many pictures of the damage and the scene as you can, including one with the other driver if possible. Note down anything the other driver said, what the conditions were and any details about the accident that might be useful, such as whether the other vehicle had its lights on if the visibility was poor.

3 INVOLVE THE POLICE Notify the police. Their report will form a vital part of your insurance claim.

■ **CALL YOUR INSURER** With a comprehensive policy, you will get your car repaired minus any excess. With a third-party-only policy, your insurer will not pay for your repairs, and as the other driver is uninsured, there will be nothing to claim from his insurance.

■ **RECOVER YOUR MONEY** Never travel with just third-party insurance. You will not get anything from the other driver unless you can trace him and succeed in a court action.

 TAKE CARE

● Stop well off the road. If this is not possible, station someone to redirect traffic around you.
● If it is necessary to help someone or carry out repairs at the side of the road, do not turn your back to oncoming traffic.
● Put out warning triangles and wear a reflective jacket (see box, right).

Be prepared overseas

Motoring organisations have web pages that give advice for motorists driving overseas (see page 339). There are a number of checks you should make before driving overseas:

● **SERVICE SAFETY** Service your vehicle before leaving home. Check it complies with all the requirements of the countries you are visiting. Only hire a car from a reputable company that can guarantee the safety of their vehicles.
● **HEADLIGHTS** When driving on the opposite side of the road, headlights need to be adjusted so that the dipped beam will not dazzle motorists. Converter kits are available but a dealer may need to make the adjustment.
● **SAFETY EQUIPMENT** Warning triangles are compulsory in many countries. Some countries insist that you have two, especially if towing a caravan. Reflective jackets must be worn in many countries if a car breaks down. A fire extinguisher is required in Greece and recommended elsewhere. In Spain you have to carry a spare set of bulbs and the tools to change them, as well as spare spectacles or contact lenses.
● **SPEEDING** Obey the limits and remember the speed-limit signs might be in mph instead of km/h. Radar detectors are banned in most countries.
● **DRINK LIMITS** In Canada, the legal limit is 0.05 per cent of alcohol in the blood compared with 0.08 in the USA, for example. In Sweden, it is just 0.02.
● **WINTER DRIVING** Winter tyres are either recommended or compulsory in many European countries. Chains are also advisable when driving in snowy conditions.

motoring problems overseas

Thousands of drivers put the wrong fuel in their car every year. It is bad enough at home as you can ruin the engine if you drive off, but it is far more serious overseas. And globally, nearly five million cars are stolen annually, some belonging to tourists who have taken their vehicle on holiday.

action

FILLED UP WITH WRONG FUEL

1 DO NOT START THE CAR If you realise you have filled up with the wrong fuel, avoid starting the engine. You could cause major damage. Contact your breakdown recovery service (see Precautions, page 286) at once. If you have started the car, pull up as soon as possible.

2 WATCH FOR OVERCHARGING You will need to have the fuel tank drained. Motoring organisations say the cost of draining a tank should not be excessive. If the car has been started and driven, the cost will be much more and will depend on the make and model of the vehicle. Get a quote from a mechanic or service station, and if you feel that the price is high, check with your insurer before agreeing to any work.

 WARNING
Diesel vehicles can take both the wider diesel and the narrower petrol nozzles, so they are more often filled with the wrong fuel than petrol vehicles.

 TAKE CARE
New unleaded fuels that are mixed with ethanol can damage vehicles registered before 2000.

YOUR CAR IS STOLEN

1 CONTACT POLICE Call the police immediately. Give them your name, address, the car's make, colour and registration and ideally the chassis and engine numbers too.

2 EXPECT THE WORST Only about a quarter of stolen cars are recovered so be aware that the chances of getting your car back are slim.

3 GET A REPLACEMENT Call your insurer to find out exactly what you are entitled to in terms of a replacement car. Most policies will provide a hire car while the police investigate.

■ **CLAIM FOR ANY DAMAGE** If the car is found, you are entitled to claim for any damage just as you would after a car accident. Ensure you get a garage to check any damage and give a full report of what needs doing. If the car is drivable, most insurers will be happy to leave this until you return home.

for next time...

WRONG FUEL
● If you drive a diesel car, consider buying insurance to cover filling up with the wrong fuel.
● Diesel owners might want to buy a 'smart' fuel cap that distinguishes between nozzles and prevents use of a narrower petrol nozzle.

CAR THEFT
● To prevent theft, invest in an electronic engine immobiliser if your car does not already have one fitted.
● Ensure that all doors are locked when you are driving and never open them to anyone unless it is an emergency.

▶▶See also: **CAR ACCIDENTS OVERSEAS** pp286–288

robbed overseas

If your appearance makes it clear that you are a tourist, you may be more of a target for thieves. Keep valuable items in your hotel safe, and money and expensive items out of view when you are out and about.

TIME TO ACT Contact the police at once. There is a chance they might be able to catch the thief and you will need a police report for any insurance claim.

action

PICKPOCKETS

■ **DO NOT GET DISTRACTED Watch for distractions, such as young children who stop you to ask for help.** While you are giving assistance, a pickpocket sneaks up and steals from you.

■ **DO NOT GET JOSTLED** Beware the 'sandwich' technique where one person stops suddenly so you collide with her, while her accomplice then bumps into you from behind and steals your wallet.

BAG SNATCHED

1 DO NOT RESIST Let the bag go. It is not worth the risk of getting attacked to keep your possessions. If you do get involved in a struggle, scream at the top of your voice. It will attract the attention of bystanders and may force the robber to flee.

2 GET A GOOD LOOK Try to notice details of the thief's build and appearance and tell police immediately. Write down details of any witnesses and make sure you get a police report.

ROBBERY FROM HOTEL

1 INFORM THE HOTEL If you have anything stolen, tell the front desk at once. If you know when it was stolen, ask the hotel to examine any CCTV footage – the hallways and lobbies may have security cameras.

2 TELL THE POLICE Do not leave it to the hotel to sort things out. Make your own statement to police. If it is a big hotel chain, make sure you also file a complaint on your return. At the very least, it will force the hotel to fully investigate the theft.

for next time...

● Do not carry money or valuables in a pack on your back. Carry a backpack on your front in busy areas or use a shoulder bag kept under your arm or across your front.
● Choose a bag that has a zip or Velcro fastening as these are much more difficult for a thief to open without you noticing.
● Always keep enough cash on you for a short taxi ride if you need to get out of a neighbourhood where you feel threatened.

● Do not keep all your money in one place. Divide it between different bags and various pockets.
● Never keep valuables in your back pocket. Front pockets are safer, but a money belt underneath your clothes is the safest option.
● Never keep any valuables unsecured in your hotel room; use the room safe or, if the room does not have one, put them in the hotel safe.
● In hotels, leave the TV on just loud enough to be heard through the door to deter thieves.

ripped off overseas

Con artists have tried-and-tested ways to rip off tourists. Many of their methods rely on targets with a gullible nature and willingness to believe anything if it seems like a bargain. Here are seven of the most common scams and how to avoid them.

WATCHPOINT Keep up your guard, but do not mistrust everyone. The vast majority of people you meet have no intention of ripping you off. Rely on your instincts.

SCAMS YOU CAN AVOID

Generally speaking, your common sense should keep you safe, but there are some confidence tricks and scams that can catch out even the most wary traveller.

SCAM	SOLUTION
METAL DETECTOR SCAM – You put a laptop onto an airport security scanner conveyor while a couple of people wait for the metal detector. One passes through, but the next triggers the alarm and slowly empties his pockets. When you get through, your laptop has gone.	Check conveyor is clear – At airports, never put anything onto the conveyor belt until the metal detector is clear. When you do put something on the conveyor, keep an eye on your possessions at all times to ensure that no one makes off with them.
THE UNLICENSED TAXI CON – A 'taxi driver' comes into the airport and offers a cheap rate to your hotel. Unsure of your new surroundings, you accept only to find that by the time you reach your destination the fare has tripled. There is, of course, no meter in the cab.	Take only licensed cabs – Never get into a taxi that does not have a meter and never take a ride in a taxi that does not have a licence. The risks of being ripped off are simply too high. Even licensed drivers sometimes take a long way round to get extra money.
FAKE RECEPTIONIST – You get a call to your room late at night saying that the front desk wants to confirm your credit-card details. On your return home you find your credit card has been used for thousands of dollars worth of purchases and that the caller was a criminal.	Only give out card details in person – Only ever give out credit-card or passport details in person – to the hotel front desk or to anyone else. Never give them out over the phone.
TOO GOOD TO BE TRUE – A gem dealer offers you a great deal on uncut gems that he says are worth several times what you will pay for them. He offers to mail them back to you at home. The ones that arrive turn out to be nothing more than cut glass.	Beware of cheap deals – Never accept a deal that sounds too good to be true. It probably is. In the case of gems, there are genuine bargains to be found in parts of Asia, but only buy from a licensed dealer. If in doubt, ask for a second opinion.
GREAT EXCHANGE RATE – You are offered a great rate of exchange from an unlicensed dealer. He counts out the cash, but on returning to your hotel you find that he miscounted and gave you far less than he promised or fake notes. The dealer cannot, of course, be found.	Only use official money changers – Never be tempted by good rates from unlicensed dealers. The only way to ensure a fair deal is to choose a reputable bank or recognised money changer.
BOGUS POLICE – Beware of fake police. There are numerous reports of people being asked for identification details by people who claim to be 'plain clothes police' and who subsequently steal their passports or wallets.	Uniforms only – If you are ever approached by someone claiming to be a non-uniformed police officer, ask to speak to a uniformed colleague. At the very least ask to see some identification.
PRACTISING ENGLISH – A young woman or man approaches you, claiming to be a university student. They offer to show you around the city for free in order to practise their English. Inevitably they lead you to a bar or tea house, where you are charged huge sums.	Never accept 'free' offers from strangers offering to act as tour guides – They are likely to be very persuasive and persistent, but you should walk away.

child goes missing overseas

A child going missing abroad, whether disappearing from a park, beach or street, is a nightmare scenario, made even more difficult by communication problems and being in a strange place. Make sure that your child knows how to contact you and what to do if she becomes separated. Contact the police immediately if you fear she has been abducted.

precautions

- Write your mobile phone number on a wristband to be worn by your child.
- Give an older child a mobile phone. Even if she does have her own phone, it is a good idea to lend a spare handset to a child when she is in an unfamiliar place.
- Introduce a child to receptionists or tour reps and tell her to go to them if she gets lost.
- Teach children that it is OK to speak to certain kinds of 'safe' strangers, such as police officers or store workers, if they get lost.
- Teach a child phrases in the local language to use if she gets lost. Make sure she can say the name of your accommodation.
- Pick a rendezvous point and say clearly that this is the place to meet if anyone gets lost.

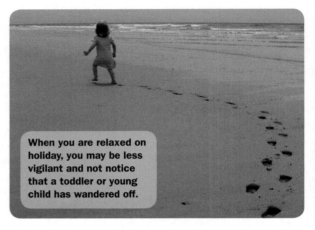

When you are relaxed on holiday, you may be less vigilant and not notice that a toddler or young child has wandered off.

 WARNING

Notify the police and your consul (see page 282) immediately if you believe the disappearance is suspicious. The first few hours are crucial.

action

MISSING IN A PUBLIC PLACE

■ **SEARCH METHODICALLY** Ask someone to wait at the meeting point while you search the area where your child was last seen. Find someone who speaks the local language to help you and give them as much information as possible that they can pass on.

■ **NOTIFY POLICE** After a quick search, **immediately call the police and your consul (see page 282). Impress on them the urgency of the situation: time is critical in missing children cases.**

■ **MAKE AN ANNOUNCEMENT** If there is a public address system – for example in a store or at a station – get an announcement made.

■ **LOOK IN FAVOURITE PLACES** Think about places that have particularly attracted your child, such as an arcade or a playground.

MISSING AT A HOTEL

1 **INFORM HOTEL STAFF** Tell the hotel front desk at once and ask them to circulate a description of the child throughout the hotel. Post someone to monitor entrances and exits, while staff assist in the search.

2 **SEARCH ALL PUBLIC AREAS** Include potential hazards, such as swimming pools, in your search. Ask other hotel guests to help. Think about where the child may have gone – perhaps to a play area.

3 **CALL POLICE** If the missing child is not found within 10 minutes, call the police. Insist that they come immediately.

4 **LOOK FOR CLUES** Ask the police to organise a search of the area around the hotel. Together with the police, examine the area where the child went missing for any clues.

Reporting a missing child

When reporting someone missing, as well as giving details such as name and age, it is vital to provide the police with all the detail necessary for a successful search.

- **HAVE A GOOD-QUALITY PHOTO** Make sure it is as recent as possible, showing the same hairstyle and, ideally, similar clothes to when the child disappeared. To be sure you have one, take a picture on every birthday and store it on your phone or keep a print in your wallet.
- **DESCRIBE THE CHILD ACCURATELY** Give her height, weight and build. Carefully describe anything she had with her when she went missing.
- **NOTE ANY DISTINCTIVE FEATURES** Mention any birthmarks, scars, or mannerisms that make your child easily identifiable.
- **DESCRIBE CLOTHING** Be as specific as you can about clothing, accessories, shoes and hats – anything that would aid recognition.
- **GIVE ALL THE FACTS** Think carefully about what might help explain the disappearance.
- **LOOK THROUGH POSSESSIONS** Search through an older child's belongings for notes or clues as to why she has gone missing.

MISSING OLDER CHILD

■ **AGREE A RETURN TIME** Before an older child or teenager goes out, check that she has her mobile phone and jointly set a time that she is expected back. Text her if she is not back by the agreed time.

■ **LIAISE WITH PARENTS AND FRIENDS** If you have got to know any other parents on holiday, find out who saw the missing child last, when and where. Try to recall if your child has made any friends. Where were they planning to go? Who did they go with? Compile a list of all the likely places and look there.

■ **CHECK HER HAUNTS** If your child has mentioned any places she has been and liked on the holiday, such as clubs, cafes or bars, go there to look.

■ **CONTACT THE POLICE** If the child has not turned up within 4 hours, report her missing to the police and your consul (see page 282).

lost overseas

Try not to panic if you lose your bearings while exploring an unfamiliar place. There are a number of practical steps that you can take to get safely back to your accommodation.

action

■ **ASK FOR DIRECTIONS** Speak slowly and calmly. Say that you are lost and ask clearly for directions. Ask if you can walk to where you want to get to or if you need to call a taxi or use public transport.

■ **PUT IT IN WRITING** If you do not speak the language, point at a map. Use your hotel's card or if you do not have one, write down the name or address of your destination in your language.

■ **LOOK FOR LANDMARKS** You will almost certainly not be far away from a known location. Look for traffic signs or signposts.

■ **RETRACE YOUR STEPS** Attempt to go back over the route you have taken until you find your way again.

 TAKE CARE

Don't look at your map on a busy street – move into a shop or hotel lobby. This will help you to avoid becoming a target for thieves. Be cautious of anyone you ask for directions; police and uniformed officials are the safest choice. Otherwise, ask someone only when there are plenty of other people around.

for next time...

- Mark your hotel on a map the moment you arrive and scan the map for nearby landmarks.
- Never leave the hotel without its business card and instructions on public transport links.
- Always carry a small amount of cash so that you can pay for a taxi if you do get lost.
- Note the position of your hotel in relation to major landmarks and places of interest. Ask the front desk to tell you the local landmarks a taxi driver would know.

▶▶See also: **KIDNAPPED OVERSEAS** pp294–295

kidnapped overseas

In some parts of the world, kidnapping is an endemic problem for locals, and even tourists are at risk. You may also be a target in volatile political situations. If you are kidnapped, do not panic; in many cases, the kidnappers will be aiming to rob you by forcing you to withdraw money from a cash machine. On rare occasions the situation may be more serious.

be aware

- Kidnapping hot spots include Colombia, Mexico, Brazil, Venezuela and the Philippines. Be extra vigilant in these countries.
- If you are going to areas renowned for street abduction, avoid going to a cash machine on the street; use machines that are inside a bank or withdraw money directly from the counter.
- Avoid becoming a target for kidnappers by trying not to show your passport in public.

action

YOU ARE ABDUCTED

1 CREATE A BARRIER Put something between you and the attacker. Whether it is a car or a group of people, an object between you may be enough to delay him.

2 MAKE A SCENE Exactly how you react depends upon the situation. Are the kidnappers armed? Have they restrained you? Security experts all agree that your chances of escape are far higher in the first few moments of a kidnap. Try to distract your abductors. Make a scene. Yell, scream. Shout out exactly what is happening: 'A man is kidnapping me.' It might just be enough to persuade your kidnappers to flee.

3 GIVE IN TO THE CAPTORS If fleeing is unrealistic and the captors are violent or armed, be co-operative.

4 WATCH YOUR CAPTORS Discreetly observe and remember as much as you can. Try to track your travel time, so you have some idea of how far you have been taken. How many captors are there? Are they well prepared? Where are you being held? What are the opportunities for escape? Listen for sounds around you, as these can give clues to your location.

If your child is kidnapped

- **CONTACT YOUR CONSUL** Your consul (see page 282) will be able to advise you on what to do. He will call the police and provide a translator if you do not speak the local language.
- **GIVE ALL THE DETAILS** Police will want to know details of your child's friends, including any new ones made on holiday, and of any suspicious incidents before the event. They will probably ask for a recent photo (see box, page 293). Take a look around for anything else that might help them: used clothes, for example, to provide a DNA sample or for sniffer dogs to pick up the scent.
- **STAY BY THE PHONE** Ensure that someone stays by the phone at all times in case the kidnappers call.
- **SEEK SUPPORT** Enlist friends to help you. Ask people at home to set up a support system so they can give help from a distance.

Do not give up; most kidnappings are resolved without loss of life.

GET HELP If you are working in a kidnapping hot spot, ask locally for advice about those areas considered too dangerous for a foreigner to visit. Do not set foot in them.

TIME TO ACT In all cases of abduction, your nearest consul (see page 282) should be contacted immediately. He will be able to help you contact the local police.

WATCHPOINT Register your trip with your country's foreign office before you go. In many cases you can do this online (see page 340). Tell your family where you are going and when you expect to return.

YOU ARE TIED UP

■ **TAKE A DEEP BREATH** When being tied up, try to take a deep breath and expand your chest. When you exhale, the bindings will loosen, increasing your chances of untying them. At the very least, this will make the bindings less tight and more comfortable.

■ **FLEX YOUR MUSCLES** Try to tense your muscles and your fists when your arms are being bound. Hold your wrists as wide apart as possible. Rope is probably the easiest to work loose. Nylon cable ties are the most difficult and will probably need someone else to loosen them. If handcuffed behind your back, the trick is to try to slip your hands under your bottom and to bring the hands to the front of your body.

SURVIVING CAPTIVITY

■ **LISTEN TO THEIR GRIEVANCES** If you know their language, speak to the captors without anger. Listen, do not argue. Challenging behaviour will just antagonise them and threaten your safety. Try to maintain a relaxed demeanour and try to understand exactly why you have been captured. It may help you to rationalise the whole situation.

■ **TELL THEM ABOUT YOURSELF** Talk to them about your family and your situation. Ask for small favours. **Anything you can do to bond with them will increase your chances of survival.** You should avoid conversations about wealth and money.

■ **STAY MENTALLY STRONG** Be as positive as you can. Give yourself a pep talk. Use your sense of humour. Do maths games, mind puzzles, anything to help you to stay alert. Celebrate any little successes you have. Keep physically fit if you can.

■ **STAY DOWN DURING A RESCUE ATTEMPT** Try to stay out of the way during any rescue attempt. Your rescuers will not necessarily know who is the kidnapper and who is the victim, so keep down low and stay away from your captors. Protect your head with your hands.

ATTEMPTING ESCAPE?

■ **STAY CALM** Remember that most kidnappings are resolved safely and successfully – it just takes time. Be patient. It is in your kidnappers' best interests not to harm you.

■ **DO NOT RISK YOUR LIFE** Once captured, plan any escape attempts with great care. If a failed attempt is likely to result in you being killed, it is probably not worth the risk.

■ **ASSUME YOUR SITUATION WILL BE RESOLVED** Most governments have a policy of not negotiating with terrorists, so the chances of a quick release are slim. However, most kidnap situations are resolved successfully in time.

■ **IF YOU ESCAPE** Even if you get away, you might still be confronted by the problem of being somewhere completely unknown, possibly where the people are hostile. Unless you are in desperate need – of medical help, for example – stay hidden until you have worked out who can be trusted.

 TAKE CARE

If gunshots are fired, keep your head down and get to the floor. Roll or crawl to a safe position. Try to get behind any sort of barrier. Stay down until you are sure it is safe.

▶▶See also: **CHILD GOES MISSING OVERSEAS** pp292–293

under **arrest** overseas

High-profile cases of apparently innocent tourists arrested abroad for being insensitive to local customs or straying into sensitive areas make the news every year. If you are taken into custody overseas, contact your consul who will help.

WATCHPOINT Never take any photos near border posts, military sites or official installations. You should also seek permission before photographing individuals.

precautions

- Know what papers you need to carry. Many countries expect travellers to carry photo ID at all times. Fail to do so and you could face arrest.
- Read up on local laws in guidebooks or on your government's foreign affairs department website. For example, some countries arrest tourists for public drunkenness.
- Take special note of areas where travel is restricted, especially border areas in dispute. Visit these regions and you could be arrested.
- Be aware of national sensibilities. Do not inflame local people by insulting the nation or defacing the flag or currency. In many countries it is illegal to do this.
- Also be aware of standards of dress and public displays of affection. What is considered acceptable in your own country may amount to indecent behaviour in some places.

Do not resist arrest. There will be time later to seek legal advice.

Can the consul help?

Your home country's embassy, High Commission (in a Commonwealth country) or consulate (outside the capital city) is where you will find the consular service (see page 282), but the consul's assistance is limited.

- **THE CONSUL CAN:** Provide a list of lawyers and interpreters, contact your family, make sure medical problems are brought to the attention of the authorities and take up any justified complaints about ill-treatment with the police or prison doctor.
- **THE CONSUL CANNOT:** Pay your legal fees, provide legal advice, investigate a crime or get you out of prison or detention. Getting released is an issue for you, your lawyer and the justice system in the country where you have been arrested.

action

■ **INSIST ON YOUR RIGHTS You have the right to contact your embassy or consul if arrested.** Give as much information about your case as you can and ask them to contact friends and family. Travelling companions can contact the consul on your behalf.

■ **GET A LAWYER** The consul will provide a list. Try to enlist help from friends or family to find a good lawyer familiar with dealing with your type of case.

■ **ACT COURTEOUSLY** Never be abusive or violent. It will just make matters worse. Talk to other prisoners to gain information about the local justice system.

■ **DO NOT ADMIT TO SOMETHING YOU DID NOT DO** Say as little as you can to the police if the lawyer is not present. What you say can be used in a trial.

political unrest

Political conditions can change quickly. If you are caught up in unrest, get information fast. Use the internet to get up-to-date news and ask tour officials for advice. Always carry the consular service phone number in case of emergency.

WATCHPOINT Avoid all street demonstrations and protests as they may turn violent. Be especially aware during election periods as this can be a time of political unrest.

precautions

- Before you travel, use your government's foreign affairs department website to check for safety warnings about your destination.
- If you are visiting a place where there is likely to be political unrest, find out the contact details for the consular service (see page 282).
- Even for a short trip, it is worth registering your journey with your country's foreign office. In many cases you can do this online; see page 340 for a list of websites. By registering it means you can be contacted in the event of a major emergency.
- Check your insurance. Most policies include cancellation in the event of war or hostilities; some also exclude travel to certain countries.
- Ask local tourist offices for advice. They should be able to tell you which areas are safe to visit.

action

CAUGHT UP IN UNREST

1 KEEP AN EYE ON THE NEWS Search out local English-language newspapers, or their websites if you cannot get a copy. Local papers may be subject to government controls so try to read the foreign media reports on the internet.

2 CONTACT THE CONSUL Phone your embassy, High Commission or consulate (see page 282). They will give you the latest news and tell you of any evacuation plans.

3 MAKE ESCAPE PLANS Find your best route to the airport or embassy and make sure you leave the building through a safe exit. Check the airport is open before travelling. If you cannot reach your own embassy, head for one of an allied nation.

4 LEAVE AS A GROUP You are much safer in company, so team up with other travellers and make your escape together. That way you are less likely to be singled out in case of trouble.

AVOIDING A RIOT

■ **BE CAUTIOUS** Treat all demonstrations with the utmost caution. If you see a protest, walk in the opposite direction or head straight back to your hotel, especially if it turns violent. Do not stay around to watch.

■ **REMAIN INDOORS** If the situation worsens, remain in your accommodation, avoiding windows if there is any rioting or gunfire. Listen to the radio or TV and ask the hotel manager or tour officials for advice.

■ **GET OUT OF THE CITY** Where the violence is localised, you may be safer getting out of the area. Head for the country or the quieter suburbs.

 WARNING

If you cannot escape from a crowd, use your arms to help you to try to stay upright. Many injuries occur when people fall over and are crushed beneath others falling on top of them.

▶▶See also: CAUGHT IN A RIOT pp210–211 **297**

aircraft emergencies

Flying is one of the safest forms of travel – your chances of being involved in a fatal accident are less than one in a million. But when an emergency occurs on an aeroplane – whether it is a runway problem or severe turbulence, knowing what to do can save lives. It is worth paying attention to safety advice, knowing where exits are and how to use an oxygen mask.

precautions

SAFEST PLACES TO SIT

Airlines insist that all seats are equally safe, but a comprehensive survey of US crash data in 2007 suggested that you are more likely to survive if you sit in the rear of the plane.

SEAT KEY
LOWER RISK
↑
↓
HIGHER RISK

Seats at the front are usually the first place to sustain damage

Seats at the back are more affected by turbulence but have higher survival rates

Being near an emergency exit means a quick escape but not all exits will work after a crash

Seats over the wing are in the aircraft's strongest and most stable part, but the closest to the fuel tanks

action

CRASH LANDING

1 ADOPT THE BRACE POSITION Make sure that your seat belt is tightly fastened and your seat is upright. Adopt the brace position: bend as far forward as you can, resting your head against the seat in front of you placing your hands behind your head. Keep your knees back to avoid leg injuries. Put a pillow on a child's lap and hold his head against it.

2 GET TO AN EXIT Stay calm if you can, but expect a mass rush for the exit. The chances are some of the passengers will be going the wrong way – tell them where the nearest exit is and turn them around. Do not take any personal belongings. Take off high-heeled shoes.

3 JUMP ONTO THE SLIDE Do not just sit on the top of the slide – jump into the middle of it. If you hesitate, a member of the crew will give you a push. Keep your arms crossed to minimise the chance of injuring yourself or someone else. Keep your feet together. Run away from the bottom of the slide.

4 INFLATE YOUR LIFE JACKET If the plane has landed on water, wait until you are safely down the slide before activating your life jacket. Get into a life raft and away from the plane as soon as possible as the plane is likely to sink.

GET HELP Your best chance of survival may be to listen to the safety briefing by crew members. Most survivors say that this information proved invaluable during an emergency.

TIME TO ACT Remind yourself of exactly how the seat belt opens. In an emergency, many passengers try to push the centre of the buckle rather than to pull up on it.

FIRE ON BOARD

1 KNOW YOUR NEAREST EXIT The smoke from a fire will restrict your visibility so knowing the exact location of the nearest exit is essential. When you take your seat on a plane, **make sure you know which is the nearest exit to you and count and memorise the number of rows of seats to it.**

2 CRAWL UNDER THE SMOKE Crawl beneath the smoke towards the nearest emergency exit. The illuminated lights on the floor of the aisle indicate the way. If possible, wet a piece of cloth with water and put it across your mouth and nose to minimise smoke inhalation. Do not attempt to open the exit until the plane is stationary. Once it has inflated, jump onto the slide (see step 3, opposite).

3 GET WELL AWAY A major danger with fire on a plane is the possibility of the plane exploding. Get as far away as you can. Do not attempt to go back to look for any travelling companions.

LOSS OF CABIN PRESSURE

1 RESPOND QUICKLY Although rare, a loss of cabin pressure is potentially fatal at high altitudes. At 9,100m people can only stay conscious without additional oxygen for up to 30 seconds.

2 DON YOUR OWN MASK FIRST Oxygen masks should drop down automatically from panels in the cabin. To ensure that you stay conscious, secure your own mask before helping others, such as children. Do not remove the mask until told to by the crew.

3 EXPECT A SWIFT DESCENT Pilots will attempt to bring the plane down as quickly as possible to around 3,000m where the air is breathable, so prepare for the plane to plummet. While this rapid plunge might be frightening, jets are designed to cope with such rapid descents and pilots practise the manoeuvre regularly.

AFTER A CRASH

1 GET AWAY FROM THE PLANE Evacuate at least 100m upwind. Planes generally land into the wind so head in the direction that the plane was moving.

2 GET ORGANISED When it is safe, do your best to attend to the casualties (see pages 12–13) and reassure those who are uninjured. Ask other survivors what skills they have and tell them how they can help.

AWAITING RESCUE

1 SALVAGE ALL YOU CAN If the plane crashes in a remote region, it is likely that you will need to survive for some time before being rescued. When you are certain that it is safe to return to the plane, search for batteries, beacons, anything that can be used for shelter (a life raft perhaps), and food and drink.

2 SIGNAL TO RESCUERS The plane's radios may still work, so try them out. Activate any rescue beacons. Also sweep the horizon with mirrors that reflect the sun or with lights at regular intervals.

TURBULENCE

1 STORE BAGGAGE SECURELY The greatest danger during turbulence is from objects falling from the overhead lockers. Make sure that everything is correctly stowed and that the locker is shut properly.

2 WEAR SEAT BELT It is better to keep your seat belt on at all times. Most injuries caused in turbulence are to people who were not wearing their seat belt.

3 STAY CALM Turbulence is one of the leading causes of fear of flying. It is usually harmless and simply a sign of atmospheric changes. Tense muscles heighten the discomfort so try to relax and stay in your seat.

▶▶See also: **PLANE HIJACK** pp214–215

emergencies on board ship

Some of the worst civilian disasters, even in recent years, have involved ferries, with the loss of hundreds and even thousands of lives. But most commercial vessels, including cruise ships and ferries, do take safety very seriously, with announcements and drills before departure, clearly marked muster stations and well-drilled crew, in case of emergency.

precautions

- Pay attention to the safety drill prior to departure so you know the location of your muster station and where the life jackets are kept.
- If you have a cabin, count the number of doors between you and the exit or stairs and how many stairs there are to the deck, so that you can exit quickly in poor visibility, such as in a fire, or if the boat is listing.

action

SHIP BEGINS TO LIST

■ **GET ON DECK** Listing in a ship may precede a sudden capsize. If this occurs you should head for the nearest muster station. Listen out for announcements and follow the crew's directions.

FIRE ON BOARD

■ **KNOW THE DRILL** The first warning of a fire will come from emergency announcements and the crew. Make sure you know your emergency escape routes and follow any instructions carefully. If asked to abandon ship, do not panic. Even the fiercest of fires should leave plenty of time for evacuation.

■ **GET WELL CLEAR** Once in the lifeboats, follow the instructions of the ship's crew or the boat leader. There may be multiple hazards that need to be avoided, such as burning oil.

ROUGH WEATHER

■ **HOLD ON** High seas will cause unpredictable movement of the vessel and slippery walkways. Hold onto handrails, especially on stairs. Wear rubber-soled shoes on deck to provide a grip.

■ **STAY PUT** Do not move around the ship more than you have to – movement increases the chance of being thrown off balance.

FORCED TO ABANDON SHIP

1 GET YOUR LIFE JACKET If an emergency announcement is made, follow instructions calmly. If you are able, put on as many layers of warm clothes as possible and a final layer of waterproof clothing if available. Move quickly to the appointed place (muster station) according to the evacuation notices. Children's life jackets will be supplied by the crew.

2 LOCATE YOUR LIFEBOAT Once on deck, await further instructions. A crew member will tell you which lifeboat or life raft you will be boarding.

3 BOARD QUICKLY Do not crowd the lifeboat or push to get on, but board as fast as you can. The first person to board needs to be strong enough to help children or any injured into the lifeboat. Most modern craft have engines, flares, several days' worth of food and water and basic first-aid supplies.

4 AWAIT RESCUE Newer boats have emergency beacons so that rescue teams can find you. Stay as near to the wreck as possible as it will increase your chances of being spotted. Do not take off wet clothing as it protects you against heat loss.

■ **COUNTER SEASICKNESS** If you have them, take anti-seasickness pills. Seasickness can cause exhaustion and even hypothermia (see page 46), and threaten your survival.

GET HELP Once in a lifeboat, try to stay as near to the wreck site as safety allows (unless land is in sight). Activate your emergency beacon so that rescue teams can find you.

TIME TO ACT If someone falls overboard, immediately shout 'man overboard' and notify a crew member. If possible, throw out a marker buoy to mark the spot and point at the victim.

WATCHPOINT Most modern ships are equipped with an automatic marine evacuation system that includes a chute for the safe boarding of inflatable life rafts.

Lifeboats

Boats carrying passengers, from small charter boats to ocean-going liners, adhere to strict regulations regarding the provision of lifeboats.

● **LIFEBOATS** There is a wide range of traditional large rescue boats that are lowered by davits (small cranes) into the water from a ship. These take up to 150 people and modern versions are often enclosed.

● **LIFE RAFTS** Self-inflating life rafts are packed in cylinders (see right, top) and found on ships, from charter fishing boats to ferries. Larger life-raft systems are ejected from ships (if the ship gets into trouble) straight into the water where they inflate to a covered circular raft (see right, bottom). They are often boarded via chutes from the ship's side.

● **FAST RESCUE BOATS** Vessels over 500 tonnes are required to carry a fast rescue boat that is launched in the event of a person falling overboard. These boats can move more speedily than large ships to retrieve a person in the water.

IN THE WATER

■ **COME UP FOR AIR** If you find yourself in the water, a life jacket should bring you up to the surface within a few seconds. If you do not have a life jacket, attempt to swim to the surface then grab anything that floats – lifering, driftwood, even a plastic bag full of air.

■ **CLING TO WRECKAGE** If possible, try to cling to wreckage so that you can pull as much of your body out of the water as possible. The biggest danger is loss of body heat. Most of the loss comes from the head, neck, armpits, groin and chest.

■ **STAY IN A GROUP IF POSSIBLE** If there are two or more of you in the water, huddle together for warmth with arms around each other. Children should be sandwiched in the middle as they lose body heat more quickly.

ADRIFT IN A LIFEBOAT

■ **MOVE IN CONVOYS** If there is more than one lifeboat or raft, you should tie them together and travel in a convoy. A group of boats is easier to spot.

■ **SAVE WATER** Carefully manage supplies of water and collect rainwater if you can.

■ **SIGNAL TO SEARCHERS** Use a flare gun or a mirror to signal to passing planes or other ships.

■ **PUT OUT AN ANCHOR** In rough weather, you should put out a sea anchor to stabilise the lifeboat or raft.

 WARNING
Smokers should never throw cigarette butts over the side of a vessel because they might be blown back onto the ship by the wind, where they could smoulder and start a fire.

train or coach crash

Bus and train crashes usually happen in an instant and without warning. The passengers on board are likely to be highly distressed and prone to panic, even if they are not injured. But it is possible to lessen your own chances of injury and effectively help others.

action

■ **BRACE YOURSELF** If you have advance warning of a crash, brace yourself against something solid, much as you would in a plane crash (see page 298). Tuck your chin into your chest to protect against whiplash injuries.

■ **EXIT WITH CARE Clamber out carefully – the exit can be the most dangerous part of the crash.** If you are going through a window, you face the danger of jagged shards of glass. You may find yourself having to climb down from a height when you get out of the wreckage, especially if the train or coach is at an odd angle, so beware of dangerous materials impeding your descent.

 TAKE CARE

Assess the situation (see below). Exiting from a train crash exposes you to track-side dangers, which could include being hit by other trains or electrocution where there is a live rail. Rail companies recommend waiting until help arrives.

■ **SMASH A WINDOW** If the train carriage is on fire, leave immediately. If you cannot get to a door, break a window. Use the hammers, if provided. Tap the window firmly near the corner. If the window is double-glazed, you will need to break both panes. Use a bag or heavy object to punch out the glass and make the hole big enough to escape through.

be aware

● On boarding, familiarise yourself with escape routes and the location of safety equipment.
● Keep aisles clear of bags and obstructions.
● In a train, opt for a seat without a table. Airline-style seating in rows is considered safer. Rear-facing seats may give better protection.
● In developing countries, avoid overloaded buses. Never stand if you can avoid it.
● Look at the condition of a bus. If the tyres are worn, for example, it may indicate a careless attitude to safety. If in doubt, do not board.

Helping the injured

Guide the emergency personnel to the most seriously injured. If people are left inside, describe their condition to the emergency services. Do not move a casualty unless he is in immediate danger (see pages 12–13).

EN57-2046ra

ANIMAL ENCOUNTERS

aggressive dog

A dog bite can be serious, requiring urgent hospital treatment. Some breeds are more likely to attack than others, and attacks tend to occur more often in urban situations, where people and dogs live in close proximity. You can avoid serious injury by learning to read a dog's body language and knowing what to do if faced with an aggressive dog.

assessment

A dog that approaches at a lope, with its head high or low, is probably coming to greet you. If it runs steadily with its head held level, it may be about to attack. Look for signs of aggression.

Hackles – raised

Tail – raised and stiff

Teeth – bared and snarling; eyes – staring

Posture – weight forward

⚠ TAKE CARE

● A dog can be very territorial, so try not to trespass on its personal space.
● If a dog sniffs you, stand still and let it confirm that you mean it no harm. It may react defensively to loud noise or if you move quickly.
● Be wary of a dog that is chained up or confined. It may attack anyone it can reach.
● Do not come between a dog and its food or between an adult dog and its pups. Teach children not to disturb a dog that is asleep.
● Do not challenge a dog by staring at it or squaring up to it. Do not smile broadly at a dog, as it may perceive the baring of teeth as a snarl and feel threatened by it.

action

DOG ATTACK

1 STAY AS CALM AS POSSIBLE If you show fear, an aggressive dog will become more confident and more likely to attack.

2 IDENTIFY A PLACE OF SAFETY Look for a car or a building and slowly back away from the dog towards it. Can you call someone for help? Is there anything you can use to protect yourself, such as a chair or is there a piece of furniture you can stand on?

3 DISTRACT THE DOG Give it an alternative target. Throw it a bag or item of clothing. If the ruse works, immediately start to back away slowly.

■ **KEEP STILL** If you cannot escape, stand still, clench your fists and keep your arms by your sides. Turn slightly away from the dog and avoid looking at it directly, but keep it in your peripheral vision. Be patient. A dog usually has a short attention span and will soon go away if you do not challenge it.

■ **PROTECT YOURSELF** If you are knocked to the ground, clasp your hands over the back of your neck and pull your arms to your ears to protect your face. Stay still and the dog will probably lose interest. Fighting back will only aggravate the dog.

⚠ WARNING

Do not run. Running triggers a dog's hunting instinct. It will give chase and you are unlikely to outrun it.

GET HELP All serious dog attacks should be reported at once to the police. A dog that has attacked once is likely to do it again with potentially more serious consequences.

TIME TO ACT If a dog has latched on to its target and you have to act, strike it on the nose. But whenever possible, avoid confrontation and the dog will lose interest in its victim.

DOGS FIGHTING

■ **USE A DISTRACTION TECHNIQUE** Try anything that will distract the dogs long enough to separate them. Throw a blanket over them or throw anything you can find that makes a loud noise near them.

■ **THROW A BUCKET OF WATER OVER THE DOGS** This technique can end a fight, although dowsing the dogs with a hose is even better. A blast from a water or CO_2 fire extinguisher can also be effective.

'Wheelbarrow' technique

A technique used by professionals to break up a dog fight is to grab the dogs' back legs to separate them. This should only be tried by someone trained to deal with aggressive dogs.

1 The rear legs of each dog are lifted off the ground, like a wheelbarrow.

2 Both handlers move away so that the dogs are thrown off balance and separate.

3 The dogs are moved in a wide arc to prevent them twisting back and biting. Both handlers move back slowly while moving sideways so the dogs have to sidestep to avoid falling over.

BITTEN BY A DOG

■ **APPLY FIRST AID** (see page 106) Try to stop any bleeding and clean the wounds, but also seek medical advice as soon as possible after a dog attack. Not only is infection common, but the pressure exerted by a dog's jaws can cause internal injuries and broken bones.

■ **SEEK MEDICAL HELP** There is a chance of catching rabies from a dog bite, especially if the dog was a stray. Get medical advice immediately. You will also need a tetanus injection if you have not had a vaccination in 5 years. Call the emergency services if you cannot stop the bleeding or suffer any loss of feeling in the affected limb.

 TAKE CARE
● Very small children and toddlers are particularly vulnerable and may not understand the risks or the implications of behaving in certain ways around dogs. If, for instance, they growl back at a dog thinking they are playing with it, they might provoke it to attack. It is important to supervise their contact with dogs at all times. An infant or young child should never be left alone with a dog, even the family pet.
● Teach an older child to ask the owner's permission before attempting to pet a strange dog.
● Certain dog breeds are statistically more likely to be involved in attacks. These include Pit Bull terriers, Staffordshire Bull terriers, German Shepherds, Blue/Red Heelers, Dobermans and Rottweilers. Take extra care around these dogs.

 WARNING
● **Never attempt to separate fighting dogs by grabbing their collars.** You will almost certainly be bitten. When dogs fight they are in survival mode, and they will simply see you as another enemy.
● Dog bites carry the risk of rabies, which can be passed to humans. Anti-rabies treatment may need to be given immediately.

charging deer

These apparently placid grazing animals may not seem threatening but in some circumstances they can become dangerous. Male deer undergo a change of character in the rutting season and females will attack when they have young to protect. A number of species of deer have been known to attack and even kill people.

be aware

- Even male deer that are tame enough to hand-feed for most of the year can become extremely aggressive as their hormones fluctuate during the mating season.
- **Female deer that are protecting their young can be very aggressive, particularly towards dogs,** whom they perceive as a threat to their fawns. Always keep dogs on a lead in areas where you know that deer are breeding. If you see a fawn, do not be tempted to approach it.
- In parts of the world where human habitation has encroached on deer territory, deer have lost much of their timidity towards people. This makes it much harder to predict their behaviour and means they may attack at any time of year.
- Deer kept as pets have no fear of humans and can be extremely unpredictable.

Males in rut

Deer are generally timid, but in the mating season, called the rut, stags can become aggressive. During the rut it is advisable to keep away from deer in case you provoke an aggressive response.

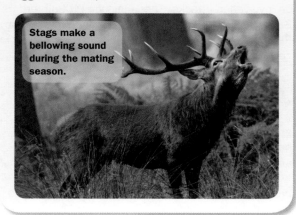

Stags make a bellowing sound during the mating season.

action

1 **ASSESS THE SITUATION** If a deer appears agitated, try to work out why – have you come between it and a female or got too close to some fawns? Whatever the case, move away calmly while watching the deer.

2 **GET BEHIND A BARRIER** If a deer charges you, try to put some kind of barrier between you and it. Get behind a wall, fence or vehicle.

3 **USE A TREE FOR SAFETY** If there is a tree you can climb, swing yourself up into its branches. If you cannot climb the tree, try to use its trunk as a protective barrier between you and the deer.

■ **IF YOU CAN'T ESCAPE** Find a weapon or something you can throw at the deer, scream, shout and wave your arms. Make yourself as large, noisy and intimidating as possible.

■ **IF YOU GET KNOCKED TO THE GROUND** Roll up in a ball, use your arms to protect your head and face and try to stay as still as possible to avoid further provoking the animal.

 TAKE CARE

Avoid entering any enclosed area where there are deer. Farmed deer can be as aggressive as wild deer and deer farmers are occasionally gored to death, especially during the rut.

 WARNING

Camera flashes have been identified as a possible cause of deer attacks. Avoid taking close-up photos of them, particularly during the rutting season. If you want to observe them at this time use binoculars or a long lens from a safe distance.

aggressive cattle

If you have to walk through a field of cattle, know the signs that warn of danger and what to do if one of the animals attacks. Bulls can be very dangerous when aroused and frightened cows can trample and crush people to death.

WATCHPOINT Cows with young calves can be more dangerous than bulls. Both cows and bulls are likely to react aggressively to dogs.

assessment

Most bulls are kept well away from public access areas, but it is still worth knowing the clear signals that tell you an attack is imminent.

Shoulders – lowered

Back – arched

Hooves – pawing the ground

Head – facing down

⚠ TAKE CARE

● Avoid entering a field where there is a bull, especially if you have children with you. Even if a public footpath crosses it, go round it if you can.
● If it is imperative that you enter a field that has a bull in it, assess the risk before you climb the stile or open the gate. Check where the bull is and what it is doing. Identify your points of exit, and any places of safety, such as a farm building.
● As you cross the field, walk purposefully but do not run. Keep to the field boundary or follow a path that keeps the maximum distance between you and the bull. Be aware of your nearest exit.
● If you are walking with others, stay in a tight group. **Keep children in the centre, shielded by adults.** Before entering the field, agree on who will do what should the bull charge.

action

ENCOUNTER A BULL

1 RECOGNISE THE THREAT A bull may challenge you with what is called the 'broadside threat posture', (see above) where it shows its power by standing or walking sideways-on. If you see this, back away slowly. If the threat escalates, with the bull facing you head on, its shoulders lowered, and its hooves pawing the ground, retreat as rapidly as possible.

2 DO NOT STARE AT THE BULL The bull will walk towards you slowly, twisting its head and roaring with its tongue out. Walk very slowly backwards.

3 THINK TACTICALLY If there are cows in the field, try to put some of them between you and the bull.

4 DODGE A CHARGE Only attempt to outrun the bull if you are close to an exit. Throwing a backpack or a piece of clothing to one side may provide a distraction, but be ready to side-step or jump out of the way if you have to. Once the bull has passed you, move swiftly in the opposite direction, or towards the exit.

CATTLE APPROACHING

■ **KEEP YOUR NERVE** If the animals approach you, be bold and walk straight through them.

■ **RELEASE YOUR DOG** If you feel in danger, let your dog off the lead and do not appear to protect it.

elephants and rhinos

Sheer size and the ability to run faster than 40km/h make elephants and rhinos potentially imposing threats. They can be unpredictable and aggressive, particularly during the breeding season or when they feel their young are threatened. Learn how to avoid agitating these animals and what to do if they charge.

action

HOSTILE ELEPHANT/RHINO

■ **FIND A SAFE PLACE** Always remain close to your vehicle in rhino or elephant territory. It is possible, when on foot, to suddenly be close to these animals, particularly rhinos, without realising. Remain calm; back away without making sudden movements; maintain eye contact. If possible, get back in your vehicle. If not, assess your options in the event of a charge and identify an obstacle to hide behind.

■ **CLIMB A TREE** Look for a tree with branches around head height and grab a branch. Use your momentum to swing your legs and body up. If you cannot climb a tree, head towards the nearest one that has a thick trunk and stand behind it. In lieu of a tree, seek refuge in a thick bush.

■ **IF YOU ARE CHASED** Do not try to out-run a charging elephant or rhino. Drop a bag or piece of clothing as a decoy. Sometimes, a well-aimed branch thrown at the animal's front feet will cause it to stop. This will give you the chance to find a safer place; for example, behind a large tree.

■ **IF YOU CAN'T GET AWAY** Stand still and face the animal. As it approaches wave your arms wildly and scream and shout as loudly as you can. But be prepared to leap out of the way.

Charge or bluff?

Most elephant charges are bluffs. If the ears are spread and the trunk is up, it is probably a mock charge, and the elephant will stop short. A really agitated elephant will hold its ears flat against its head, and tuck its trunk in.
Rhinos will charge towards an unfamiliar scent or sound. They seldom mock charge.

be aware

● Wild elephants and rhinos can be extremely dangerous. If you are observing them, do so from a distance and always with a guide.
● When driving through elephant or rhino country, take care not to surprise the animals. Be particularly careful at dawn and dusk or where the road is narrow and the bush dense.
● If elephants or rhinos are blocking the path of your vehicle, do not try to edge through or sound the horn. Either turn back, or switch off your engine and wait for them to leave.
● **If you encounter rhinos when on foot, try to stay upwind of them and do not get too close; keep 30–50m between you and the rhinos.**
● Never approach a young elephant or rhino – the maternal bond is very strong and females are extremely protective of their young. A mother will attack anything that is a threat.
● If a herd of elephants is feeding, they are probably relaxed. If they stop feeding and begin showing any signs of irritation, such as shaking their heads, retreat at once.

Female elephants will protect their young with their bodies and even their lives.

aggressive monkeys

Some areas around the world have large populations of monkeys living closely to people. Always remember that no matter how tame they may seem, monkeys can be extremely unpredictable. They can quickly become aggressive, particularly if food is involved. In common with most animals, monkeys may attack if they sense a threat to their young.

precautions

- Do not attempt to feed or pet monkeys. They may grab at food, jewellery or clothing, which can be the start of an attack.
- Do not show your teeth by smiling or making facial expressions as a monkey may regard this as an aggressive signal. Avoid prolonged eye contact for the same reason.
- Monkeys that are accustomed to receiving food from people, at tourist spots or temples, for instance, may assume that any food that you are carrying is for them. Hide foodstuffs in sealed containers inside your bag or avoid carrying a bag altogether.
- Never get between a mother monkey and her baby as this will arouse her protective instincts and may incur the wrath of the entire troupe of monkeys.

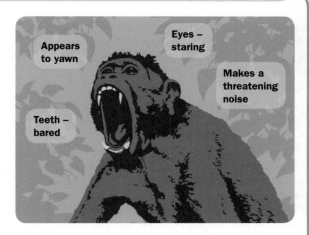

Appears to yawn

Eyes – staring

Makes a threatening noise

Teeth – bared

- If a monkey displays the above signs, it is probably about to attack and you should calmly retreat without showing panic.

action

MONKEY ATTACK

1 GIVE THEM WHAT THEY WANT If a monkey or a troupe are menacing you because they can see that you are carrying food, drop it and retreat. Do not try to beat them off the food. If you do not have any food, show them your open palms to demonstrate that it is pointless to proceed with the attack.

2 DO NOT GIVE WAY TO PANIC Try to stay calm, although screaming and shouting at the monkey may be enough to scare it away.

3 USE A WEAPON If you feel you are in real danger, grab anything that comes to hand – a stick, stone or your belt and use it to repel the monkey. Most monkeys will retreat as soon as they realise that you are not intimidated.

⚠ TAKE CARE

- If you are bitten by a monkey, wash the bite immediately with an antiseptic or disinfectant solution and seek medical help as soon as possible. A monkey bite can be more than a nasty wound. Monkeys can carry and pass on many serious diseases, including rabies and hepatitis B. A medical practitioner will be able to administer tests to determine whether you have contracted anything serious, and, if necessary, give you appropriate medication, such as an anti-rabies injection.
- Even if you've not been bitten, always wash your hands thoroughly after contact with a monkey.

▶▶See also: ANIMAL OR HUMAN BITE p106

encountering a **bear**

Although attacks are rare, encounters with bears are potentially lethal. If you are planning a trip through bear country, such as in the forests or woodlands of North America or northern Eurasia, understanding how to behave during an encounter could prevent an attack. Knowing what to do if a bear attacks you could save your life.

precautions

- When walking or camping in bear country, check with local wildlife authorities for information about bear behaviour, habits and activity in the area.
- Carry anti-bear pepper spray (see box, opposite) close at hand, where it can be easily and quickly accessed – in a pocket or holster on your belt. Make sure you know how to use it and practise blindfolded so you will be able to operate it even at night.
- Never wander off or go walking alone.
- Avoid areas where bears are likely to be encountered, such as berry patches, stream sides and dense forest. Look for evidence of bears: large droppings (bigger than 5cm in diameter), animal prints with claw marks, and animal carcasses.
- Before cycling in bear country, make sure that your bicycle is fitted with a bell and ring it frequently to alert bears to your presence.

- Avoid walking at dusk, dawn or during the night when bears are most active.
- In woodland, alert any nearby bears to your presence by talking loudly, clapping or whistling. If a bear knows you are nearby it will normally avoid you.
- Bears are attracted to food, so take sealable containers for edible supplies, soaps and cosmetics.
- Keep dogs on a lead or, better still, avoid taking them into bear country.

 TAKE CARE

When camping, do not just lock food inside your vehicle as bears have been known to break into cars and vans. Store food and waste in sealed containers 100m from your campsite and hung from a rope at least 4m above the ground and 1m from the nearest tree trunk.

recognition

The brown bear (*Ursus arctos*) – of North America and northern Eurasia – and American black bear (*Ursus americanus*) – restricted to North America – are both dangerous. Telling them apart is critical to ensure the best response during an attack (see next page). The Kodiak and grizzly bears are both forms of brown bear.

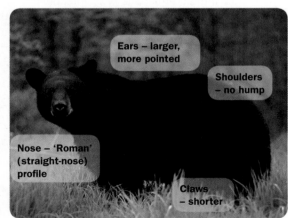

Ears – larger, more pointed

Shoulders – no hump

Nose – 'Roman' (straight-nose) profile

Claws – shorter

Ears – short, rounded

Shoulders – a distinct hump

Claws – twice as long

Face – dish shaped

BEAR HAS NOT SEEN YOU

1 DO NOT ATTRACT THE BEAR'S ATTENTION Stop, and stand still. Make no noise.

2 RETREAT SLOWLY Revise your route to give the bear the widest possible berth.

3 NOTE THE WIND DIRECTION Try to stay downwind of the bear so that it remains unaware of you.

BEAR HAS SEEN YOU

1 SPEAK LOUDLY AND CALMLY Wave your arms, so that the bear can identify you as human. Bears have relatively poor eyesight, but their hearing and their sense of smell are good. Never attempt to feed or throw food at a bear.

2 BACK AWAY SLOWLY Keep at an angle to the bear's line of sight. Give the bear as wide a berth as possible. Note the wind direction (see above).

BEAR APPROACHES YOU

1 DO NOT RUN Running will provoke the chase response and a bear, which can reach a speed of 60km/h, will certainly outrun you.

2 SPEAK CALMLY TO THE BEAR Back away slowly at an angle to its line of sight. If the bear continues to approach, stop and hold your ground. Bears frequently bluff charge so try not to panic. But if the bear comes to within 9m, use your pepper spray for at least 6 seconds (see box, right), aiming at the bear's eyes and mouth, and then retreat.

3 REPORT ENCOUNTERS Advise local authorities of any bear encounters. The information could help prevent an injury, or worse, in someone else.

 WARNING

Pepper spray is an effective deterrent only when discharged as an airborne cloud. It offers no protection at all when sprayed onto clothing or camping equipment.

BEAR ATTACKS YOU

If you have pepper spray, use it. Otherwise, take the following measures.

■ **FIGHT A BLACK BEAR** Throw rocks, hit it with a stick, punch or kick it. Be as aggressive as possible and direct blows at the eyes and nose.

■ **PLAY DEAD WITH A BROWN BEAR** Protect your stomach by lying face down (see above) or rolling into a ball, with your hands clasped across the back of your neck. Remain in position until you are sure the bear has left, then seek help.

Bear-deterrent pepper spray

The spray contains capsaicin, a non-lethal irritant derived from chillies. It is most effective when sprayed as an airborne cloud from a range of 9–12m across the path of a charging bear. Rain or wind may reduce its impact.

1 POINT THE SPRAY Do not aim too high. Direct the nozzle slightly down and towards the approaching bear, waving the canister in a left-to-right motion while spraying.

2 RETREAT Once the bear breaks off its attack, retreat at once. If the bear manages to make contact with you, take appropriate action (see above).

venom in the sea

Of the millions of swimmers who take to the sea each year, a few are painfully stung. Fast action can reduce some of the discomfort and pain, but with all stings always be prepared to treat the casualty for shock (see pages 38–39).

WATCHPOINT Never swim in the sea by yourself. Even minor emergencies can quickly become major ones if there is no one nearby to help or raise the alarm.

be aware

JELLYFISH

● Check with lifeguards for the presence of jellyfish and look for signposted warnings. Wear protective swimwear to keep bare skin covered.

● Some jellyfish stings can be painful and deadly.

Most dangerous is the box jellyfish species known as the sea wasp, found in tropical coastal waters off Australia, the Indo-Pacific and South-East Asia. Related smaller Irukandji jellyfish species, found in offshore tropical waters worldwide, are also potentially lethal. The jellyfish-like Portuguese Man-o'War, also known as the bluebottle (above), which floats in warm ocean water worldwide, delivers a very painful, but rarely fatal, sting.

BLUE-RINGED OCTOPUS

● These shy creatures have a poisonous bite that can be fatal. They shelter in crevices on reef flats and in tidal pools and occur throughout the Indo-West-Pacific, from New Zealand in the south to Japan in the north.

● Adults are up to 20cm long. They are usually brown or yellow but when disturbed develop 'glowing' blue markings.

STINGRAYS

● Stingrays are found in warm temperate and tropical waters worldwide. Check if, when and where, stingrays occur in your holiday destination.

● People usually come into contact with stingrays in shallow water. Shuffle your feet as you enter the water to avoid stepping on them and so that they can move away.

● When snorkelling, avoid disturbing sandy seabeds.

● If you happen to catch a stingray when fishing, net it before lifting it into the boat.

SCORPION-FISH AND STONEFISH

● With needle-like fin spines connected to venom glands, these groups include some of the most toxic fish in the ocean. Scorpion-fish are found in all tropical and temperate seas; stonefish occur throughout the Indo-Pacific.

● They live mostly in shallow waters on or near the seabed and are often very well camouflaged. People usually encounter poisonous spiny fish by accidentally standing on them or by picking them up.

● Avoid walking on reef or tidal flats in bare feet where these fish are known to occur.

action

JELLYFISH STINGS

1 LEAVE THE WATER Always liberally douse any suspected jellyfish sting with vinegar UNLESS you know it is a bluebottle (Man-o'War) sting (see below). Remove any tentacles from the skin carefully – use a plastic bag or a stick, for example. Wash the area in sea water – not fresh.

■ **RINSE EYES** Stung eyes should be rinsed with a saline solution then dabbed with a vinegar-soaked towel. Vinegar should not be put on the eyes directly.

■ **GARGLE FOR MOUTH STINGS** Use a solution of three parts water to one part vinegar before spitting it out.

■ **TAKE PAINKILLERS** Take painkillers, such as paracetamol or ibuprofen, to reduce the pain.

BOX JELLYFISH STINGS

1 GET MEDICAL HELP A box jellyfish sting is life-threatening so call the emergency services at once. Prepare to give cardio-pulmonary resuscitation (CPR) if casualty stops breathing (see pages 16–17).

2 SOAK WITH VINEGAR Immediately soak the affected area with ordinary vinegar to help stop more venom being released. Keep the stung area still.

IRUKANDJI STINGS

■ **BE ALERT** A sting may seem minor and there may be no mark. Symptoms can appear up to 40 minutes later, usually beginning with severe lower back pain possibly followed by nausea, vomiting, muscle spasms or breathing difficulties. Douse a suspected Irukandji sting with vinegar and seek emergency help.

BLUEBOTTLE (MAN O'WAR) STINGS

■ **REMOVE TENTACLES** Do not use vinegar. Rinse tentacles off with sea water or remove with tweezers. Apply ice wrapped in a plastic bag. Water heated to 45°C may reduce the pain. If eyes are affected, rinse with a saline solution and seek medical help.

STINGRAY WOUNDS

1 TREAT THE WOUND Remove the casualty from the water and staunch any major bleeding by applying localised pressure. Most stingray wounds are to the feet and lower legs and these injuries should first be thoroughly cleaned. A wound to the chest or abdomen requires immediate medical attention.

2 REDUCE THE PAIN Quickly immerse the affected limb in water as hot as you can bear. Soak the wound for 30–90 minutes.

3 DRESS THE WOUND Keep the limb elevated. Take painkillers to reduce the discomfort, which may last 2 days. Check the wound regularly for infection.

4 GET MEDICAL ATTENTION Even if you have treated the wound, seek medical advice. Parts of the barb may be embedded in the wound and further treatment may be needed.

BLUE-RINGED OCTOPUS BITES

■ **BITE CAN BE PAINLESS** Numbness of the lips and tongue occurs soon after being bitten and is often the first sign of a bite.

1 GET MEDICAL HELP Phone the emergency services immediately. There is no antidote or antivenom but administering the correct first aid can be life-saving. Breathing difficulties can occur rapidly, escalating to paralysis of breathing muscles within minutes.

2 BEGIN RESUSCITATION If mouth-to-mouth resuscitation is needed, do not stop until medical help arrives, even if victim appears not to be responding. Breathing assistance may be needed for up to 12 hours at a hospital, after which victims usually recover.

SCORPION-FISH AND STONEFISH WOUNDS

■ **GET MEDICAL HELP** Treat all wounds by stinging fish as serious. A doctor will assess whether an anti-venom should be administered. Try to record a description of the fish responsible for the sting.

▶▶See also: **SEVERE ALLERGIC REACTION** p20 • **SHOCK** pp38–39 • **INFECTED WOUND** p66

shark in the water

In 2008 there were 59 unprovoked shark attacks worldwide (32 off the coast of Florida, USA) with four deaths: two in Mexico, one in Australia and one in California, USA. These figures reveal how rare it is to be attacked – you have more chance of being struck by lightning than being bitten by a shark. But here is what you need to know in the event of a shark attack.

precautions

- When travelling, check the shark safety record of beaches you plan to swim at. Stick to beaches with lifeguards or bays protected by shark nets. The US states of Florida, California and Hawaii are shark hot spots. So too are Australia and South Africa.
- Sharks are most likely to be in attack mode around their natural prey, so do not swim near aggregations of seabirds, seals, penguins or fish. Be wary also around river mouths and fishing boats.
- Stay out of murky water. Bad visibility may prevent you from seeing a shark and increase the chance of a shark biting you by mistake.
- Avoid swimming between sandbars and near steep drop-offs – locations favoured by sharks.
- Contrasting coloured clothing is best avoided. So too is shiny jewelry which can shimmer like fish scales. Avoid excessive splashing, too, as a shark may see it as young or injured prey.
- Always swim with others. Lone swimmers can be more susceptible to attacks.

RECOGNISING SHARKS THAT MAY ATTACK

Most reported attacks on humans are from white (also called great white), tiger and bull sharks. The oceanic whitetip is probably the leading shark threat to survivors of mid-ocean boat and air accidents.

SHARK NAME	CHARACTERISTICS	
WHITE SHARK	Pointed snout and long, prominent gill slits. Back blue-grey; underside white. Average length 5m. Occurs worldwide in temperate coastal waters. Adults are often daytime hunters of marine mammals and turtles.	WHITE SHARK
TIGER SHARK	Large eyes, rounded snout. Back dark with spots and vertical bars along its length. Pale underside. Occurs from river estuaries to open ocean in temperate to tropical waters worldwide. Average length 4.25m.	
BULL SHARK	Found in tropical to sub-tropical coastal waters worldwide. Commonly enters estuaries and swims upriver into fresh water. Stout body, rounded snout. Small eyes. Grey back, pale belly. Maximum length 3.5m.	BULL SHARK
OCEANIC WHITETIP	Stocky body. Large, rounded first dorsal fin. Paddle-like pectoral fins. Most fins tipped white. Occurs in offshore tropical to sub-tropical waters worldwide. Body dark; white to yellow underside. Average length 3m.	

action

SHARK ENCOUNTER

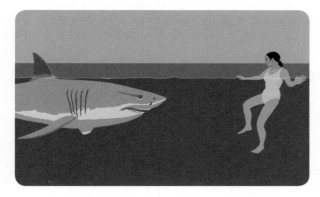

Never tease or deliberately aggravate a shark. Try to remain calm during any encounter and avoid making large, sudden splashing movements. Keep your distance but be prepared to be assertive.

■ **IF YOU SEE A SHARK** Alert any nearby swimmers, and then swim towards the shore, a boat or any other way out of the water, as smoothly as you can. **Breaststroke is a suitable splash-free stroke.** If a shark is swimming towards or around you, it may simply be curious. Turn to face it, hang vertically and slowly tread water looking as unlike a seal as possible. If other swimmers are near, tread water closely together, with your backs to each other.

■ **IF YOU SENSE A SHARK** If you feel something nudge you or brush past you, leave the water as quickly and calmly as you can before investigating. Sharks sometimes bump their prey before attacking. Some victims report not to have realised that they have been bitten until a few moments after an attack.

■ **IF YOU ARE DIVING** Most attention from sharks will be non-threatening curiosity, unless spearfishing is involved. However, lowered pectoral fins, erratic swimming, charging and back-hunching indicate aggression. If this happens, remain close to diving buddies, back up to rocks and respond to any attack by hitting the snout, eyes or gills with anything available. Ascend with your backs to each other as quickly as is safe and leave the water.

SHARK ATTACKS YOU

1 FIGHT BACK Never play dead. Use any object available to strike eyes and gill slits, or claw these areas with your fingers. Aggression is needed to tell a shark you are a strong opponent, best left alone.

2 TEND YOUR WOUNDS While leaving the water as quickly as possible, apply direct pressure to any wounds, to stem bleeding. Swimming on your back propelled by rhythmic leg kicks frees hands for this.

3 SEEK HELP, WARN OTHERS Once ashore, raise the alarm and seek medical attention for wounds.

YOU WITNESS AN ATTACK

1 ALERT THE LIFEGUARD If none present, go for help or send a bystander. Any deep-water rescue is best attempted by boat. Do not put yourself at risk but help the victim ashore if you can.

2 TEND VICTIM'S WOUND Staunch any bleeding (see pages 96–97) by applying pressure to the wound.

3 SETTLE VICTIM Keep the victim still and wrap him in towels to keep warm and prevent shock (see pages 38–39). Call for medical assistance.

 TAKE CARE

If you have been spearfishing and are carrying a catch of fish when you see a shark, let the catch go and slowly swim away from it. Get back in your boat.

▶▶See also: **SEVERE BLEEDING** p22 • **SHOCK** pp38–39 • **DROWNING** pp250–251

facing **hippos** and **crocs**

Hippos cause more deaths than any other large animal in Africa; some estimates put the number of people killed annually at more than 100. Crocodiles, too, cause hundreds of deaths worldwide each year. Attacks are avoidable. If you are attacked, keeping a cool head and knowing what to do will greatly increase your chances of survival.

precautions

HIPPOS

- Hippos will attack to protect their young and their territory, and out of fear. Always give them a very wide berth both in the water and on land.
- Do not swim anywhere near hippos, and when boating, use your oars to make plenty of noise by splashing and banging on the side of the boat, so that you do not surprise a dozing group.
- At night, hippos graze on land, frequently roaming several kilometres from the river along well-worn tracks. Never place yourself between a hippo and the water.

CROCS

- Pay particular attention to signposted warnings in crocodile country. Never swim or go near the water's edge in these areas. Crocodiles are stealth hunters. Even if you think you can't see one, a crocodile may be near. This includes some beaches and coastal areas in the tropics.
- Be especially careful as night falls; this is when crocs are most active and are harder to see.
- If you are boating, be vigilant and take turns to keep watch. Do not trail your limbs in the water. Make noise to avoid startling a dozing crocodile.

action

HIPPO ATTACK

■ **FIND A SAFE SPOT** Hippos seldom bluff. If it charges, run straight to the safety of a tree, vehicle or building. **Hippos can run at nearly 30km/h, but cannot turn swiftly;** you might be able to sidestep a charge.

■ **IF A HIPPO CAPSIZES YOUR BOAT** Try to use the hull as a shield between you and the hippo. If a hippo bites you, it may drag you under the water to drown. Use a rock, branch or your fingers to attack its eyes.

CROC ATTACK

1 **RUN AWAY** You may be able to outrun a croc, as 17km/h is their top speed on land. Run away from the water and in a straight line. Do not zigzag.

2 **RETALIATE** If you are bitten in or near water, the reptile may try to drag you under. Scream and fight back. Use any and every weapon to attack its eyes and nostrils.

3 **ATTACK THE PALATAL VALVE** If your arm is in the reptile's mouth, try to reach the palatal valve (a membrane that prevents water from entering its throat, see right) behind the tongue. If you can hit it, or force it open, the reptile may release you.

biting insects

If someone has an extreme allergic reaction to an insect bite, the result can be fatal. Even if the person bitten does not have a severe response, many insects carry diseases – some of them serious – so all bites need to be treated with care. To avoid problems, take precautions to avoid being bitten in the first place.

action

INSECT BITES

1 **DO NOT SCRATCH** To reduce swelling and soothe any itching apply calamine lotion, ice packs, ibuprofen gel or antihistamine cream; oral antihistamines will also reduce the swelling.

2 **WATCH FOR ALLERGIC REACTIONS** In extreme cases, a condition called anaphylaxis can occur (see pages 20 and 54). Symptoms include wheezing, difficulty in swallowing and faintness. If the casualty experiences any of these reactions, get medical help at once.

Insect-borne diseases

Mosquitoes can carry malaria, yellow fever, dengue fever and encephalitis. Ticks may pass on Lyme disease, tsetse flies can carry sleeping sickness and sandflies – found on beaches – leishmaniasis.

TICK BITES

1 **USE TWEEZERS** Apply insect repellent to kill the tick then take hold of it as close to the skin as possible, and pull gently. Its mouthparts are barbed, but a steady action should pull it free.

2 **STORE THE TICK** Keep the tick so it can be identified if you develop a reaction or symptoms of disease. A small screw-top jar covered with plastic wrap or tape makes an ideal specimen container, or use anything sealable, such as a drink bottle. Wash your hands if you touched the tick.

3 **CLEAN THE BITE** Swab the bite with antiseptic, apply antiseptic cream and cover it. Rarely, an anaphylactic reaction may occur. If after a few days it does not seem to be healing, seek medical advice as infection is quite common.

precautions

FLYING INSECTS
● Most mosquitoes are most active just before dusk right through until dawn. If possible, head indoors just before the sun goes down.
● Use a mosquito repellent. The most effective ones contain DEET.
● At night, sleep under mosquito netting or in a room protected by screens. If the screens are open by day, close them and use a mosquito spray to clear the room before you go to bed. Cover exposed skin with light clothing.
● Treat clothes and mosquito nets with permethrin to repel all types of flying and crawling insects.

CRAWLING INSECTS
● Ticks are most active in the spring and summer, so in areas where tick-borne disease is common, avoid prime tick habitat if possible.
● Ticks live in woodland and other well-vegetated areas. They climb up the stems of plants from where they can cling on to any passing host. When out walking, wear long-sleeved shirts and long trousers tucked into your socks or boots. DEET-based repellents also help.
● Check your skin carefully after a walk. Remove ticks quickly to reduce the chances of acquiring an infection or developing a reaction.

▶▶See also: **SEVERE ALLERGIC REACTION** p20 • **INFECTED WOUND** p66 • **SWARM OF BEES** p322

venomous snakes

Despite their sometimes fearsome reputation, only 15 per cent of the world's 3000 or so snake species are venomous, with bites that warrant emergency medical treatment. Very few snakes present a serious danger to healthy adults. But snakes will attack when threatened, so the key to safe coexistence with these usually shy and retiring reptiles is respect.

precautions

- Before you travel, check whether the area you are visiting is home to any venomous snakes and, if so, learn to identify them.
- Snakes use the environment to regulate their temperature, and will seek out sunny spots on cool mornings and shady spots in the heat of the day. Be vigilant around areas such as flat rocks and paths, which trap the sun, and in the shade of bushes.
- If you are travelling through an area where snakes are common, keep dogs on a lead and ensure that children walk behind you. Children and dogs are the most frequent victims of snakebite.
- When walking in snake country, wear thick boots. Do not lean against fallen trees and take particular care when collecting firewood.
- Avoid walking in long grass. If you do, use a walking stick to clear the way. Always 'check before you step' and 'look before you reach'.

RECOGNISING VENOMOUS SNAKES

If you are travelling to an unfamiliar area where venomous snakes are common, consult a reliable reference before you arrive. Below is a selection of some commonly encountered venomous snakes.

CONTINENT	DESCRIPTION
AFRICA	**Black mamba** Olive to greenish grey. Lethally venomous and aggressive snake, about 2.5–4.5m long. **Cape cobra** Usually yellow or brown, sometimes speckled. Its venom can be fatal, about 120–180cm long. **Puff adder** A fat snake, with dark and light bands; 1m long.
EUROPE	**Common adder** Has a zigzag pattern down its back and a dark mark, often a V-shape, on its neck. Average length 65cm.
AUSTRALIA	**Common or Eastern brown snake** From pale brown to almost black, sometimes striped or speckled. Average length 1.5m. **Eastern tiger snake** Olive, brown or grey colour, usually with creamy yellow banding. Average length 1m. **Fierce snake (Inland taipan)** Brown, varying from light to dark and also varies with season and location. Average length 1.8m. **Common death adder** Broad, flat, triangular head. Thick, pale brown body with dark horizontal stripes. Up to 1m long.
NORTH AMERICA	**Copperhead** Patterned in varying shades of brown. Average length around 76cm. **Common coral snake** Wide red and black bands, divided by narrower yellow bands. Up to 80cm long. **Eastern diamondback** Brown, olive or grey, with a pattern of diamond shapes along its back. Average length 1.7m.
ASIA	**King cobra** Varies from black to light brown or olive, with creamy banding. Average length 4m. **Common krait** Bluish black with white bands. Around 1m.

COMMON ADDER

COMMON CORAL SNAKE

KING COBRA

action

YOU SEE A SNAKE

1 STOP AND DON'T MOVE Wait a few minutes. Most snake species will move away if they've seen you. If this doesn't happen, back away slowly without making any sudden movements. **Do not be tempted to move closer for a better look.**

2 GET PAST IT SAFELY If a snake is blocking your path, detour around it by a few metres. A snake can typically strike across a distance of half its body length, which it may do if it feels threatened. Move slowly and calmly. Watch the snake in case it moves.

SNAKES AROUND THE HOUSE

1 DISCOURAGE SNAKES If you live – or are holidaying – in a house in an area where snakes occur, wherever possible keep the surrounding yard free from long grass, rubbish and low ground-hugging plants. Keep woodpiles off the ground and locate them away from the house.

2 REDUCE POTENTIAL PREY Putting food away and keeping it in sealed containers will help keep down rodent numbers. Rats and mice are common prey items for many snakes.

Do not wash a snakebite

Traces of venom around the bite can be used to identify the snake responsible. The use of 'polyvalent antivenoms', which work across a range of venomous species, means it is no longer critical to identify the species. BUT it is preferable to know which species has bitten you as it can improve the speed of recovery.

3 KEEP YOUR DISTANCE If a snake comes into the house, back away – most snakes will leave of their own accord. If not, seek professional help (see Get Help, above).

BITTEN BY A SNAKE

1 LOOK FOR SIGNS Bites, which can be painless, may be difficult to identify if they occur in water or long grass and the snake has not been seen. There may be paired puncture marks, but not always. Other signs include scratches, bruising, bleeding or localised swelling.

2 WATCH FOR EARLY SYMPTOMS These often include headache, irritability, sensitivity to light, nausea, vomiting and diarrhoea. Always suspect snakebite if you're in snake country and someone becomes unexpectedly confused or loses consciousness.

3 FIRST AID IS CRITICAL Follow the 'pressure-immobilisation' technique to slow the spread of venom. Place a pad over the bite then apply a bandage around it – wrapping it as firmly as you would a sprained ankle, but not so tight it restricts blood flow. Extend the bandage in each direction away from the site. Use a splint or a sling to immobilise the limb. Do not elevate it. If the bite is on the torso, still apply a pressure bandage .

4 KEEP VICTIM STILL Don't let the victim walk. Either leave them to get emergency help or carry them.

5 GET MEDICAL HELP Antivenoms to treat poisonous snakebites should be available at hospitals and large medical centres in areas inhabited by dangerous species of snake.

►►See also: **SEVERE ALLERGIC REACTION** p20 • **INFECTED WOUND** p66

venomous spiders

There are around 40,000 spider species worldwide but very few are dangerous to humans. While it is true the vast majority produce venom, most species are not capable of delivering a serious bite to a person. Some notable exceptions are listed here. Learn how to identify dangerous spiders and the simple steps that can be taken to avoid them.

RECOGNISING VENOMOUS SPIDERS

If you live in or are travelling to an area that is home to venomous spiders, it is wise to learn to recognise them. This chart describes some of the species of most concern on each continent.

CONTINENT	DESCRIPTION
AUSTRALIA	**Sydney funnel-web spider** Glossy, dark bodies, black to reddish brown. Body up to 35mm. Males slightly smaller with more potent venom; roam in summer/autumn seeking mates. **Eastern mouse spider** Smooth, glossy black body with large, bulbous head and jaws. Body 15–25mm. Sydney funnel-web antivenom known to be effective. **Redback spider** Females: black body with red/orange stripe. Males: light brown with white markings. Body up to 10mm.
AFRICA	**Black (or West coast) button spiders** Six species, ranging in colour from cream to black. White or red marks common. Body up to 12mm. **Six-eyed sand (or crab) spider** Brown, flattened and crab-like, often covered in sand. Body up to 15mm.
EUROPE	**Mediterranean black widow spider** Black, with 13 red, yellow or orange spots on back. Body up to 15mm. **False widow spiders** A widespread group; body up to 14mm and often dark in colour with lighter markings. **Yellow sac spider** Pale, straw-coloured body. Front legs are longer than the other three pairs. Body 6–8mm long.
NORTH & SOUTH AMERICA	**Black widow spiders** Females: shiny black, with red hourglass on underside. Males and juveniles: black or greyish, with white stripes and yellow/orange speckles. Males smaller. Only females venomous. Body up to 15mm. **Brazilian wandering spiders** Large brown body and legs. Body up to 48mm. Occur tropical South and Central America.
ASIA	**Chinese bird spider** (tarantula) Either golden brown with black stripes, or dark brown to black. Body and legs up to 20cm. **Gooty sapphire spider** (tarantula) Striking metallic blue coloured body and legs. Body and legs up to 20cm.

BLACK WIDOW

SYDNEY FUNNEL-WEB

GOOTY SAPPHIRE

 WARNING

There have been rare instances of large venomous spiders being transported in cargo – such as boxes of bananas – between countries. Treat any unknown spider with caution.

 TAKE CARE

Never attempt to handle a spider you believe to be venomous. Cover it with a bucket or jar and contact an expert, such as a specialist pest controller.

GET HELP If you are in an area where dangerous spiders occur, treat any bites seriously. Antivenoms are available for most species with potentially life-threatening bites.

TIME TO ACT With some spider bites, serious pain and other symptoms can take more than an hour to appear. If you have any doubts, seek medical help immediately.

WATCHPOINT Children, the over-60s and people with heart problems or allergies are most at risk from the effects of spider bites.

action

BITTEN BY A SPIDER

1 **DO NOT PANIC** Even if you are bitten by a venomous spider, remember that many bites are 'dry', that is, the spider has not necessarily injected any venom. Panicking and rushing about will increase your heart rate and cause any venom to move more quickly through your system.

2 **IDENTIFY THE SPIDER** The treatment can vary according to the species. In the case of most spider bites – including the widow spiders such as redbacks in Australia and several species across the USA – wash the area with soap and water. Ice packs may relieve the pain. Do not use a pressure bandage.

3 **WHEN TO USE A PRESSURE BANDAGE** Any bite by a large black spider in eastern Australia should be treated as a potential funnel-web bite. Use the 'pressure immobilisation' technique and apply a bandage as for a snakebite (see page 319). Then take the casualty straight to hospital where an antivenom may be administered.

■ **WATCH THE WOUND** A very small percentage of spider bites have been blamed for a rare condition called 'necrotising arachnidism'. This involves the blistering, ulceration and sometimes death of skin around the bite site. Scientific and medical communities continue to debate the exact cause. If an area of redness and blistering develops around any suspected spider bite, the affected limb should be elevated and the patient told to rest. Take photographs of how the wound develops and if concerned at all seek medical advice. Medical treatment of most spider bites consists of cleaning the wound, administering pain relief, and treatment with antibiotics or even surgery if the wound becomes severely infected.

Removing problem spiders

The vacuum-cleaner technique works well for a spider up to about 30mm. Keep an eye on it to make sure it does not move out of your sight. Fit the wand attachment to your vacuum cleaner. Turn on the power, but not so near the spider as to alarm it or it may run for cover. Swiftly lower the end of the wand to suck up the spider. Leave the motor running for a little while to ensure that the spider is sucked all the way into the dust bag or reservoir. Take the cleaner outside and carefully empty it into a refuse sack that you can seal and discard.

precautions

If you are in a location where there are likely to be venomous spiders, take these sensible precautions:

● Check shoes and boots before putting your feet into them – spiders like the dark recesses.
● Hang your clothes up and shake out each item before putting it on, especially when you are camping.
● Position your bed slightly away from the wall and check the sheets before getting in.
● Be cautious around places that are favoured by spiders – often dark, shady areas with lots of crevices, such as toilets, around barbecues and swimming pools, garages and woodpiles.

▶▶See also: **SEVERE ALLERGIC REACTION** p20 • **SHOCK** pp38–39 • **INFECTED WOUND** p66

a swarm of bees

When honey bees swarm, thousands take to the air as they follow their queen in search of a new home. Although most honey bees are not aggressive, encountering a swarm is potentially dangerous, due to the risk of multiple stings.

GET HELP If someone stung by a bee shows signs of an allergic reaction (see pages 20 and 54–55), such as breathing difficulties or a rash, seek medical help immediately.

action

ENCOUNTER A SWARM

■ **IF A SWARM CHASES YOU** Sprint away as fast as you can – you should be able to outrun it. Run to the nearest safe place, such as a vehicle or building.

■ **IF THE BEES ARE CLOSE Shut your mouth and cup your hands over your eyes and nose** as you run to minimise the risk of being stung in these areas.

⚠ WARNING

● When running away, do not zigzag – running in a straight line is more effective.
● Do not jump into water, such as a swimming pool. The bees will probably circle the pool for up to 15 minutes, and you risk being stung on the face when you surface to breathe.

STUNG BY BEES

1 REMOVE THE STING
Scrape out the sting with your fingernail or by dragging a blunt knife blade or a credit card across the skin at an oblique angle, working from the sting towards

the sac. Do not rub or squeeze the sting as you may increase the amount of venom delivered.

2 APPLY A COLD COMPRESS This will soothe the pain and reduce swelling.

3 SEEK MEDICAL HELP If you suspect that the casualty may be allergic to bee stings or she has been stung a number of times in sensitive areas such as the face, mouth or throat, seek medical assistance as soon as possible.

be aware

● Honey bees typically tend to swarm on sunny afternoons in early summer, so be particularly vigilant at this time of year. Warn children to take care when climbing trees in case they encounter a resting swarm.
● If you find a swarm resting on a tree or post in your garden do not approach it. Warn others and keep children and pets at a safe distance. Contact your local beekeeping society, who will send someone to collect the swarm safely.
● Do not try to move a swarm on, either by spraying it with water or by shaking the branch it is resting on.
● Do not use lawn mowers or similar garden power tools near a swarm, as the noise and vibrations may antagonise the bees.

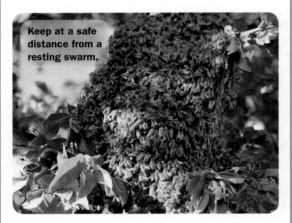
Keep at a safe distance from a resting swarm.

⚠ TAKE CARE

It would take about 500 bee stings to deliver enough venom to kill the average person. However, an estimated three per cent of the population are allergic to honey bee venom and one sting is potentially deadly. For these people, symptoms of anaphylactic shock can develop within minutes of being stung (see page 54).

TECHNOLOGY CRISES

computer freezes or crashes

Some people are completely dependent on computers at both work and home. If your computer suddenly stops working, you may find yourself unable to work or communicate with essential services. But in many cases you can sort out the problem yourself. Work carefully through the reasons why your computer has crashed to get back in action as soon as possible.

assessment

Armed with a little knowledge, you can tackle many minor computer problems on your own. To diagnose more serious problems, you will probably need an expert. Try the simple fixes below to get your computer started, before you call a technician.

TROUBLESHOOTING

PROBLEM	WHAT TO DO
LOCALISED PROBLEM The program you are working on will not respond, but other functions, such as your email, still work.	Software problem **Quit out of the program (see right); make sure Windows is updated (see box, right); check that the program you are using is up to date. Check that the memory you have is sufficient for all the tasks you want to do simultaneously (see right).**
MOUSE IS NOT WORKING When you move the mouse, nothing seems to move on the screen and/or you cannot see the mouse pointer at all, but the keyboard still works (try the arrow keys).	Check your mouse **Check all the cables from the keyboard and mouse are connected. If you have a wireless mouse or keyboard, replace the batteries.**
SCREEN IS STILL ON BUT NOTHING IS WORKING No programs respond to either the keyboard or the mouse.	Restart **This is a typical system freeze. Note what you were doing when the computer stopped working in case it happens again. Restart the computer (see right), then run your virus protection; check and add more memory if necessary (see right).**
FREQUENT FREEZES If your computer often stops functioning, you may have a serious problem. This could be caused by a virus or because you are asking too much of the machine.	Perform basic maintenance **Go to Control Panel, System and Maintenance and click on Defragment your hard drive. Run your anti-virus software. Reinstall any problematic programs.**
THE COMPUTER IS ON BUT THE SCREEN IS BLANK There is nothing on the screen, or there is a message saying 'No signal received'. This may happen when you first turn on the computer, or when you are in the middle of using your computer.	Check the screen **Make sure the cable from the screen to the computer is securely connected. If you can, connect your screen to another computer. If it does not work, your screen is at fault, not the PC.**
COMPUTER DOES NOT START UP When you press the On button, the computer does not respond at all.	Power supply problem **Check that the computer is plugged in, turned on and there is no problem with the mains supply. If all the above are working, the computer's power supply unit may need to be replaced. Take your PC to a computer repair shop.**
UNUSUAL SOUNDS The computer does not sound as it normally does – maybe the fan is making more or less noise than normal, or the hard drive makes a grinding noise when you first turn on the machine.	Hardware problem **This is probably a hardware problem such as a faulty fan, dust inside the PC or a problem with the motherboard (where the components reside). Contact a repair service.**

action

COMPUTER IS UNRESPONSIVE

1 TRY ESCAPE FIRST Some programs appear to freeze in the middle of a process; pressing the **Esc** key may get it going again. For example, accidentally pressing the **Alt** key activates the menus – press the **Esc** key to release.

2 RIGHT CLICK Try right-clicking the program's button in the taskbar at the bottom of the screen. Click on **Close** from the pop-up menu.

3 CTRL + SHIFT + ESC If right-clicking does not work, press the **Ctrl + Shift + Esc** keys simultaneously. Click on the **Applications** tab to view a list of running programs and their status. You should see the status 'Not responding' against the frozen or crashed program. Click on the non-responsive program to select it and then on **End Task.**

4 CTRL + ALT + DEL If your computer is still unresponsive, press the **Ctrl + Alt + Del** keys to display the Windows options menu. Click the red button at the bottom right to shut down.

5 POWER DOWN If pressing **Ctrl + Alt + Del** does not work, the only course of action left is to switch the computer off. Press and hold down the power switch for at least 5 seconds by which time you will hear the fan has stopped whirring. Wait for at least 30 seconds and then press the power switch again. Unfortunately, you will lose any work that has not been saved.

INSUFFICIENT MEMORY

1 FIND OUT HOW MUCH MEMORY YOU HAVE From the Start button, click on **Computer**. The amount of RAM (Random Access Memory) is displayed next to 'Memory' at the bottom of the window. How much you need depends on how you intend to use your computer. Gaming or graphic-design programs may require more RAM, so check the software's requirements. Memory is available online or from computer outlets. Sellers can advise you what to buy, depending on your computer type and model.

2 OPEN YOUR COMPUTER Switch off and unplug the computer. Use an anti-static pad or wrist strap to discharge any static electricity, which could damage the computer and your new RAM, and open the case.

3 SLOT IN THE NEW MEMORY RAM is installed in a series of slots. The memory module has a notch at one end, so that it will only go in one way. Install the memory by placing the module in the slot at 45 degrees and push it down until it snaps into place.

4 CHECK THE MEMORY IS ACTIVE Close the case and switch on the computer. Go back to **Control Panel** and check the increased amount of RAM is shown.

Getting Windows updates

When your computer is connected to the internet, Windows can automatically check for important updates and install them for you.

To set this up, go to the **Start** button and click on **Control Panel, System and Security, Windows Update** and turn **Automatic Updating** on or off. Make sure you select 'Install updates automatically (recommended)', and set a time to install the updates. Alternatively, make manual choices to control Windows updates. Click **OK**.

▶▶See also: **COMPUTER INFECTED BY VIRUS** p326 • **POWER SURGE** p330

computer infected by **virus**

Computer viruses are constantly mutating and can appear without the user realising. If your computer is attacked it can devastate your work and you may inadvertently spread the virus. Learn to recognise a virus and act quickly to contain it and remove the threat.

be aware

There are various signs that indicate your computer may be infected by a virus.

- If you have anti-virus software that has been updated regularly, a message will flash up on the screen warning you of the attack.
- Check any email that seems suspicious with the sender. A virus can be sent by email without the sender's knowledge, so may come from a friend.

- Your computer may run slowly or keep crashing and then restarting.
- You may hear the hard disk whirring when you think the computer should be inactive.
- Dialog boxes and other on-screen elements may look different from usual.

action

1 DISCONNECT Save all open documents, close down all open programs, and disconnect your computer from any networks and from the internet.

2 RUN VIRUS SCAN Run your anti-virus software and, if necessary, run it again to ensure the virus has been dealt with properly, and the computer is clean.

3 RECONNECT EVERYTHING Connect back to your network or router, go to your anti-virus provider's website and check for updates and information. Install updates and run the virus scanner again.

■ **OBTAIN ANTI-VIRUS SOFTWARE** If you do not have anti-virus software, you can download free software from AVG, AVAST! or Anti-VIR. You can also purchase anti-virus software from your local computer store. Be careful of surfing the web or using email until the programs are installed and fully updated.

■ **INSTALL THE SOFTWARE** Start your computer and install the software. Run the software, then reconnect to the internet and check for updates, then run the anti-virus software again.

 TAKE CARE
Make sure that Windows Firewall and Automatic Updates are turned on. Check in **Control Panel, System and Security,** then **Review your computer's status,** if you are not sure.

for next time...

- Scan all types of media (DVDs, CDs and removable drives) when you insert them. Do not re-use disks from other computers.
- Be alert to email messages with attachments – especially ones with a vague subject line. Delete the email straightaway.
- Download files from reputable websites only. Legitimate websites should state that they use anti-virus software to check all downloadable files and programs.
- Ensure your anti-virus software and **Windows Update** (see p325) are configured for automatic updating and to automatically detect viruses.

Do Macs get viruses?

Although viruses and other malware (malicious software) that attack Macintosh computers are not common, Macs can still be vulnerable. Make sure a Mac has anti-virus software and it is kept up to date. Take the same precautions as PC owners. Note also, that even an iPod and iPhone can now be infected by malware.

internet connection down

Losing your internet connection can be frustrating if you are about to bid for an item on eBay or order almost sold-out tickets for a popular show, but it can cause serious problems if you are using it to access details of flights or other urgently needed information.

assessment

Establish whether the problem is your computer and modem or with your Internet Service Provider (ISP).

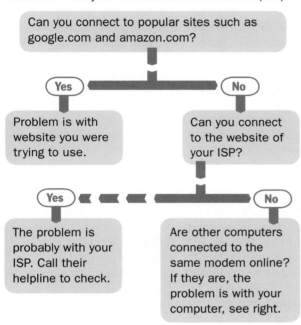

Can you connect to popular sites such as google.com and amazon.com?

Yes → Problem is with website you were trying to use.

No → Can you connect to the website of your ISP?

Yes → The problem is probably with your ISP. Call their helpline to check.

No → Are other computers connected to the same modem online? If they are, the problem is with your computer, see right.

Know your modem/router

The lights and labels on most modems or routers are similar to those described below. If you are in any doubt, see your modem's manual.
- **POWER** A steady light tells you the power cable is connected and the modem is turned on.
- **STATUS** A steady light means all is well.
- **(A)DSL** A steady light means your service is working. If it is flashing or off, contact your ISP.
- **WLAN** When flashing, data is being transferred via your wireless network.
- **LAN** When flashing, data is being transferred via your ethernet connection.
- **INTERNET** A steady light shows the internet connection is active.

action

1 SHUT DOWN Close all programs and then turn off your computer. Unplug and remove all cabling. If you have a router, switch this off and remove the cabling. Unplug the phone from the router or modem and from the wall socket. Wait at least 30 seconds, reconnect all cabling and switch everything back on in reverse order.

2 DIAGNOSE AND REPAIR Right-click on your network icon, which is on the right of the taskbar. Click on **Diagnose and Repair.** This opens the **Windows Network Diagnostics** window, which helps to diagnose and repair any networking problems. Follow the on-screen instructions.

3 CHECK YOUR ROUTER If your router has a **Reset** button (see the manual), press it to restore the router to its factory settings. Check the troubleshooting section of any instructions that came with the router. Connect to the router and follow the manual to input your settings.

4 CHECK NETWORK AND SHARING CENTER Click on the **Start** button, **Control Panel, Network and internet** then on **Network and Sharing Center.** This displays a map of the route between your computer and the internet. A red 'X' between two icons indicates a break in communication and helps you to locate the problem; if you cannot resolve it, the information will be of use to your ISP.

5 GET ADVICE If you are still having problems and cannot access the internet, call your ISP helpline (check the cost of calls when they answer you). The adviser will talk you through how to check your settings. Be ready to describe everything you have done already, and tell the person the results of the two diagnostic programs you have run.

deleted or lost files

It is a common misconception that when you delete a file it is removed from the hard drive of your PC. What actually happens is that the tiny piece of information that points to the location of the file is erased, making the file invisible to the operating system. If the file is still located in the Recycle Bin, it can be restored to its original location.

precautions

● Make regular back-ups (see box, below) of all your important data, in case a file gets permanently deleted from your hard drive.
● Create folders for associated files and clearly label them, for example, 'Family Letters', 'Holidays', 'Household Expenses'. Save your files in these folders to find them easily in future.

Backing up

● **BUY BACK-UP HARDWARE** Before backing up your files, decide on the best way to store them. DVDs and CDs are cheap, but may get lost, broken or corrupted. External hard drives are now reasonably priced and allow you to back up repeatedly.
● **USE BACK-UP SOFTWARE** To back up all of your data files, you can use the Automatic Back-up feature that comes with Windows. This lets you choose how often to perform regular back-ups and whether to save the data to an external hard drive, portable media such as a DVD, or a network location. To use this feature, click on the **Start** button, then **Control Panel, System and Maintenance** and **Back Up Your Computer**.
● **RESTORE FILES WIZARD** If you have backed up regularly, use the Restore Files wizard to retrieve the backed-up version of your lost file. You can access this wizard in the same way as you set up Automatic Back-up.

⚠️ **WARNING**

Certain files and folders cannot be rescued from the Recycle Bin. These include items that were deleted across a network or from removable media such as a CD-ROM or removable hard drive. A warning message is displayed when you delete these items.

action

FILE DELETED

1 **GO TO RECYCLE BIN** To start restoring a deleted file on your PC or laptop, go to your desktop and double-click on the **Recycle Bin** icon.

2 **LOCATE THE FILE** A window opens, showing the contents of the Recycle Bin. Next to each item are columns displaying additional information about the deleted files, such as the original location and the date and time the file was deleted.

3 **RESTORE THE ITEM** To restore an item to its original location, click on it to select it, then click on **Restore this item** from the menu bar above.

■ **RESTORING MULTIPLE ITEMS** To select and restore several items from the Recycle Bin at the same time, hold down the **Control** key and select each item in turn. When finished click on **Restore the selected items** from the menu bar above. All the selected items will now be restored to their original locations on the computer.

FILE IS LOST

1 **USE THE WINDOWS SEARCH FACILITY** Click on the **Start** button to open the **Start menu**.

2 **START THE SEARCH** In the **Start Search** box, start typing a word that is part of your lost filename (there is no need to click in the box first). As you type, filenames containing that combination of characters are displayed in the pane above. Hover your mouse pointer over a filename to display its location. Click on a file to open it and launch its associated program. You can now save it to a location where you can find it again, using **Save As**.

TIME TO ACT If you haven't already done so, now is the time to make a back-up of all your important data, documents, pictures, music files and video clips.

WATCHPOINT To make use of Windows 7 'Restore Files' facility, you must have previously used the 'Back Up Files' wizard to create a back-up.

FILE OVERWRITTEN

1 LOCATE THE FILE OR FOLDER Click on **Start** and **Explorer.** In **Explorer,** find the file or folder that you have accidentally overwritten with a later version.

2 RIGHT-CLICK ON THE FILE A **Properties** dialog box is displayed. Click on the **Previous Versions** tab. A list of shadow copies – the file as it was at particular points in time – is displayed. You can quickly preview a read-only version of the file to check that it is the version you want. When you have decided which file you need, drag it to a folder or select it and click on the **Restore** button.

be aware

All versions of Windows 7 have a basic back-up and restore function, which can be found by clicking the **Start** button, **Control Panel**, **System and Maintenance,** then clicking **Back Up and Restore**.

● The Ultimate and Professional versions of Windows 7 have more extensive back-up and restore features.
● If you are using older versions of Windows, such as XP and Vista, you may have to use third-party back-up software, such as Comodo Backup, or buy a back-up program from your local computer store.
● Shadow Explorer is a piece of free software that gives you access to the previous versions of important system files saved by Windows 7, Vista and XP's shadow volume service.

TAKE CARE
If you have a generous size of hard drive (200GB or more), only empty the **Recycle Bin** when it is absolutely necessary. You can then go to the bin when you need a file that you 'deleted' as unwanted.

Lost files on a Mac

If you are using a Mac computer that is running operating system 10.5 or later, a number of options are available for finding lost files, depending on how much you know about the file you have lost.

● **USE RECENT ITEMS** If you know you have recently accessed the file you have lost, click on the **Apple** menu, and then point to **Recent Items** and click on the required application or document.
● **RUN A SPOTLIGHT SEARCH** Click on the **Spotlight** icon – the magnifying glass. This can be found on the menu bar at the top right of the screen, in some applications or in the **Open** or **Save** dialog boxes. Type as much of the filename as you can remember in the search field. Spotlight starts searching as soon as you start typing.
● **SEARCH MORE PRECISELY** In **Finder**, click on the **File** menu and then click on **Find**. In addition to typing the filename, you can also specify the location and other search criteria, such as the type of file.
● **MAKE REGULAR BACK-UPS** To increase your chance of finding lost or deleted files, back up your work regularly. The easiest way to do this is to use Time Machine, part of the operating system. To back up immediately, hold down the mouse button on the **Time Machine** icon – the clock face with an anti-clockwise arrow – in the **Dock**, or open the program from the **Applications** folder, and choose **Back Up Now**. To schedule periodic back-ups, turn on and set up **Time Machine** in **System Preferences**. You will be able to back up weekly or monthly.

power surge

Power surges occur for a number of reasons. Problems at an electricity sub-station, a lightning storm, unexpectedly high demand in your area or faulty domestic wiring can all be culprits – the important thing is to protect your valuable data.

WATCHPOINT An electrical power surge or 'spike' is a temporary (often less than one second) increase in the normal electrical supply voltage, which can damage home electronics.

precautions

● Buy a surge protector for your computer hardware and sensitive electrical equipment. Make sure it includes a phone-line input socket.
● If you live in an area that is susceptible to power fluctuations and your computer is essential to you, buy an Uninterruptable Power Supply (UPS). If a 'spike' (power surge) or power cut occurs when you are using your computer, this will give you enough time to save your documents.
● Use a power strip with a built-in surge protector for multiple plugs.

A power strip with a surge protector ensures a safe electricity supply.

action

1 DISCONNECT ALL AFFECTED APPLIANCES Appliances that were running at the time of a power surge should be disconnected, tested and, if necessary, reset or repaired.

2 CHECK APPLIANCES Inspect all devices that were connected to the power supply, even if they were not running at the time of the surge. Any that have burn marks around their plugs should be repaired or replaced.

3 CHECK FUSE BOX Check the fuse box if all appliances on a particular circuit are not working. Switch off the power, take out the fuse and replace with a new fuse of the correct amperage.

4 CHECK MCB UNIT If you have a consumer unit with mini-circuit breakers (MCBs), a switch for the circuit may have tripped and be in the Off position. Push the switch to the On position (normally up).

5 CALL AN ELECTRICIAN If the MCB switch will not stay on, or you have continued problems, call a qualified electrician to check your circuits.

⚠ TAKE CARE

● When working with any electrical appliance, **ensure that plugs are removed from sockets and the power is turned off before attempting any repairs.**
● In many countries only licensed electricians can work with electrical circuits and fuse boxes – check with your local authorities. Electricity can kill so if you are at all unsure of what you are doing, call a professional, qualified electrician.

Effects on computer

● **COMPUTER RUNS ERRATICALLY** You may notice the loss of files or programs, freezing, crashing and other erratic functions. Reinstall your programs. If the PC still performs poorly, consult a computer technician.
● **COMPUTER DOES NOT WORK** Power surges can affect a number of computer components, such as semi-conductors, magnetic discs and circuit boards. The effects can render the computer unrepairable – check with a technician.

liquid spills

At a moment's slip of the hand, your keyboard can easily be covered in liquid from a nearby drink that can render it unusable. Fortunately, the damage may not be irreparable and if it is, a replacement is fairly cheap. While a desktop computer's keyboard is easily cleaned, a laptop keyboard may need repair by a technician.

action

SPILLAGE ON PC KEYBOARD

1 SWITCH COMPUTER OFF Shut down the computer immediately and, if it is connected to a mains socket, unplug it.

2 REMOVE KEYBOARD Unplug the keyboard from the computer and unplug the mouse if it is connected to the keyboard.

3 DEAL WITH LIQUID If you spilled water, turn the keyboard over and let the water drain out. Leave it to dry on an absorbent surface, such as a wad of paper towels, for at least 24 hours. If a sticky liquid, such as coffee or cola, is spilled, turn the keyboard over to reveal the fixing screws underneath. Remove these screws and pull the keyboard apart.

4 DRY OUT On a flat, clean surface, try to prise the smaller keys off the keyboard with a wide-bladed screwdriver. Do not remove the spacebar, Enter key or other large keys. Use a cotton bud and surgical spirit to remove any sticky residue. Let everything dry for at least 24 hours before reassembling.

Replacing a keyboard

Before buying a new keyboard, note the type of connection the existing keyboard uses, or whether it is wireless. The usual types of connectors are PS/2 (older keyboards) or USB. Having obtained the correct keyboard, simply plug it in (or if it is wireless, install the software and plug in the receiver). If the keyboard does not work, reboot the computer. Most laptop keyboards can be replaced by a technician, or purchase a new USB or wireless keyboard to use with the laptop.

SPILLAGE ON LAPTOP

1 SWITCH LAPTOP OFF Shut down the laptop. Pressing and holding the power button for 5 seconds is quickest. Remove the mains lead, unplug any peripherals and remove the battery. The biggest danger at this time is the device shorting out.

2 REMOVE EXCESS LIQUID Blot up excess liquid with a soft lint-free cloth or paper towel. Do not use a wiping motion as that just spreads the liquid further.

3 TURN LAPTOP OVER With the laptop facing away from you, tilt it from side to side and from front to back in a gentle rocking motion to help the liquid to escape from all four sides.

4 USE COMPRESSED AIR TO DRY Make sure that you have removed all excess liquid. Then, if you have one, use a can of compressed air to help to dry the laptop. Alternatively, use a hair dryer on its coolest setting: keep the dryer moving all the time and hold it at least 20cm above the laptop.

5 LEAVE TO COMPLETELY DRY OUT Leave the laptop opened in an inverted 'V' shape in a warm area, to completely dry out. Do not leave it in direct sunlight or on a radiator. Wait for 24 hours or longer, making sure the keyboard is completely dry, before reinstalling the battery and peripherals.

for next time...

- Consider purchasing a wet cover protector for your computer keyboard.
- Thin protective skins for laptop keyboards are available from computer outlets for a wide range of different models.

mobile phone

Being unable to make or receive a call or text message is very frustrating, but if you are completely reliant on your phone – perhaps if you are in an isolated area and need to call for help – it is important to know how to restore this lifeline quickly.

assessment

Given the high demands placed on mobile phones, operating problems are likely, but these can usually be solved by simple troubleshooting techniques.

TROUBLESHOOTING

PROBLEM	WHAT TO DO	
PHONE ON BUT NOT WORKING If your phone is on and you can see the on-screen display, but nothing happens when you use the keypad, it is likely that the keypad is locked.	**Keypad locked** Press the unlock key and/or enter the unlocking code. The default is often 0000 or the last four digits of your number. To reset it, remove then reinsert the battery, and turn the phone on.	**CLEANING SIM CARD**
SIM CARD NOT RECOGNISED Phone displays message 'SIM card is not recognised'. The SIM contact points need cleaning and the card seating in the correct position.	**Clean SIM card** Clean the contact points with a cotton bud. If the card is not seated tightly enough against the contact points, wedge it with a small piece of folded paper.	
SIGNAL FAULTS The signal display should tell you how good a signal your phone is receiving. This is normally indicated by the number of bars displayed, with more bars signifying a better reception.	**Find good reception** If you cannot get a signal indoors, try going outside or near a window. You may get better reception higher up.	
BATTERY FAULTS If your battery loses power very quickly, or gets very warm during use or charging, the battery may need to be replaced. If you are in an emergency situation and the battery is low, you can extend its life until you are somewhere safe (see below).	**Remove battery and check** Remove the cover (usually on the back of the phone) and take out the battery. Check whether it has warped. If you detect these faults, buy a new battery. Carry a charged battery as a back-up.	**REMOVING BATTERY**

Get more from your battery

If you know your battery is low but you need to make or receive a call, turn off the phone until you need to use it. Turn off Bluetooth, vibrate and the backlight. Turn down the brightness and deactivate 3G and any data transmissions.

⚠ TAKE CARE

You can normally still make calls to the emergency services, even if the phone's keypad is locked and you have no credit. In most countries, if you do not know how to contact the local emergency services, dialling 112 on your mobile phone will usually connect you to the appropriate helpline.

READY
REFERENCE

emergency **preparation**

To take effective action in an emergency situation it can help to have specific items to hand. By preparing a kit in advance you can access what you need quickly and easily. Medical, household and driving kits are useful for everyday use. If you're heading to the great outdoors or travelling to a high-risk area, having an emergency kit can be reassuring and potentially life-saving.

💓 medical

first-aid kit for the home
Keep a watertight box containing:
- ❏ Alcohol-free antiseptic wipes
- ❏ Alcohol gel
- ❏ Latex-free disposable gloves
- ❏ Sticking plasters in assorted sizes
- ❏ Gel blister plasters
- ❏ Sterile dressings in assorted sizes
- ❏ Sterile eye pad
- ❏ Triangular bandages
- ❏ Pack of safety pins in assorted sizes
- ❏ Crêpe roller bandages of different widths
- ❏ Elastic bandage
- ❏ Combined sterile dressing and bandage
- ❏ Adhesive tape
- ❏ Scissors
- ❏ Tweezers
- ❏ Digital thermometer.

first-aid kit for outdoor activities
When hiking or camping, consider purchasing a pouch travel kit that can easily be carried. The Red Cross travel first-aid kit contains:
- ❏ Sticking plasters
- ❏ Bandages
- ❏ Dressings
- ❏ Disposable gloves
- ❏ Sterile dressings
- ❏ Wipes
- ❏ Safety pins.

Useful medication for first-aid kits
- ❏ Paracetamol and paracetamol syrup for children
- ❏ Ibuprofen for adults and children
- ❏ Antiseptic cream
- ❏ Rehydration salts
- ❏ Anti-diarrhoea medicine
- ❏ Antihistamine tablets or syrup
- ❏ Insect repellent
- ❏ Antihistamine cream.

finding medical equipment

Though colour schemes may vary, the symbols for medical equipment are similar throughout the world.

 First-aid sign shows location of either a first-aid box or other medical equipment.

 AED (Automated external defibrillator), used if someone has a heart attack. They are often found in shopping centres and other public places, (see page 17).

first-aid kit for the car
It is possible to purchase a first-aid kit that is designed to be kept in a car. A kit from the Red Cross contains:
- ❏ Sticking plasters
- ❏ Triangular bandages
- ❏ Dressing pads
- ❏ Gauze swabs
- ❏ Sterile dressings
- ❏ Adhesive tape
- ❏ Disposable gloves
- ❏ Antiseptic wipes
- ❏ Safety pins
- ❏ Disposable face shield
- ❏ Scissors
- ❏ Tweezers
- ❏ Mylar emergency blanket
- ❏ Note pad and pencil
- ❏ Torch (flashlight)
- ❏ Clinical waste bag.

specialist kits
A person who has an allergy or long-term medical condition may be wearing a medical alert bracelet to indicate this (see page 55). He or she is likely to be carrying specialist medical equipment and medication. Someone who suffers from anaphylactic shock will carry an autoinjector (see page 54); a person with diabetes may carry an insulin kit (see page 58).

household

general-purpose tool kit

Keep the items listed below in a durable plastic tool box that is light to carry and allows easy access to each tool. Store the tool box in a place that is quickly accessible. Do not pile other items on top of it. You'll need:

❑ Flat tip, Phillips and Pozidriv screwdrivers with large and small heads
❑ Hammer
❑ Retractable blade knife
❑ Tape measure
❑ Self-amalgamating tape
❑ Two adjustable spanners
❑ Torch (flashlight)
❑ Wire cutters
❑ Pliers
❑ Aerosol water repellent (WD40)
❑ Petroleum jelly.

Ladder safety

Do not attempt to climb a ladder unless you feel totally confident. If you do climb a ladder, ensure it is properly secured at the correct angle – 1m out for every 4m up the wall. Ask someone to hold on to the bottom of the ladder.

for power failure and replacing fuses

Keep this kit readily available – you will have to find it in the dark:

❑ Candles
❑ Matches
❑ Torch (flashlight)
❑ Fuse wire or cartridge fuses if your powerboard (electrical panel) needs them.

emergency plumbing kit

Store small items in plastic bags, clearly labelled. Keep the complete kit in a large box or crate with clear access. Make sure you know where the water mains stop valve is located (see page 147) and keep access to it clear. You'll need:

❑ Emergency pipe repair clamp (pipe leaks)
❑ Radiator key
❑ Slip coupling (pipe leaks)
❑ Self-amalgamating tape (pipe leaks)
❑ Sink plunger (blocked sink, basin, etc.)
❑ WC plunger (blocked WC)
❑ Tap washers (dripping taps).

Fire safety equipment

Knowing the different types of fire extinguishers and when to use them can save lives. The most common extinguisher for use in the home is a dry powder version. Read the instructions when installing and be familiar with how to use it. Keep any extinguisher regularly serviced; once a year is normal. A fire blanket is effective in containing a small fire and most usefully kept in the kitchen.

● **DRY POWDER** By far the most common, these extinguishers contain dry powder and are suitable for use on burning solid materials, but also for electrical fires and for those involving flammable liquids (but not cooking oil). It should be at least 1kg in size.

● **FOAM** This type of extinguisher contains a spray foam that is ideal for fires involving flammable liquids and can also put out fires involving solid materials but not electric fires (though they are safe if accidentally sprayed on electrical equipment). Minimum 2kg capacity.

● **WATER** These are limited to tackling fires involving solid materials and should never be used on electrical fires or fires involving flammable liquids. As they send a high-pressure jet, they can be used at a distance on something like burning furniture. Minimum size 5 litres.

● **CARBON DIOXIDE** These are not suitable for putting out fires involving solid materials, but are ideal for flammable liquids (not cooking oil) and for electrical fires, especially with equipment such as computers as they cause minimum damage.

● **FIRE BLANKET** Made from fire-resistant material, a fire blanket can be used only on small, localised fires. It should be at least 1m square. Keep it where it can be easily reached in an emergency.

driving

essential

Keep a torch (flashlight) and reflective clothing inside the car.

- ❑ Torch (flashlight) and batteries
- ❑ Basic tool kit
- ❑ Jack and wheelbrace
- ❑ Jump leads
- ❑ Duplicate ignition key
- ❑ Warning triangle
- ❑ First-aid kit.

useful

- ❑ Owner's manual
- ❑ Tow rope
- ❑ Water repellent lubricant
- ❑ Fire extinguisher (see below)
- ❑ Blanket

- ❑ Petrol can (5 litre)
- ❑ Spare bulbs
- ❑ Spare fuses.

when driving in snow and ice

Keep as many items as possible for personal use inside the car to avoid getting wet and cold.

- ❑ Fully charged mobile phone
- ❑ Shovel and long-handled brush
- ❑ High-energy food and drinks
- ❑ A vacuum flask containing a hot drink
- ❑ Warm clothing and blankets
- ❑ Sacking to provide tyre grip in icy conditions.

driving in more extreme conditions

Think carefully about whether you must make the journey. If driving overseas, seek local advice on road conditions.

- ❑ Snow chains
- ❑ Can of spare fuel
- ❑ Tow rope
- ❑ Recovery strap for muddy or sandy terrain.

Driving overseas

Check what you need in the country you are visiting as legal requirements vary. For overseas driving take:
- ❑ Full driving licence, including any paper counterpart
- ❑ Vehicle registration document
- ❑ Motor insurance certificate
- ❑ Breakdown cover documents
- ❑ International driving permit when required, such as when hiring cars in some African and Asian countries.

Fire extinguisher for a car

To deal with a car fire, experts recommend a dry-powder extinguisher with a capacity of at least 1.5kg. Smaller models last for just 8 seconds, which is probably not enough time to put out a fire. Install the fire extinguisher in an easily accessible place such as under the dashboard or clipped under the driver's seat. Do not keep an extinguisher in the boot.

☢ public

evacuation kit

If you need to make a quick exit from your home, take the following in a waterproof bag:

- ❑ Battery-operated or wind-up radio
- ❑ Eating utensils
- ❑ Blankets or sleeping bags
- ❑ Passport and valuable papers.

for a refuge shelter

For a stay in a shelter for several days, the following will be useful (packed in a soft holdall or backpack):

- ❑ Torch (flashlight) and batteries
- ❑ Water (1–2 litres per person per day)
- ❑ Canned foods
- ❑ Milk and beverages
- ❑ Medicine
- ❑ Toilet paper

- ❑ Sanitary towels (pads)
- ❑ Nappies
- ❑ Baby food and baby supplies
- ❑ Battery-operated or wind-up radio
- ❑ Eating utensils
- ❑ Blankets or sleeping bags
- ❑ Passport and valuable papers
- ❑ Games and books
- ❑ To keep finances secure, a note of credit card numbers and bank phone numbers etc.